D1591098

Exploring
the Physical Sciences

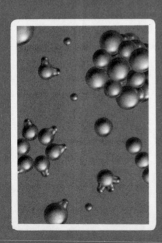

second edition

Exploring the

the

Physical Sciences

Willard J. Poppy
Professor of Physics
The University of Northern Iowa

Leland L. Wilson
Professor of Chemistry
The University of Northern Iowa

Prentice-Hall, Inc., Englewood Cliffs, New Jersey

Library of Congress Cataloging in Publication Data

POPPY, WILLARD J
    Exploring the physical sciences.

    Includes bibliographies.
    1. Science. I. Wilson, Leland L., joint author.
II. Title.
Q160.2.P66 1973   500   72-6565
ISBN 0-13-297457-6

EXPLORING THE PHYSICAL SCIENCES, second edition
by Willard J. Poppy and Leland L. Wilson

© 1973, 1965 by Prentice-Hall, Inc.
Englewood Cliffs, New Jersey

All rights reserved.
No part of this book may be reproduced in any form
or by any means without permission in writing from
the publisher.
Printed in the United States of America

10 9 8 7 6 5 4 3 2 1

PRENTICE-HALL INTERNATIONAL, INC., London
PRENTICE-HALL OF AUSTRALIA, PTY. LTD., Sydney
PRENTICE-HALL OF CANADA, LTD., Toronto
PRENTICE-HALL OF INDIA PRIVATE LIMITED, New Delhi
PRENTICE-HALL OF JAPAN, INC., Tokyo

Contents

v

Unit 3   Matter and Change

Preface

Science has influenced the life and thought of modern man to such an extent that it has become a major intellectual force of our time. The technology based upon science provides the foundation for our industrial society and offers one of the best hopes for relief from hunger and deprivation in the underdeveloped nations. The applications of science are not necessarily beneficent, since they may be, by design or through lack of understanding, directed to destructive as well as constructive purposes. Thus, there is no doubt that some understanding of science and the work of scientists in acquiring new knowledge is a necessary part of the education of every individual. However, there is no agreement regarding the particular topics from the physical sciences to be included in a general education course that must be restricted in scope because of time limitations.

The second edition of *Exploring The Physical Sciences* includes the same major units as the first edition. Space, energy, and the structure of matter have been selected for rather intensive study, instead of attempting to survey the whole domain of the physical sciences. We have made no attempt to describe all the products of technology or to glorify the "miracles of modern science." Rather, we have placed the primary emphasis upon the development of some major concepts and ideas in these areas. Science is an intellectual enterprise, and therefore its theories and concepts have great aesthetic appeal. The development of a rational interpretation of the physical world is inherently satisfying to the human mind; it is this aspect of science which appeals to the intelligent student.

Many sections of this book have been extensively revised in this second edition and a glossary has been added. A historical development of solar system models has been included in the first chapter. The chapters dealing with the solar system have been revised and brought up to date with the latest information from the space program. The mks system of units is introduced in Chapter 7 and used exclusively throughout the rest of the book. The chapter on the nature of matter has been deleted and the essential ideas included in appropriate sections. The discussion of electrical energy and magnetism has been divided into two separate chapters with extensive revision. The chapters on radioactivity and atomic energy have been rewritten and now follow the discussion of atomic structure.

The importance of science and technology in matters of public policy has been emphasized at appropriate points. The discussion of the social and economic consequences of environmental pollution has been expanded and the importance of a sound national policy concerning this problem has been stressed. The experimental basis for the development of concepts has been described where possible to emphasize the role of experiment as the ultimate basis for knowledge in the sciences.

We have assumed no mathematical preparation beyond elementary algebra on the part of the student. The illustrative problems in the text are worked out in detail to aid the student in learning to solve similar problems. Problems and questions of varying difficulty are included at the end of each chapter to give the instructor flexibility in assignments. The suggested references are intended to supplement the material in the text for those students who are interested in going beyond the necessarily limited discussion in this book.

We appreciate the reception accorded to the first edition and the constructive criticisms that have been offered by users. We wish to thank Abelard-Schuman, Ltd., for permission to reproduce the lines from *Sun, Stand Thou Still*, by Angus Armitage, which are found on the title page of Unit 1, and the estate of Albert Einstein for permission to use the lines from *The Evolution of Physics*, by Albert Einstein and Leopold Infeld, which are found on the title page for Unit 2.

Willard J. Poppy
Leland L. Wilson

Exploring
the Physical Sciences

unit

1

Earth and Sky

Science satisfies us because it shows us that behind the transient and confused pageant of nature, there is a permanent and ordered reality. And it was in the sky that this order was first revealed to men on a vast and spectacular scale.

—Angus Armitage

[Spiral nebula photograph courtesy Hale Observatories.]

1
Models of the Solar System

The birthplace of man is believed to be somewhere in the Eastern Hemisphere, but in just what region, or even on what continent, it is still impossible to say. It is equally difficult to determine when and where the first glimmer of science appeared. Who was the first to kindle a fire, and how was it done? Who invented the earliest stone implement? Who was the first to use a spoken language? By whom was a written language first developed? No greater invention than writing has ever been made, for it is through recording thoughts and observations and making achievements a permanent record that each generation has been able to contribute to the advancement of mankind.

1-1
The Dawn of Astronomy

Primitive man was primarily concerned about his survival. He was continually battling nature and predatory animals. In his struggle for life, he left the mysteries of nature to higher powers, the gods. To account for all phases of nature, he imagined a multitude of gods; he had a god of harvest, a god of thunder, a god of fertility, and so forth. To him the Sun was even a god. This was very convenient, for whenever anything went wrong he blamed a god, which took the responsibilities out of his hands. He thought these gods often punished him through floods, droughts, and famines. After each disaster, he felt the urge to go through some kind of a religious ceremony or to sacrifice something or somebody to appease the god who punished him. He always looked skyward because he believed that his gods lived among the stars.

Man's first feeble attempt to control the mysteries of nature was through magic. He performed rituals and dances to try to control the amount of rain, or the amount of sunshine. These attempts by the "witch doctors" to control the environment, although in vain, gave primitive man the idea that by better understanding nature, he might somehow attain a measure of control over it, and thus make life more pleasant. This type of magic still appeals to modern man. To this day we rub a rabbit's foot or search for four-leaf clovers to bring us luck, and we drink a toast to a person's success.

By the middle of the fourth millennium B.C. man learned to read and write. At least two written languages appeared, one in Babylonia in the Tigris and Euphrates valleys and one in Egypt in the valley of the Nile. In all likelihood they were of equal antiquity. Both countries were in fertile valleys and were somewhat isolated and protected by nature. For example, the fertile valley of the Nile was protected by cataracts to the south, large deserts on both sides, and the Mediterranean Sea to the north. Without fear of hunger and invasion, these two groups of people developed remarkable civilizations. It is also possible that two other written languages had appeared in China and India at about this time, but they contributed very little to our knowledge of the physical sciences, especially astronomy.

By being able to record observations, these early peoples noticed that nature followed definite patterns from which they could predict future happenings. The Babylonians recorded the solar eclipses, and from the data they observed that the eclipses occurred at definite intervals of time; from this, they predicted future eclipses. Knowing more about nature helped remove the fear of such physical phenomena. The Babylonians were ardent and successful students of astronomy. They knew the approximate length of the year. They used a lunar calendar of 12 months, representing the 12 full moons in a year, with alternate 29-day and 30-day months, averaging $29\frac{1}{2}$ days. They divided the month into 4 weeks of 7 days each, the day into 24 hours, the hour into 60 minutes, and the minute into 60 seconds. Their lunar year consisted of 354 days, and to keep it in step with the seasons, an extra month was added whenever it was felt necessary. They sincerely believed that a person's life was affected by the positions of the planets and the constellations or configurations of stars in which the Sun was located when that person was born, and so they developed to a high degree of sophistication the theory called astrology. The Babylonians called astrology a science, and to many of them, it was the most important branch of science. Mathematics and engineering were also developed by these people during the 3,000 years of their civilization. They realized the necessity of having standard units for measuring length, weight, and time, and they set up such standards.

By 4200 B.C., the Egyptians had developed their knowledge of astronomy, not to the extent of the Babylonians because they did not believe in astrology, but enough to devise a calendar of 360 days plus a 5-day period for feasting. They were more interested in medicine, as some of their early carvings of Egyptian surgeons performing operations would indicate. By 3500 B.C., they were using the decimal number system, and each decimal unit was represented by a special symbol. The learning of the Egyptians was extensive and well organized, as authenticated by two papyri, one dating from about the middle of the nineteenth and the other from the middle of the seventeenth century B.C. Each of these, we are quite sure, was copied from a still earlier text. Together they give evidence of a remarkable intellectual activity in medicine and mathematics, the latter of which played a very important role in the development of astronomy. Humanity will always remember the ancient Egyptians for their great pyramids constructed with great astronomical orientations. Such masterpieces show the mathematics and engineering skills of the Egyptians. These great stone structures are still one of the seven wonders of the world. The Egyptians noticed that the waters of the Nile started rising when the star Sirius appeared in the eastern sky just before sunrise. Since the flooding of the Nile each spring enriched the soil, they thought that Sirius was a good omen, and they erected seven temples in its honor. Each temple had a passageway through which Sirius could be observed at helical rise, just before sunrise.

In about 1900 B.C. the circles of the giant stones at Stonehenge, England, were arranged to allow accurate observations of the Sun and Moon, and give exact determinations of the beginning of the seasons. The ancient inhabitants could accurately determine when the Sun was at the summer and winter solstices, highest and lowest in the sky. With these great stones they were able to maintain astronomical information long before they were able to write and record such information. From the positions of the shadows formed by these stones, they were able to predict lunar eclipses. The Mayas of Central America believed that time is cyclical, and to determine the reappearance of rains, hurricanes, and eclipses they developed a calendar of 18 periods, or months, of 20 days each, plus a terminal period of 5 days and 6 hours. They also had a religious calendar of 260 days, which had no relation to the solar year. The Mayan people also believed that their lives were affected by the positions of the planets, and so they were remarkably accurate in their observations of those heavenly bodies. In South America, the Incas erected a large stone at Machu Picchu so that on the first day of spring or fall it casts no shadow, and by the positions of its shadows, they could determine the beginning of the seasons. By 2000 B.C., the Chinese were able to predict eclipses, and by 1400 B.C. they had developed a working calendar. Throughout the ages, they kept a fairly accurate account of the comets and nova; the latter they called "guest stars." Stellar observations were also made and recorded in India as early as 1400 B.C., but their observations lead to no predictions of the eclipses at that early date.

Hence, we see that for thousands of years before Christ men all over the world were observing celestial objects, and reckoning their time by them.

Most of these ancient astronomers knew that a few of the heavenly objects moved around among the seemingly permanent *fixed stars*. These star-like objects were later called *planets*, after the Greek word meaning "wanderer," because of their apparent aimless motion through the constellations of the zodiac, the groups of stars through which the Sun makes its yearly journey. For ages one of the basic problems in astronomy was to explain the complex motions of the Sun, Moon, and planets accurately enough to be able to predict their future positions.

1-2
Observed Motions of Celestial Objects

By 600 B.C. man had observed and recorded the motions of the Sun, Moon, planets, and stars, but he had no working model to explain their motions. Before we study any such schemes, let us look at the motions that puzzled man for so long. The Sun, Moon, planets, and stars all rise above the eastern horizon, trace arcs across the sky, and set in the west. The stars follow the same path across the sky, while the paths followed by the Sun, Moon, and planets seem to change with seasons. In June (in the Northern Hemisphere), the Sun rises north of due east, traces a path high in the sky, and sets north of west; in December, it rises south of east, follows an arc low in the southern sky, and sets south of due west. This shifting of the angle at which the Sun's rays strike the Earth gives rise to our seasons, warm in the summer and cold in the winter. Careful observations at dawn show that the stars rise about four minutes earlier each day. We have taken one complete cycle of the Sun as 24 hours, while the stars all make one cycle in 23 hours and 56 minutes. Each day the Sun falls behind the stars in their westward journey, and seems to drift eastward among the background of stars. In the course of a year, the Sun falls one complete cycle behind, and is back among the same stars it was among about 365 days before. The group of stars through which the Sun appears to move is called the twelve constellations of the zodiac, which are so important in astrology.

The Moon rises in the east, follows an arc across the sky, and sets in the west. It, however, falls about 50 minutes behind the stars each day, and drifts eastward one complete cycle with respect to the stars in 27.32 days. The Moon's appearance changes from full to third quarter, to new, to first quarter, and back to full again in 29.53 days. From full moon to full moon is called a *lunar month*.

Two planets, Mercury and Venus, always remain as morning or evening stars, which means that they stay rather close to the Sun in its apparent eastward journey among the stars. At times Venus is an extremely bright star in the western sky shortly after sunset; at other times it is a bright morning

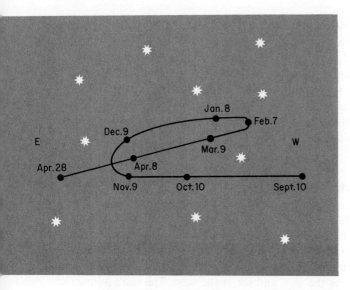

FIG. 1-1
Retrograde loop of Mars.

star in the eastern sky before sunrise. When at its greatest brilliance, it can be seen by an unaided eye in the full daylight. This early-to-bed or early-to-rise planet is never is never seen later than 3.25 hours after sunset or earlier than 3.25 hours before sunrise. Mercury follows a similar pattern, but never sets or rises more than 1.9 hours behind or ahead of the Sun. Hence, it stays closer to the Sun than does Venus. Mercury is less brilliant than Venus; therefore, it attracts less attention. The rest of the planets do not stay near the Sun, or even near each other, in their eastward motion through the constellations of the zodiac. They can even be on the same side of the Sun as that of the Earth and be seen at midnight, or be on the side opposite the Sun. At certain intervals, which are not the same for different planets, they stop, move backward toward the west for awhile, stop again, and then resume their eastward motions. This backward motion is called *retrograde motion*. At times these planets seem to travel through the background of stars in a series of loops, while the Sun and Moon travel continuously in an easterly direction. The apparent loop-the-loop motion can be seen in the diagram of the retrograde motion of Mars as plotted on a sky map in Fig. 1-1.

1-3
Greek Models of the Universe

In the sixth century B.C., about a thousand years after the fall of the Babylonian and Egyptian civilizations, an intellectual awakening took place among the Greeks. They employed learning to such an extent that the Golden Age of Greek civilization is regarded by many as the highest level of achievement that the human species has yet attained. To the Greeks, philosophy and science were the same thing. They relied upon logic rather than on experimentation.

In 400 B.C., Plato, the great Greek philosopher and teacher, asked his colleagues for a general explanation or model of the cyclic changes in the sky. According to the Greek writings that survived the Dark Ages after the fall of the Roman Empire, Plato assumed that the stars were eternal, divine, and unchanging beings, which moved around the Earth with uniform motion in endless circles, the most perfect paths for moving objects. The planets must also move in a way becoming to such heavenly bodies, combinations of perfect circles. The Greeks, at that time, believed that the large, solid Earth was the steady, unmoving center of the universe. They observed that the stars in the nightly sky seemed to be located on a hemisphere with the Earth at its center. This bowl of stars suggested to the Greeks that the stars were all on a sphere, called the *celestial sphere*, with the Earth at its center, and that the sphere was rotating on an axis which passed through the center of the Earth and the Pole Star (or North Star), since that star did not move any appreciable amount during a night. This celestial sphere, the early astronomers assumed, made one complete rotation in 23 hours and 56 minutes. Inside this star sphere was the invisible sphere of the Sun. To account for the annual north-south motion of the Sun, they tilted the axis of the Sun sphere to the axis of the stellar sphere. The five planets known at that time were placed on transparent spheres with Saturn closest to the stars. The fast-moving Moon sphere was placed closest to the Earth. The Earth remained stationary with all of the celestial objects revolving around it. This is called the earth-centered, or *geocentric* model of the solar system. Eudoxus, one of Plato's devoted students, designed a model of the solar system with twenty-seven spheres; an outer sphere for all of the stars, three spheres for the Sun, three spheres for the Moon, and four spheres for each of the five planets. Later Callippus added seven more spheres, and shortly thereafter Aristotle became interested in solar models and designed a model with fifty-six shells, each rotating at a different rate.

Aristotle (384–322 B.C.) was the greatest of all of the Greek philosophers. He was the son of the physician to King Philip of Macedonia. He was one of Plato's students, and was the tutor of the king's son, who later became Alexander the Great. Because of Aristotle's high position he could not do any measuring or experimenting himself for that was considered as manual labor, which was slave's work. Therefore, he relied upon reason and logic. He became known as the "father of logic." He reasoned that the Earth was spherical in shape because a sphere is the most nearly perfect configuration. Based upon philosophy and religion, he believed the Earth to be at rest because rest is the most perfect position. He also argued that a heavy object falls faster than a light one because things seek their natural places, and a heavy object would seek that position faster. Aristotle was active in many branches of science, and his views were all generally accepted without question for nearly 2,000 years.

Not all of the Greeks, however, thought the same as Plato and Aristotle, for in the third century B.C. Aristarchus suggested a much simpler model for the motions of the celestial objects. He placed the Sun at the center of the system with Earth, planets, and stars revolving around it in concentric circular orbits. Such a Sun-centered model is called *heliocentric*. Aristarchus believed from certain geometrical measurements he made that the Sun was much larger than the Earth, and the largest object ought to be at the center of the solar system. To explain day and night, he had the Earth rotating on an axis through its center. The Earth was assigned the third orbit from the Sun. He explained that a planet would appear to move backward to us, or in retrograde motion, as the Earth was passing that planet in their motions around the Sun. Aristarchus violated the philosophical theory that the Earth was stationary, and not a celestial object. The biggest objection, however, was that a moving Earth ought to make the stars appear to shift positions relative to each other as the Earth followed its annual path around the Sun, and no such relative motion, or *stellar parallax* (see Fig. 1-2), was observed

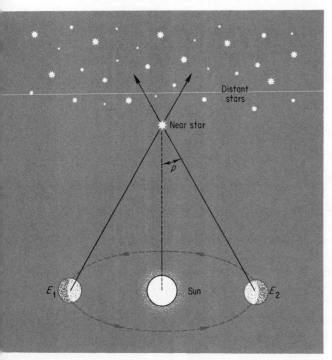

FIG. 1-2 Stellar parallax. If the Earth moved around the Sun, the nearer stars would appear to shift positions relative to distant stars as shown in this figure, but no such parallax was observed.

by him or any other astronomer. Aristarchus seemed to have a good idea, but it had very little influence on Greek thought because it did not seem to describe the observed fact that there was no relative shifting of the stars.

1-4
Ptolemaic System

For 500 years after Aristotle, astronomers tried to develop a more accurate model of the solar system that would explain all of the observed motions of the planets. During this time the scientific center of the world had shifted from Greece to Alexandria at the mouth of the Nile where Alexander the Great had founded a great museum with an outstanding library. In 225 B.C., Eratosthenes of Alexandria accepted Aristotle's idea that the Earth is spherical in shape, and determined the Earth's circumference with an amazing degree of accuracy (see Section 2-2). Hipparchus in 130 B.C. catalogued the exact position of more than 1,000 stars. To locate the celestial positions of these stars, he conceived and introduced spherical trigonometry. While doing this work, he discovered that year by year the celestial *equinoxes*, the points in the sky where the Sun is located when it is directly over the equator, slowly move westward through the sky. (Right now the spring equinox is in the constellation Aquarius.) The greatest of the Alexandrian scientists was an astronomer, Claudius Ptolemy, who in A.D. 150 developed a geocentric system that predicted the positions of the planets. He accepted Aristotle's assumption that the Earth was a motionless center around which all of the members of the celestial universe revolved from east to west once each day. The Moon and the Sun moved with the universe, but they did not make one complete revolution each time the stars did. They gradually fell behind the westward motion of the stars, making them appear to move eastward among the background of stars. The Moon lost one complete revolution in 27.32 days, and the Sun lost one revolution in 1 year. Hence, the Moon appeared to make one complete eastward revolution around the Earth in 27.32 days, and the Sun in 1 year. To account for the annual north-south motion of the Moon and Sun, the lunar and solar orbits were tilted, each the proper angle to the axis of rotation of the star sphere. The path the Sun takes through the stars is called the *ecliptic*.

To explain the peculiar motion of "wanderers" or planets, Ptolemy designed a system of "epicycles" (see Fig. 1-3). Each planet moved around a small circle called an *epicycle*, while the center of that circle revolved around the Earth along a second circle, called the *deferent*. The plane of each deferent was approximately parallel to the ecliptic. The retrograde motions of some of the planets were explained as the combined result of one circular motion superimposed upon another circular path. On the earthside of an

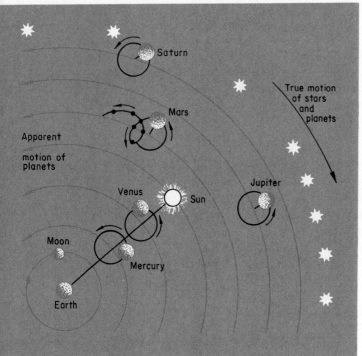

Labels in figure: Saturn, Mars, True motion of stars and planets, Apparent motion of planets, Jupiter, Venus, Sun, Moon, Mercury, Earth

FIG. 1-3 Ptolemaic system.

epicycle, the planet would move toward the west for a short interval, while the rest of the time it would be traveling eastward as indicated by the observations. It also explained why Mars was brightest during its retrograde motion, because at that time it would be nearest the Earth. To exactly describe the motion of the outer planets, Ptolemy had to assume that the radius of each epicycle was parallel to the line connecting the Earth and the Sun. To explain why Mercury and Venus were morning and evening stars only, Ptolemy had to assume that the centers of their epicycles remained in a straight line with the Earth and the Sun. In this manner and with the right epicycle radii, those two planets, could never get any farther from the Sun than their observed 28 and 48 degrees, respectively.

It was known that the Sun moved through successive 90-degree intervals in 92, 94, 90, and 89 days. To account for this irregular motion, and still keep a uniform angular motion of the Sun, Ptolemy located the Earth slightly off the center of the Sun's orbit. Likewise he placed the Earth slightly off the centers of the planets' deferents. With this arrangement, the Earth was no longer at the center of the universe, but it accounted for the unequal times for the Sun and planets to move through the different quadrants. This made the deferent an *eccentric*, centered slightly off from the Earth. All of these eccentrics and epicycles, however, did not completely describe the irregularites in the motions of the planets, and so Ptolemy put the center of the angular motion of the Sun and centers of epicycles off the center of the eccentrics opposite the offset Earth. This was called the *equant* point (see Fig. 1-4).

The epicycle system with its eccentrics and equant lasted for 1,400 years because it gave man an adequate picture of the planetary motions, and a psychological satisfaction to think of the Earth and himself at the center of the universe. It boosted his ego. Some of the Greek writings survived the three burnings of the library at Alexandria, and were transferred to Spain by the Moslems as they swept along the southern shore of the Mediterranean Sea and up into Spain. Other Greek writings survived the Dark Ages and were taken to Italy. After the founding of the University of Paris, many of Aristotle's writings were acquired and placed in the library there.

In the thirteenth century Thomas Aquinas read many of the writings of Aristotle, and blended the Greek philosophy and the Christian religion together as his theology. He accepted the geocentric model of the solar system because it agreed with his theology. This gave impetus to the acceptance of the Ptolemaic system of the universe.

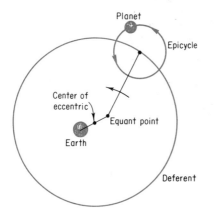

FIG. 1-4   Ptolemy's system of deferent, epicycle, eccentric, and equant.

1-5
Copernican System

In spite of the blessings of the church, the geocentric model of the solar system was soon in trouble. With the Renaissance in Europe much astronomical data came to light that could not be accurately explained by the Ptolemaic system. By the sixteenth century, nineteen epicycles on epicycles were used to explain the motion of Mars, and still that was not accurate enough. The astronomers were by now becoming interested in the distances to the Sun and planets, but the Ptolemaic scheme had no distance scale. Hence, the stage was all set for a reform.

FIG. 1-5   Nicholas Copernicus (1473–1543). (Courtesy Yerkes Observatory.)

Astrology survived the Dark Ages and prospered during the Renaissance because it appealed to man. Every king had a court astrologer to give him advice. Since astrology was so prevalent, it was natural that a revival in science began in astronomy, the study of the stars and planets. The first was Nicholas Copernicus (1473–1543) (see Fig. 1-5), a Polish monk who, while studying the canon laws, became interested in the heavens above. He studied Aristotle and the Ptolemaic system, and felt that the motions of the planets must be much simpler than those proposed by Ptolemy. He thought that the large Sun ought to be at the center of things. Copernicus took the number of cycles that Mars, Jupiter, and Saturn were observed to make among the background of stars in a certain number of years, and found that if they revolved around the Sun at a uniform rate instead of around the Earth, their periods of revolution would be 687 days, 11.8 years, and 29.5 years, respectively. By a somewhat similar method, he determined the period of revolution of Mercury and Venus about the Sun to be 88 days and 224 days, respectively. Using the distance from the Sun to the Earth as 1, Copernicus was the first to determine the relative distances from the Sun to the planets. Everything seemed to fit beautifully into a Sun-centered system with the Earth revolving in the orbit where Ptolemy had placed the Sun, and the stars remained fixed relative to the Sun. To account for the daily motions of the stars, and day and night, he had the Earth rotating once a day as well as re- volving around the Sun once in a year. Since he knew that his idea seemed preposterous to many, and contrary to the human understanding of the stationary Earth, he delayed publishing his book *On the Revolutions of the Heavenly Spheres*. It was, however, published and delivered to him on his deathbed in 1543.

The Copernican system had all of the planets, including the Earth, revolv- ing around the Sun in concentric circles, with the Moon revolving around the Earth in an epicycle (see Fig. 1-6). This simpler pattern was able to explain all observed motions, which were really relative motions. When the Earth passed any planet, that planet appeared to move backward while the Earth was passing it, as shown in Fig. 1-7. This retrograde effect is a familiar phenomenon experienced by most travelers. While traveling eastward along a highway, other cars on the same side of the road appear to be going in the same direction, but while passing one of the cars, it appears to be moving backward or westward with respect to the surrounding landscape due to

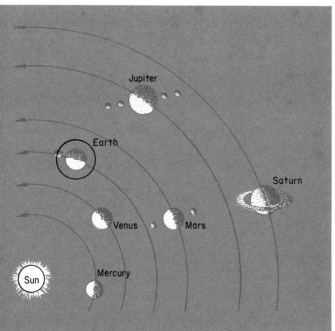

FIG. 1-6   Copernican system.

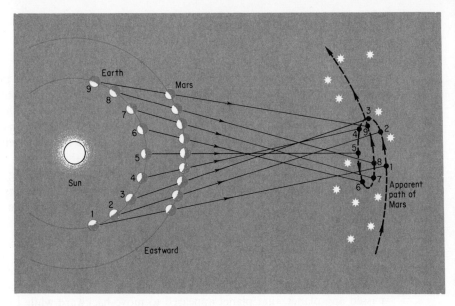

FIG. 1-7   Retrograde motion of Mars, as explained by Copernican model.

parallax. As soon as the car has been passed, it again appears to be traveling eastward. If the orbits of the Earth and planets were in the same plane, like the cars on the road, the back-and-forth apparent motion would be along a straight line. Since the observed retrograde paths are usually loops, the Earth's orbit was assumed to be slightly inclined to those of the other planets.

The one thing that puzzled Copernicus was the same thing that bothered Aristarchus: a moving Earth should make the stars appear to shift relative to each other as the Earth makes its annual revolution around the Sun, and no astronomer through the ages had ever observed stellar parallax. His book brought forth considerable opposition from the church, and later all of his books, published at that time, were burned. However, the heliocentric idea lived on.

Another astronomer to consider the problem proposed by Plato was Tycho Brahe (1546–1601), the astrologer to the king of Denmark, Frederick II. He was given an observatory by the king and with improved, naked-eye instruments, he made a great number of observations of the stars and planets, expecially Mars. He observed no parallax of stars, which indicated a stationary Earth, but he liked Copernicus's idea of the planets revolving around the Sun. He then proposed a new model, one with the planets revolving in circles around the Sun, while the Sun, Moon, and stars were all revolving in concentric circles around the Earth. This really confused the issue, but it did not contradict the views of the church. Brahe's greatest contribution to astronomy was not his complex planetary model, but the vast amount of accurate information he collected in his 30 years of observing in Uraniborg and Prague. With only a sextant having plain sights like that of a gun, he observed the planets night after night with special emphasis on Mars, and his published works filled many volumes.

1-6
Kepler's Laws of Planetary Motion

Johannes Kepler (1571–1630), Brahe's trusted assistant at Prague, inherited all of the records his master had accumulated. He carefully studied the data hoping to find some clue to the behavior of the planets. He began his study with Mars. He tried to fit the data of Mars to epicycles, eccentrics, and equants but without too much accuracy. From the abundance of data left him, he then actually plotted the orbit of Mars, and after years of untiring analysis, he proposed the following three laws, known as Kepler's laws, describing planetary motions with the Earth as one of the planets:

1. *The planets move around the Sun in elliptical paths with the Sun at one focus.*

This law describes the shape of the orbits. The planets do not follow concentric circular paths, as previously assumed.

2. *The line joining a planet to the Sun sweeps over equal areas in equal times.*

This law indicates how the planets travel along their elliptical paths. A planet moves most rapidly when nearest the Sun, and the slowest when farthest away (see Fig. 1-8). We on Earth are traveling fastest relative to the Sun

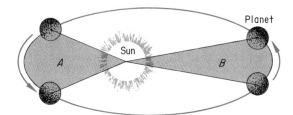

FIG. 1-8   Kepler's law of equal areas.

on January 3, and slowest on July 3. Since the Earth rotates at a constant rate, the length of a solar day, noon to noon, is longer than average on January 3, and shorter on July 3. Because of our elliptical path, the solar days change from day to day throughout the year.

3. *The squares of the period of revolution of any two planets are proportional to the cubes of their mean distances from the Sun.*

This law gives a relationship between the size of a planet's orbit and its time of revolution. It is called the *harmonic law*, and is expressed symbolically as follows:

$$\frac{P_1^2}{P_2^2} = \frac{d_1^3}{d_2^3}$$

where P_1 and P_2 are the periods of revolution of any two planets, and d_1 and d_2 are their mean distances from the Sun. Knowing the period of revolution of the Earth as 365 days and the mean distance from the Earth to the Sun as 93,000,000 miles, or 1 *astronomical unit* (a.u.), the period or distance of any other planet can be computed, providing one of the quantities is known. For example, since one Martian year is equal to 687 Earth solar days, we can calculate the mean distance from the Sun to Mars. Substituting these values into the foregoing equation, we obtain

$$\frac{365^2}{687^2} = \frac{1^3}{d_2^3}$$

Hence, d_2, the mean distance from the Sun to Mars, is equal to 1.52 astronomical units, or 141,000,000 miles.

Kepler's laws are strictly empirical relationships. They were obtained by inductive reasoning from the experimental data, and not derived mathematically. They merely describe the motions of the planets, but do not account for the motions.

While Kepler was formulating his laws, Galileo Galilei (1564–1642) was observing the planets through the small telescope he had invented. While at the University of Padua, he heard of a new glass made by Likppershey, a Dutchman, that could magnify distant objects. This gave him the idea that he might magnify the heavens. He constructed a telescope, and what he discovered with his telescope (it has been estimated) would have won him nine Nobel Prizes, had they been granted at that time. To his amazement he saw four moons around Jupiter, and some rings around Saturn. Many who looked through the telescope could not believe what they saw, and the skeptics simply refused to look. Even Kepler, when he first heard about it, said that such things were unbelievable, but facts soon convinced him. Galileo discovered that Venus displayed phases like our Moon, from crescent to full and back to crescent. This phenomenon could not be explained by the Ptolemaic theory, because in that system Venus could never appear as full, but the heliocentric system could explain it easily. Therefore, Galileo was convinced that the Copernican model of the solar system was right. He gave many talks on the subject, and in 1632 he published *A Dialogue on the Two Principal Systems of the World*. It aroused a great deal of attention throughout Europe. The following year, Galileo was summoned to Rome and forced to renounce his findings. He was sentenced to an indefinite prison term, and spent the remaining years of his life confined to his villa in Florence under constant surveillance.

Sir Isaac Newton (1642–1727), an English mathematician, physicist,

FIG. 1-9
Sir Isaac Newton (1642–1727).
(Yerkes Observatory photograph.)

and astronomer (see Fig. 1-9), was born the year Galileo died. Newton was the greatest scientific genius the world has ever known. He introduced the binomial theorem, formulated the three basic laws of motion (see Chapter 8), developed a form of calculus in order to use adequately his laws of motion, discovered the composition of the light spectrum, and formulated the inverse-square law of gravitation (see Chapter 9). It is said that one day, while walking through an orchard, he saw an apple fall from a tree, and he began to wonder why the apple fell. His curiosity led to the formation of the law of gravitation, which was the key that unlocked the age-old mystery about the planetary motions. His law of universal gravitation states that every particle in the universe attracts every other particle with a force that is proportional to the product of the masses of the particles and inversely proportional to the square of the distance between them. He assumed that the gravitational force of the Earth extended out to the Moon, and calculated the motion of the Moon under the influence of the Earth's pull. He found the calculated motion to agree with the observed facts. Assuming the Sun to have a similar gravitational force on the planets, he calculated the motions of the planets around the Sun, and found that these motions satisfied Kepler's laws. Now things were beginning to tie together. For the first time man was able to turn his attention from the empirical analysis of *how* planets move to the more scientific analysis of *why* they behave as they do. Newton proved that the heliocentric model of the solar system is the one that explains all observations. We now accept, without question, the Copernican theory of planetary motions. Just a minute, you might say, how about the parallax of stars? With modern instruments we have finally detected stellar parallax, but the parallax angle is indeed small; for the nearest star it is only 0.76 second of arc. No wonder the early astronomers did not see it. With this bit of information, we are sure of the sun-centered theory.

1-7
Scientific Methods

We have seen from the development of the solar system model that there was a steady growth throughout its history of about twenty-one centuries. Each scientist tried to systematize the knowledge of the celestial phenomena available to him and use it to predict future positions of the celestial objects. It is very clear that in the development of planetary theories, astronomers would have been more accurate if each had systematized the known physical facts without allowing his opinions or preconceived beliefs to influence his conclusions. Any theory must explain all new data collected, or the theory must be changed to explain the new facts. As new data about the planetary system accumulated, the model was changed to accommodate the facts. But, as we have noticed, astronomers find it difficult to discard personal opinions, especially if they are connected with religious beliefs. The development of the planetary model was very much involved with religion, but in many cases prejudice and strong personal opinion may influence the interpretation of scientific data. Science is a systematized knowledge of facts about nature from which future events may be predicted. The methods used in the advancement of science vary from scientist to scientist. However, these various methods have certain common elements which we shall discuss in Section 1-8. An individual scientist may spend a very long time in developing one segment of a great theory, which may take many years for complete development.

Before man made any progress in science, he had to be able to *record* his observations. Only by recording eclipses of the Sun or erecting big stones was he able to see the periodicity of the events and predict future eclipses. Recording data is an important step in all scientific achievements. The second great step took place when the Greeks introduced logic. Thereafter, logical conclusions could be drawn from the classified knowledge acquired. After determining the time required for each planet to revolve once around the Sun, Copernicus logically concluded that the planets follow concentric circles around the Sun in precisely the order we know them today, in spite of the fact that he did not observe any stellar parallax. He had no facts to disprove the concentric circle idea. The third step came when scientists started basing their conclusions upon experimental observations. Remember that Aristotle made no measurements, but depended upon logic. Galileo, on the other hand, gathered experimental data with his telescope and recorded that data. Although some did not believe what they saw, Galileo recorded the phases of Venus, the positions of the moons of Jupiter at various times, and the rings on Saturn. The phases of Venus helped establish the heliocentric idea, for such phases as those observed by Galileo could not be explained by the Ptolemaic theory. After man learned to record experimental data and logically draw conclusions from that data without letting personal opinions enter, science progressed by leaps and bounds.

1-8
Attacking a Scientific Problem

Let us now look at the whole scientific pattern. We shall discuss the procedure in an order which seems most logical, instead of the order taken by any particular individual.

1. Defining the Problem The first step in any procedure is to know what we are setting out to do. If a goal is clearly in mind, the solution is much easier. Not all problems, however, can be well defined. The experimentation may be exploratory in nature and the only thing we know is that we are looking for something different or unusual. Also, many discoveries are accidental, and it would be impossible to define such an achievement in advance. As an example, Professor Urey, while studying the hydrogen spectrum, noticed an extra emission line which he could not explain. This extra spectral line led to the discovery of heavy hydrogen (deuterium). A discovery generally introduces other problems which can be defined. Scientists usually start out with a goal in mind and, while trying to achieve that goal, discover new things.

2. Gathering Controlled Observations The next step is to gather facts— not personal opinions, but true observations which can be checked by others or measured with accurate instruments. Observations like the lunar eclipses can be accurately checked by colleagues, but a verification by others may not always be reliable either, especially if the observations depend upon the human senses. For example, if a person puts one bare foot on a throw rug which has been in the room for some time, and the other bare foot on the wooden floor, he will say that the rug is much warmer. Other persons performing the same experiment will heartily agree with him that the the rug is warmer than the floor, but an accurate thermometer would show that the temperature of the rug is the same as that of the wooden floor. The thermometer gives the true, unbiased temperature.

Science would not have progressed as rapidly as it has if the investigators depended on chance observations. It is very important to perform controlled experiments, keeping all the variables constant except two, and finding a relationship between these two variables. Many experiments have been set up and much data collected but no satisfactory results were obtained because there was no proper control of the experimental conditions. In the descriptive sciences, the observations of an experimental group are compared to those of a controlled group. We find out that controlled experimentation is by far the most fruitful.

3. Classifying and Generalizing the Facts   After the data have been accumulated, they must then be classified and integrated into the existing knowledge. For the descriptive sciences this is the most important step, but for the more exact sciences, such as chemistry and physics, this is only the beginning. From the classified results, relationships may be observed and scientific laws derived. This generalization from the specific facts, or going from specifics to the general, is called *inductive reasoning*, the most essential part of the scientific method. It is dangerous to make a generalization before sufficient evidence is obtained, for the resulting conclusion may not be valid. (For some people, jumping to conclusions is their only form of exercise.) A scientific law is not like a civil law; it is not set up for nature to follow, but is merely a description of natural behavior. A scientific law is a concise statement, usually in the form of an equation, of *how* we believe things behave.

As an example of this procedure, suppose we wish to learn the relationship between the distance an object falls from a rest position and the time of fall. To obtain the necessary data, we clock the time it takes a ball to fall various distances, always starting from rest. We observe that the ball falls 16 feet in 1 second, 64 feet in 2 seconds, 144 feet in 3 seconds, and 256 feet in 4 seconds. From this we see that the ratio of any two distances is equal to the ratio of the corresponding times squared. Hence, by inductive reasoning we can say that the distance (d) a freely falling object travels from rest is directly proportional to the time (t) squared. This may be written in symbolic form as $d = 16t^2$, where the factor 16 was obtained from the accumulated data. This is the law for freely falling objects because it describes how they fall.

Scientific laws are valuable only if used for future thinking or to predict future events. Without this predictability there would be no science. If we cannot predict, we really do not understand a natural phenomenon. Applying the generalization to a specific event, or going from the general to specific, is called *deductive reasoning*.

As an example, let us apply the general law of freely falling objects to a particular case, and determine the height of a bridge over a deep canyon. The law states, in general, a relationship between distances and times of fall; therefore, if we know the time for a stone to fall from the bridge to the canyon floor, we can determine the height of the bridge. Let us say that by counting "One thousand one, one thousand two, one thousand three," etc., we estimated the time of fall of a stone to be a little under 5 seconds, maybe 4.75 seconds. Then we know the bridge to be $16 \times (4.75)^2$ or about 360 feet above the canyon floor. Of course, if a stopwatch is available, the height of the bridge can be determined more accurately—but not precisely, because of air resistance.

4. Forming and Testing Working Hypotheses A scientist has a great curiosity about nature. He wants to know more than *how* a thing behaves— he wants to know *why*. He first makes an intelligent guess as to why it behaves the way it does. This requires a creative imagination on his part, and some of the guesses are "out of this world"! A workable guess is called a *hypothesis*. Different scientists may have different guesses, and for a physical phenomenon there may be a number of hypotheses, or schools of thought; consequently, more experimentation is necessary to determine which hypothesis is correct. In the above example we could explain *how* the object falls, but the scientific question is, "*Why* does it fall?" One hypothesis might be that the Earth attracts the object, and another might be that the pressure of the Sun's light pushes the object toward the Earth. More data indicates that an object falls the same distance in a given time interval at night as in the daytime; hence, the light-pressure hypothesis does not satisfy the experimental facts. Thus, gravitational attraction remains as the working hypothesis. It may not tell us exactly why the object is attracted to the Earth, and so we continue to seek the why.

5. Forming Theories from Tested Hypotheses After a hypothesis has been checked and rechecked, it becomes a theory. Sciences are built around these theories. Radio, radar, and television are based upon Maxwell's electromagnetic wave theory, and the whole field of chemistry is based upon Dalton's atomic theory.

If new evidence which the theory cannot explain is uncovered, then more hypotheses must be proposed, more testing done, and a new theory formulated. The caloric theory of heat, which stated that heat is a weightless fluid, lasted for about 200 years before it was proved false by experimentation. Perhaps many of our present theories are not exactly right, but as long as they are able to predict events as accurately as our instruments can measure them, we will consider the theories adequate and science will continue to march forward.

In summary, the scientific method is a pattern of procedure, but is not necessarily a specific rule of order followed by each scientist. It consists of defining the problem, gathering experimentally objective facts, classifying the data, logically drawing conclusions to enable man to understand how things behave as they do, formulating hypotheses as to why he thinks they behave that way, checking the hypotheses experimentally, and forming a theory which is revised throughout the years as required by experimental data. Consequently, *physical sicence is a systematized knowledge of physical truths from which general laws or models can be derived and future events, under known conditions, predicted.*

QUESTIONS AND PROBLEMS

1. Why did the Babylonians develop astronomy to a greater extent than did the Egyptians?

2. What is meant by retrograde motion?

3. What do you mean when you say that the Moon rises?

4. Describe the essential features of the Ptolemaic theory of the planetary system. What assumptions did Ptolemy make?

5. In the Ptolemaic system, what does the deferent represent?

6. How was the Ptolemaic system able to explain why some planets are only morning and evening stars while others show retrograde motion?

7. How can the Sun have a daily westward motion and still have an eastward drift?

8. Describe the apparent motion of the stars if the Earth's shape was that of a flat disk. If its shape was that of a cylinder.

9. Describe the essential features of the Copernican system of planets. What were the early objections to this idea?

10. Why did astronomy get so involved with religion?

11. Did Copernicus make any assumptions in his system of planets?

12. Since Aristarchus proposed a sun-centered system about 18 centuries before Copernicus, why isn't the heliocentric model called the Aristarchus system?

13. Why did Tycho Brahe become interested in astronomy, and what was his greatest contribution?

14. Galileo built a telescope in 1609 with which he observed that Venus exhibited all of the phases of our Moon. Describe the phases one can see by using the Ptolemaic system, and the Copernican theory.

15. How can you explain by using the Copernican system that Mars is brightest at retrograde motion?

16. How did the phases of Venus as observed by Galileo prove that the Earth is revolving around the Sun?

17. Why were so many scientists afraid to look through Galileo's telescope?

18. What does each of Kepler's laws tell us about the motion of the planets? Do they apply to our Moon and the moons around Jupiter?

19. Why is the length of the solar day longer on January 3 when the daylight is about the shortest?

20. Why is the Earth traveling the fastest on January 3 when the shortest amount of daylight is on about December 21?

21. Does Venus show retrograde motion? Explain.

22. Why is the retrograde motion for Saturn less than that of Mars?

23. Jupiter is 5.2 astronomical units from the Sun. Using Kepler's harmonic law, calculate Jupiter's period of revolution. How does it compare with the accepted period of revolution (see Table 5-1)?

24. If some external force should shift the Earth nearer the Sun so that its mean radius becomes 80,000,000 miles, what would be the Earth's period of revolution?

25. It has been suggested that there might be a tenth planet in our solar system at about 75 astronomical units from the Sun. What would be its period of revolution?

26. How can one tell whether or not a certain field of endeavor is a science? Is astronomy a science? Is religion a science?

27. What is the basic difference between a scientific law and a civil law?

28. Give one example of *inductive* reasoning and one example of *deductive* reasoning that you have employed recently.

29. What is the difference between a hypothesis and a theory? Why do theories change if they were good enough to have become theories?

30. What is the difference between science and technology? Give an example of each.

31. What is meant when we say that a person is "scientific-minded"? What are some of the characteristics of a scientific attitude?

SUGGESTED REFERENCES

ABELL, GEORGE, *Exploration of the Universe*, 2nd ed., Chaps. 2, 3, & 4. Holt, Rinehart & Winston, New York, 1969.

DAMPIER, SIR WILLIAM, *A History of Science*, 4th ed. Cambridge University Press, New York, 1958.

PANNEKOEK, A., *A History of Astronomy*. Interscience Publishers, New York, 1961.

RIDGEWAY, SIR WILLIAM, *The Early Age of Greece*. Cambridge University Press, New York, 1901.

VON HAGEN, VICTOR W., *The Ancient Sun Kingdoms of the Americas*. World Publishing Co., Cleveland, 1961.

WIENER, PHILIP P., and AARON NOLAND, *Roots of Scientific Thought*. Basic Books, New York, 1958.

2
Our Planet, the Earth

The space age has brought astronomy into sharper focus, but before taking a journey into space, we must know more about our planet, the Earth. A firmer knowledge of the celestial universe can come only through a more complete understanding of our own planet and its effect upon what we see in space. The more we know about the Earth, the better we are able to interpret our observations of celestial phenomena. It is also essential that we know the Earth's shape, size, and motions before we can satisfactorily launch man-controlled vehicles into interstellar space to explore the universe and return them to Earth safely.

2-1
Shape of the Earth

The early idea that the Earth is flat and floating on the seas still seems to be quite logical, for if a man were just to observe the landscape around him, he could easily say that the Earth definitely looks like a flat, circular disk covered with hills, valleys, and mountains. It appears to be rimmed by a blue sky which is shaped like a large bowl inverted over his head. The point in the sky directly above him is called his *zenith*. If this person were to travel in any direction, the terrain would still appear to be flat, and eventually he would reach a body of water. Hence, the Earth might seem to be a flat disk floating on water.

As youngsters, our parents and teachers told us that the Earth is round like a ball, and we rightfully accepted their word. At home and at school, we also saw round globes which clinched the idea in our minds. Not that we doubt the veracity of either our parents or teachers, but what experimental evidences do we have that lead us to believe in the Earth's sphericity? Two

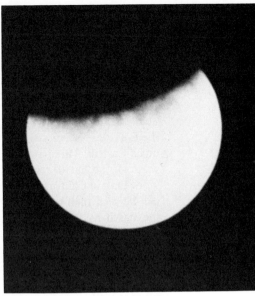

FIG. 2-1 Picture taken from the *Apollo 11* spacecraft during its translunar coast toward the Moon.

FIG. 2-2 Earth's shadow cast upon the Moon forty minutes before the total eclipse of the moon on December 31, 1963. (Photographed by Del Borer of the Des Moines Register and Tribune Company.)

thousand years before Columbus sailed the Atlantic Ocean, Aristotle reasoned that the Earth was spherical because a sphere is the most perfect configuration since it has the smallest exposed lateral area for a given amount of material. This conclusion for the Earth's shape was based upon an inference, but not upon unbiased facts. What facts do we have to prove that the Earth is spherical? Pictures taken by the Apollo astronauts on their way to the Moon (see Fig. 2-1) definitely show the Earth to be almost round, but what we see might be that of a partially illuminated disk instead of a sphere. We also know that the Earth casts a circular shadow on the Moon during a lunar eclipse (see Fig. 2-2), but again this might be the shadow cast by a circular disk. Persons living near large bodies of water assure us that the Earth is spherical because the lower part of a ship disappears before the funnels and masts do when the ship travels away from the shore (see Fig. 2-3), and

FIG. 2-3   Earth's curvature.

they say that if the Earth were flat, the ship would merely get smaller and smaller, and finally fade out of sight. Their observation certainly proves that the Earth has a curved surface, but maybe it is like that of a bowl turned over. A more systematic observer might present the fact that we can travel continually westward and eventually arrive at the starting point, thus proving the Earth's sphericity. This could also be true if the Earth were a hemisphere or half a ball. There are other observations that might indicate the spherical shape of the Earth, such as the fact that the Sun rises 3 hours earlier in New York than in California, and that at high altitudes more of the Earth's surface can be seen than at lower altitudes. Both of these facts certainly prove that the Earth has a curved surface, but do not necessarily show its sphericity.

If the Earth is a sphere as our globes indicate, there must be people living on the other side, and they ought to be able to observe certain stars that we cannot see because the Earth is obstructing our view. Is there any such evidence? Many of us living in the northern part of the United States have never seen the well-known constellation called the Southern Cross, except in books and planetariums. Therefore, the Southern Cross must be on the opposite side of the Earth from those of us in the northern latitudes. Since some people south of the equator are able to see the Southern Cross each clear night, someone must definitiely live on the other side of our curved Earth. Hence, it must be more than a hemisphere or we would all see the same stars during one year. In Fig. 2-1 North America is not visible. Therefore, it must be on the opposite side, again proving the Earth to be spherical.

Another convincing set of evidence for the Earth's roundness can be obtained by observing the shape of the paths the stars take through the sky when observed north of the equator, at the equator, and south of the equator. These paths can be recorded photographically by aiming a camera into the sky on a moonless night and leaving the shutter of the camera open for several

FIG. 2-4 (a) Star trails taken north of the equator showing concentric circular arcs; (b) Star trails taken at the equator showing straight lines. (Yerkes Observatory photos.)

(a) (b)

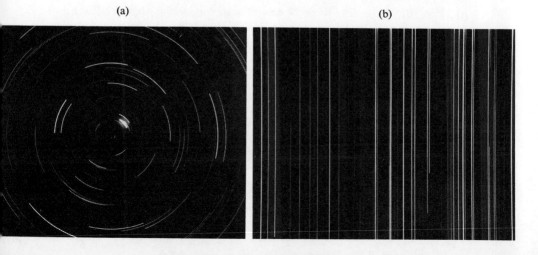

hours. The resulting bright streaks on the photograph show the apparent motion of the stars through the sky. Such "star trails" taken north of the equator show concentric circular paths with Polaris, the North Star, almost at the center of the circular arcs, as shown in Fig. 2-4(a). Star trails taken at the equator are straight lines [see Fig. 2-4(b)]. South of the equator the trails become circular again, but not around any particular star. The patterns of such star trails, regardless of whether the stars or Earth are moving, could be produced only if the Earth were a complete ball instead of a flat surface or a hemisphere. Of course, it possibly could be in the shape of a football.

2-2
Size and True Shape of Earth

How would one go about measuring accurately the circumference of the Earth in various directions to determine its true shape when three-fourths of its surface is covered with water? Eratosthenes, head of the library at Alexandria, solved the problem in 225 B.C. He observed that on a certain day in June, when the Sun was the farthest north, no shadows were cast at noon in Syene, Egypt, indicating that the sun was directly overhead. While in Alexandria, some 5,000 stadia (about 500 miles) due north, the Sun on the same day was $7\frac{1}{4}$ degrees south of a vertical position (see Fig. 2-5). He reasoned that the two cities were $7\frac{1}{4}/360$, or about $\frac{1}{50}$ of the circumference of the Earth apart, and concluded that the Earth's circumference was 250,000 stadia (approximately 25,000 miles), a distance very close to our present-day value.

Modern determinations follow the same procedure, but use a distant star instead of the Sun. Two observing stations are selected along the arc of a great circle (a circle with its center at the center of the Earth) with the distance between them accurately known. When a star is directly above one station, the other observer measures precisely the angle the star is to one side of his zenith. In such a manner, the equatorial circumference has been found to be 24,887 miles, while the polar circumference is 24,806 miles. From this

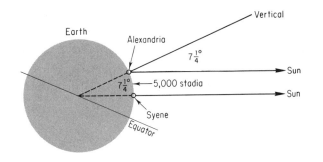

FIG. 2-5 Measuring Earth's circumference.

we definitely see that the Earth is almost spherical. Information from man-made satellites shows it to be slightly egg- or pear-shaped.

From these circumferences the equatorial and polar diameters have been computed to be 7,927 and 7,900 miles, respectively. This difference of 27 miles in 7,900 shows that the shape of the Earth deviates very little from that of a sphere. If the Earth were represented by a globe 18 inches in diameter, the equatorial diameter would be 0.06 inch larger than that of the polar diameter, an amount hardly noticeable.

2-3
What is Moving—The Stars or the Earth?

We have already mentioned that the Sun, Moon, and stars rise daily in the east and set in the west. This surely indicates that something is moving, but is it the motion of the celestial objects or of the Earth? If this apparent motion of the celestial scenery is due to the rotation of the Earth, then each of us is carried eastward at a very high speed. At the equator, a person would travel 24,887 miles in 24 hours, or at a speed of 1,038 miles per hour relative to the center of the Earth. In the central part of the United States, we would be traveling eastward at a slower speed of 770 miles per hour because we have less distance to go in the same 24-hour period. Certainly, motions of these magnitudes should produce some detectable proof of their existence. Our difficulty in observing them is that everything around us is moving with the same eastward velocity, and so we have nothing for comparison. However, if we look at the world's prevailing surface winds, we do see evidences of such motions. The trade winds are the result of these motions. The air near the equator is heated, expands, and when it rises, the air from the northern and southern tropics moves into this region to replace the rising air. Thus the air drifts steadily equatorward from the tropics. If the Earth were not rotating, these trade winds would always come from due north or due south. This does not agree with the observed facts, for we know that the trade winds in these two regions are from the northeast and southeast (see Fig. 2-6). If, however, the Earth were rotating, the air moving down from the "horse latitiudes" would have the eastward speed of the Earth where it originated, and that would be much less than the speed of the Earth's surface at the equator. As the air moves toward the eqautor, it cannot keep up with the eastward motion of the Earth and appears to lag behind it. Hence, the air is deflected toward the west. The resulting wind, with reference to the Earth, appears to come from the northeast in the Northern Hemisphere, and in the Southern Hemisphere, it would appear to come from the southeast. This agrees with the known facts about the winds in the trade-wind belts. Similarly, the air moving northward from the "horse latitudes" would be

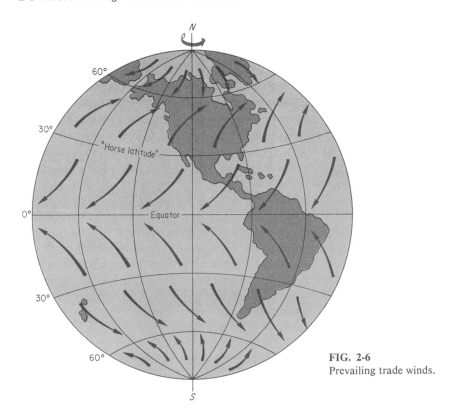

FIG. 2-6
Prevailing trade winds.

moving eastward faster than the Earth's surface farther north, and due to its greater eastward motion would gain on the Earth. It would be deflected toward the east, thus producing the prevailing westerly winds. Most of the United States is located in the westerly trade-wind belt. Although we may have surface winds from almost any direction, our storm centers move from the Plains States northeastward across the rest of the country. The storm centers definitely would not move in this direction if the Earth were not rotating on its axis.

Another evidence of the Earth's rotation may be seen in the circulation of the air around the low- and high-pressure regions which we see on the weather maps of television newscasts. We observe from these weather maps that the air circulates around all low-pressure regions in a counterclockwise direction in the Northern Hemisphere. The air from the north moving southward into a low-pressure region is deflected to the west due to the rotation of the Earth, and the air from the south moving northward is deflected to the east, producing the counterclockwise motion (see Fig. 2-7). In a high-pressure region, the air moves outward from the area. The air moving northward is

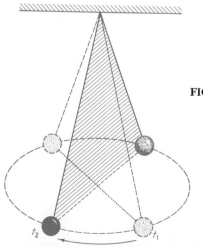

FIG. 2-7 Cyclonic region in the Northern Hemisphere.

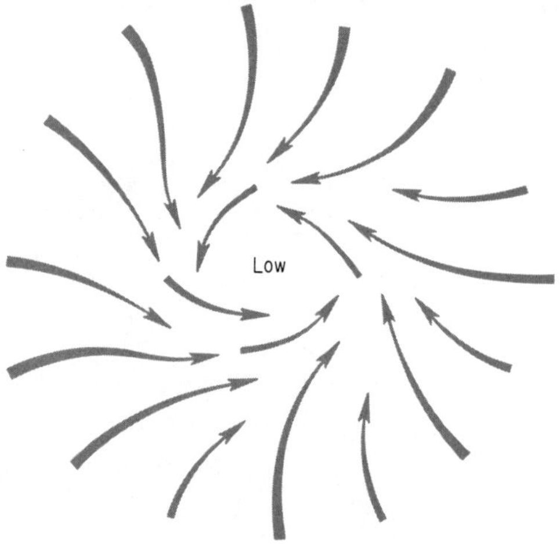

deflected to the east, and that moving southward is deflected to the west, producing a clockwise rotation. In the Southern Hemisphere, the circulations are reversed. If the Earth were not spinning, there would be no circulation of air around these cyclonic regions as the air moves in or out of them, and our weather pattern would be considerably different.

The most direct experimental proof that the Earth rotates about an axis can be performed in a classroom by allowing a long pendulum to swing freely, and observing the behavior of its motion. Such a pendulum is called a *Foucault pendulum*, in honor of the man who first performed the experiment, and is merely a heavy ball suspended from the ceiling by a long, fine wire. After the ball has been set into a swinging motion, it slowly appears to change its direction of motion (see Fig. 2-8). Since no forces are acting upon the ball to change its course, it must continue to swing along a fixed path relative to the stars, and any apparent change in motion is due to that of the Earth. In the Northern Hemisphere the pendulum appears to turn in a clockwise direction, meaning that the Earth moves from west to east. At the North

FIG. 2-8 Foucault pendulum.

Pole, the Earth would make one complete rotation in a day under such a pendulum, and the pendulum would appear to turn clockwise through 360 degrees in 23 hours and 56 minutes. At the equator it would not appear to turn at all.

All of these proofs have depended on a knowledge of the entire Earth or on the motion of a pendulum, none of which was known until recent times. Copernicus could offer no more convincing argument of the Earth's rotation than to say that it seemed more probable than did the rotation of the entire universe about the Earth. To us, this seems to be a very weak argument. During the last century, however, we have obtained enough evidence to settle definitely the rotational question once and for all. The evidence is convincing that the Earth rotates from west to east about an axis through the North and South poles.

2-4
Orbital Motion of the Sun or the Earth?

The rotational motion of the Earth produces our days and nights, but what motion produces the years? By noting the stars in the western sky each evening shortly after sunset, we observe that the Sun slowly moves *eastward* through the background of stars. In one year, it makes one complete journey through the celestial bodies and returns to its original position among the stars. The apparent path the Sun takes through the panorama of stars is called the *ecliptic*. The twelve groups of stars along its path are called the *constellations of the zodiac*, and play a very important part in astrology, which has flourished throughout the period of recorded history. The astrologer believes that the constellation of the zodiac in which the Sun is located when a person is born determines the character, behavior, and destiny of that individual. Does the Sun really move through these constellations, or is it an apparent movement due to the Earth's motion? If the Earth revolves once around the Sun in one year, the Sun would appear to make a complete trip through the stars. Ptolemy insisted that the Earth could not move around the Sun because at the speed it would have to travel, the Earth would fly apart; therefore, he was certain that the Earth was stationary. What would keep the Sun from flying apart if it were moving around the Earth he did not say.

The ancient astronomers argued that if the Earth were revolving around the Sun, the nearer stars should appear to move with respect to the distant ones as illustrated in Fig. 1-2. When the Earth is in position E_1, a near star, A, appears to be located at X among the background of stars. In 6 months the Earth moves to E_2 and that same near star then appears to be located at Y. Early astronomers did not observe such a shift and concluded that the Earth remained stationary at the center of the universe. When Copernicus presented his hypothesis of a Sun-centered planetary system, he overcame this argument by saying that the stars were all so far away that any such shift would be too small to be detected. However, by taking pictures of a certain group of stars through our present-day large telescopes in the spring and again in the fall, we have detected a measurable displacement, or *stellar parallax*, as it is known The parallax angle *p* is indeed small; for our nearest star, Proxima, the parallax is only 0.76 second of arc. This is equivalent to measuring the diameter of a quarter coin at a distance of 2 miles. Proxima is the most favorable case. This parallactic shift is smaller, the more distant the star becomes. One might argue that this stellar displacement is due to the motion of the stars themselves. Therefore, another picture must be taken the following spring to see if the stars return to their relative positions, or if they continue to move in the direction observed in the fall. We find that the stars do return approximately to their original positions in the course of one year. Of course, the Earth could be stationary and the nearer stars actually moving in elliptical paths among the distant stars, but it seems very unlikely that all the nearer stars would make one complete revolution in one Earth-year as they are observed to do. Therefore, we can conclude that the Earth is revolving around the Sun. *Revolution* is the term used to describe that fact that one body is traveling in an orbit around another body, while *rotation* indicates that a body is turning about an internal axis.

A more convincing proof of the revolution of the Earth was discovered by James Bradley in 1725 while attempting to detect the stellar parallax. He observed that the displacement of the star Draconis went through a complete cycle in one year. He interpreted this as the resultant of two motions, that of the Earth and that of the light coming from the star, producing a slight displacement in the direction of the observer's motion. This aberration of light is most easily understood by an analogy of falling raindrops. A person walking in a rainshower, in which the drops are falling vertically, finds that the rain appears to be coming from ahead of him although it is actually falling straight down. If he is carrying an umbrella, he tilts it forward slightly to compensate for his motion (see Fig. 2-9). If he turns to a new direction, the rain still seems to come from ahead of him changing its apparent direction

FIG. 2-9   Aberration analogy.

when he did. If he walks faster, the effects is increased, and if he slows down it diminishes. In exactly the same manner, Bradley observed that the light from Draconis entering his telescope appeared to come from a slightly displaced position, and as the Earth swung around in its orbit, changing the direction of its motion through 360 degrees in the course of a year, the star seemed to change its position in a tiny orbit of about 41 seconds of arc in diameter. Aberration produces larger angles than does stellar parallax; consequently, it gives us a more accurate measurement and a much better proof of the Earth's revolution about the sun.

2-5
The Shape of the Earth's Orbit

From pictures taken in the Northern Hemisphere of the Sun at noon on different days of the year, we observe that the Sun appears slightly larger in the winter than in the summer (see Fig. 2-10). This indicates that the Earth is closer to the Sun in our winter than in our summer. Hence, its path cannot

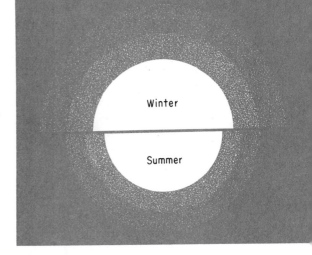

FIG. 2-10 Sun's apparent size in winter and summer.

be circular. The distance from the Earth to the Sun has been measured to be about 91,500,000 miles in the winter and 94,500,000 miles in the summer, with an average distance of almost 93,000,000 miles. By measuring the distance to the Sun each day of the year, we find that the Earth follows an elliptical path (see Fig. 2-11). In order to complete a trip around the Sun in one year, the Earth must travel at an average speed of about 18.5 miles per second, or about 66,000 miles per hour relative to the Sun.

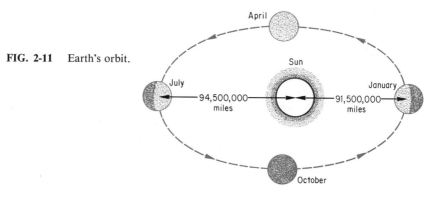

FIG. 2-11 Earth's orbit.

2-6
Direction of Earth's Axis

In the northern latitudes, the Sun does not rise perpendicular to the horizon, but rather takes a sloping arc in the sky southward in relation to the horizon until it reaches its highest point at noon, and then takes a symmetrical arc back to the western horizon (see Fig. 2-12). On the first day of spring or fall the Sun follows an arc in the sky directly above the equator or along the *celestial equator* (the plane of the Earth's equator extended out to the stars). During the rest of the year, the Sun follows daily paths through the sky parallel to the celestial equator, north of it in the summer and south of it in the winter. The Moon and all of the wandering stars or planets follow similar arcs through the night sky. The full moon moves south of the celestial equator in the summer and north of it in the winter. The only conclusion we can draw from these observations is that the Earth's axis of rotation is not perpendicular to its plane of revolution, but is tilted at some angle from the normal position. This angle has been determined to be $23\frac{1}{2}$ degrees.

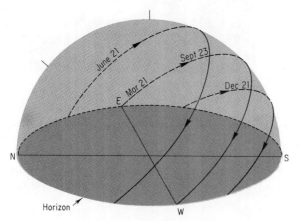

FIG. 2-12 Apparent paths of the Sun through the sky at four different days of the year.

The casual observer knows that night after night the stars travel in concentric circles around the same point in the northern sky very near Polaris, the North or Pole Star. Polaris, however, has not always been the North Star. When the Pyramids were built in 2800 B.C., Thuban, the third star from the tail of Draco, was the North Star, as indicated by small tunnels leading out from the main chambers of the Pyramids. Hence, the Earth's axis must be wobbling in space like the axis of a spinning top which has its axis inclined to the floor. This circular motion of the axis is called *precession*. If the Earth's axis continues its present motion, Vega in the constellation Lyra will be the North Star in about 12,000 years, and the axis will make one complete precession in 26,000 years (see Fig. 2-13). This motion is slight, but nevertheless it affects our celestial observations. The wobbling motion is due to the gyroscopic action produced by the Sun, Moon, and planets trying to pull the Earth's equatorial bulge into the plane of the Earth's orbit. This precessional motion isalso a good proof that the Earth is spinning on its axis.

The Earth has other motions. Our Sun and the whole planetary system is moving through the Milky Way galaxy toward the constellation Lyra at a speed of about 12 miles per second, or 43,000 miles per hour, relative to Lyra. The solar system is also moving with our galaxy of stars as it rotates around its center, and as the whole galaxy moves through space. These motions, however, do not disturb our solar system any more than the motion of a smoothflying jet plane disturbs its passengers.

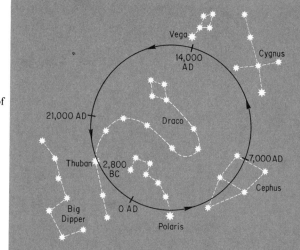

FIG. 2-13 Processional path of North Pole through the stars.

2-8
Terrestrial Coordinates

The conventional way of locating a certain place on Earth is to name the city and country to which it belongs, such as Des Moines, Iowa, U.S.A., or Wellington, New Zealand. If it is a friend's home we are to locate in either city, then more information is needed. We must know how far the home is north or south of some well-known east-west street, like Main Street, and also how far it is east or west of some well-known north-south street. From this information, we can then go directly to the friend's home.

A ship at sea cannot be located accurately by naming the country, island, or continent it is near. A ship has to be located in a manner similar to the way the friend's home was located—a certain distance from a well-known east-west reference line, and a certain distance from a well-known north-south reference line. The distances from these standard reference lines are the terrestrial coordinates, and we measure these distances in angles of arc instead of in miles. It is quite logical that the main east-west reference line agreed upon is the equator. The angle between the line drawn from the place in question to the center of the Earth and the equatorial plane is called the *latitude* of the place being located as shown in Fig. 2-14, and may be either north or south of the equator. For example, Des Moines is at a latitude of 41.5° N while Wellington, New Zealand, is 41° S. A north-south line on the spherical Earth is the arc of a circle drawn through the poles, and this great circle is called a *meridian*. The reference or prime meridian has been arbitrarily chosen as the meridian through Greenwich, England, which is very near London. The angle between the plane of the meridian through any place being located and the plane of the prime meridian is called the *longitude* of that location, and may be either east or west of the Greenwich meridian. For example, Des Moines has a longitude of 93.5° W, while Wellington is 175° E. If a ship on the high seas signals its position as 15° S and 75° E, we know exactly where in the Indian Ocean it is located.

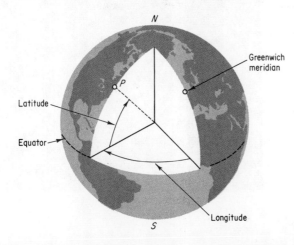

FIG. 2-14   Terrestrial coordinates.

2-9
Determination of Latitude

At the North Pole, latitude 90° N, the star Polaris is directly overhead, or 90 degrees above the horizon. At the equator, latitude 0°, Polaris appears on the horizon, zero degrees above the ground. Hence, *the latitude of an observer is equal to the altitude of the Pole Star above the northern horizon.* South of the equator, latitudes can be obtained from the altitude of the Sun or of a known star as it crossed the zenith celestial meridian. The longitude of any place on Earth can be determined from the difference between the local and Greenwich times, and will be explained in detail in the next chapter.

QUESTIONS AND PROBLEMS

1. Give evidences that the Earth is spherical in shape.

2. If the Earth were represented by an 18-inch globe, how high would a 29,000-foot mountain appear on the globe? The deepest part of the Pacific Ocean is about 7 miles. How deep a dent in the globe would represent the bottom of the ocean?

3. Suppose the Earth were a flat disk spinning around a perpendicular axis through its center. How would the shape of the star trails photographed from such an earth differ from those photographed from a spherical earth?

4. Distinguish between proof of the Earth's rotation and evidence that it rotates.

5. Give two evidences of the Earth's rotation, and explain how they indicate a rotation.

6. What is the difference between rotation and revolution? Is a revolving door correctly named?

7. What is the difference between stellar parallax and aberration?

8. Explain how the parallax of stars proves that the Earth is revolving around the Sun instead of merely moving through our galaxy with the Sun.

9. Give three examples of parallax which you have observed here on Earth.

10. Each of the following observations is due primarily to the fact that (A) the Earth is spherical in shape, (B) the Earth is rotating on its axis, (C) the Earth is revolving around the Sun, or (X) none of these. Explain which each is.
   (a) The Sun rises in the east and sets in the west.
   (b) The Southern Cross cannot be seen in the Great Lakes region.
   (c) The Sun is higher in the summer sky than it is in the winter sky.

    (d) The evening constellations of stars seen in the winter sky are different from those seen in the summer.

    (e) Boat houses across a fairly wide lake cannot be seen from the opposite shore.

    (f) The Moon appears to be moving in the same direction as an observer traveling in a fast moving train or car.

    (g) Certain stars seen in Panama cannot be seen in Boise, Idaho.

    (h) All the constellations of the zodiac can be seen in the course of one year.

    (i) Winds circulate clockwise around high-barometric-pressure regions in the Northern Hemisphere.

    (j) We see Saturn's rings edgewise every 15 years.

11. What must be the direction of motion of the Earth relative to a star for aberration of the starlight to be observed?

12. If the Earth's axis of rotation were perpendicular to the Earth's plane of revolution, what path across the sky would the Sun appear to take on March 21? On June 21?

13. What difference in the sky would you notice if the Earth rotated on its axis as it does now, but did not revolve around the Sun?

14. What difference in the sky would you notice if the Earth did not rotate on its axis, but revolved around the Sun as it does now?

15. If the Earth is really spinning as stated in the text, the surface at Chicago would be traveling about 770 miles per hour. How would it be possible for an airplane capable of flying 300 miles per hour to take off from the O'Hare Airport and land again at the same airport in 1 hour, since the airport would move 770 miles while the plane was in the air and the plane could only travel 300 miles in that time?

16. What is meant by each of the following terms?

(a) Zenith.	(c) Celestial equator.	(e) Latitude.
(b) Ecliptic.	(d) Precession.	(f) Longitude.

17. What is the longitude and latitude of the place where you live? Of the North Pole?

18. One degree longitude represents how many miles along the surface at the equator?

19. Two observers, *A* and *B*, are located on the equator. *A* is at a longitude of 75° east and *B* is at a longitude of 145° east. What is the distance in miles between *A* and *B*?

20. Point *X* is on the equator. Point *Y* is 249 miles due south of *X*. What is the angular distance between the zenith of a person at *X* and the zenith of a person at *Y*?

21. Show that a person's latitude is equal to the angle between his zenith and the celestial equator along a great circle.

SUGGESTED REFERENCES

ABELL, GEORGE, *Exploration of the Universe*, 2nd ed., Chap. 7. Holt, Rinehart & Winston, New York, 1969.

BAKER, ROBERT, and LAURENCE FREDRICK, *An Introduction to Astronomy*, 7th ed., Chaps. 2 and 3. D. Van Nostrand Co., Princeton, 1968.

KUIPER, G. P., *The Earth as a Planet*. University of Chicago Press, Chicago, 1954.

McLAUGHLIN, D. B., *Introduction to Astronomy*, Chaps. 4 and 5. Houghton Mifflin Co., Boston, 1961.

3
Time

Time is a fundamental quantity which we all use in our everyday experiences, and it is related to most of the important events in our lives. The concept of time itself is difficult to comprehend, for time does not directly stimulate our senses. We cannot see, hear, or feel it, but in a vague way we do sense it. On certain occasions time seems to pass more slowly than on others. When our experiences are dull and boring, time seems to drag, but when they are thrilling and exciting, time almost literally "flies." For example, the days before an anticipated vacation seem extremely long, while the joyous days during the vacation seem far too short. It is obvious that times measured by events which come to our consciousness are not very reliable. For a more dependable measurement, we must take the interval between two events which recur regularly. Since celestial objects appear to move through the sky at regular rates, the interval between successive crossings of the same meridian extended out to the stars for the same heavenly object has given us our concept of a day.

3-1
Solar Day

The Sun is the most natural celestial object to be used for measuring time, and has been used by man as a universal clock from the remotest antiquity until the present age. The interval between successive crossings of the same meridian by the Sun is taken as our *solar day*. For convenience, we have selected the crossing of the lower celestial meridian, the one opposite our zenith meridian, as the beginning of each day; in other words, our day begins at midnight. Although the Earth rotates at a remarkably constant rate, the days throughout the year are not of equal lengths because the speed of the Earth around the Sun varies as it travels along its elliptical path; it travels fastest when nearest the Sun and slowest when farthest away. During a year, these solar days may vary as much as 15 minutes or more. Any device used to keep accurate time cannot change from day to day in this manner; therefore, the average of the solar days for one complete year is used for timekeeping purposes. This is called the *mean solar day* and is divided into 24 hours (two 12-hour periods in most countries); each hour is further divided into 60 minutes, and each minute into 60 seconds—the same division as that introduced by the early Babylonians. Each tick of a watch is 1/86,400 of a mean solar day. We find that the tides tend to slow down the Earth's rotation, making the average solar day slightly longer each year. Although the change is extremely small, the mean solar day is gradually increasing. Hence, the standard second has been defined as 1/31,556,925.9747 of the year 1900.

The fact that our clocks, which read mean solar time, are not exactly in unison with the Sun can be verified experimentally as follows: Fasten a piece of cardboard that has a small hole in it to a south window as shown in Fig. 3-1, and once a week, at exactly noon by the clock, mark the position of the sunspot on the floor. By continuing this procedure throughout the year,

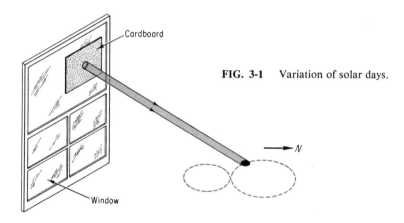

FIG. 3-1   Variation of solar days.

a figure eight, of the type seen on globes, will be traced out on the floor with the north end of the loop larger than the south end. If our clocks were in step with the Sun during the entire year, a straight north-south line would be produced as the Sun climbs high in the sky in the summer and low in the sky in the winter. The east-west deviation shows how the solar days vary in length as compared to the clock, sometimes slightly longer and other times shorter.

3-2
Sidereal Time

If a star, other than the Sun, were used as a reference for measuring time, we would not have to go to the trouble of averaging the days throughout

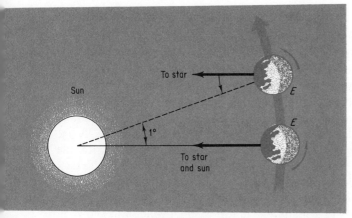

FIG. 3-2 Relation between sidereal and solar days.

the year, because all days would be of equal length. The time between successive crossings of the same meridian by the same star is called a "star day" or *sidereal day*—the time for the Earth to make *one complete* rotation. Since the Earth rotates at practically a constant rate, all star days are of equal length. During each sidereal day, the Earth also revolves about 1 ($\frac{360}{365}$) degree around the sun. Hence, the Earth must turn about 1 degree more than one rotation in order for the Sun to again cross the zenith meridian (see Fig. 3-2). This means that the solar day is slightly longer than the sidereal day. In one revolution about the Sun, these extra degrees add up to be one complete rotation of the Earth; therefore, in one year there is one more sidereal day than solar days. The length of each sidereal day is 23 solar hours, 56 minutes, and 4 seconds.

It may seem that sidereal time with its equal days would be far more convenient than the solar time with its variable days, but our lives are geared to the apparent motion of the Sun. We normally work when it is light outside, get hungry at noon, and sleep when it is dark. The astronomer, however, finds the sidereal time very useful.

3-3
Timekeepers

The keeping of accurate solar time has been a problem throughout the ages, and the importance of accurate timekeeping has increased with the increasing complexity of civilization and the demands of this atomic and space age. Television, jet planes, "atom smashers," satellites, and spaceships are just a few examples of mechanisms that demand split-second accuracy for their success, and even for their existence. Scientists are now requiring time measurements to about a billionth of a second. It is the task of the technologist to provide us with timepieces capable of such precision.

FIG. 3-3   A sundial. (Virginia Metalcrafters, Inc.)

The earliest type of timepiece was the *sundial* (see Fig. 3-3), which originated in Babylonia about 2000 B.C. It is, essentially, a device for indicating the passage of the hours by means of the shadow of a pointer, called a *gnomon*, cast upon a rigidly attached circular base. The gnomon is set parallel to the axis of the Earth—that is, in a north-south direction, and inclined away from the equator at an angle to the horizontal equal to the latitude of the place where the sundial is to be used. The hours and their subdivisions are marked on the horizontal base plate. The time is given by the position of the shadow of the pointer on the base. This elementary but effective timepiece, or some variation of it, served mankind for centuries. When Man demanded a more accurate measuring instrument, the sundial became obsolete, and today it makes a very attractive ornament for a garden.

In 200 B.C., a time indicator called a *clepsydra*, or water clock, was invented to measure more accurately shorter periods of time, usually an hour. Time was measured by the flow of a certain amount of water from the upper of two vessels through a small orifice into the lower vessel. Different times were measured by using different amounts of water. In arid regions, sand was used instead of water, and the resulting device was called an *hourglass* (see Fig. 3-4). Smaller hourglasses are used today as egg timers. Other arrange-

FIG. 3-4   Hourglass.

ments, such as the burning of candles or knotted ropes, were used as time devices, but none was very satisfactory.

The first mechanical timepiece that might be called a clock was invented in the fourteenth century. It was a weight-driven device, having a dial with only one hand. The first clocks weighed about 500 pounds and were used mainly in large cathedral towers. They were not very accurate—some varied as much as an hour per day. By 1500, Peter Henlein had introduced a coiled spring as replacement for the falling weight to power the mechanism. This made it possible to have portable timepieces.

The first important breakthrough in accurate timekeeping came when Galileo observed that a pendulum swings back and forth at a fairly constant rate, and its period of oscillation can be changed at will by varying the length of the pendulum. Later, Christian Huygens perfected the escapement mechanism, allowing a pendulum with a definite period to operate correctly the hour hand of the clock. Further refinements included the minute hand and, later, the second hand. Following these developments, most of the timepieces made were of the pendulum type, because they were far more accurate and ran much longer between windings. The domestic clocks were placed in tall, wooden cases, and are now known as grandfather clocks. Soon the pendulum was replaced by a balance wheel which was motivated by hairsprings. These modern timepieces have served man well, but even the most accurate of them introduce errors of about 1/1,000 of a second per day. This error of one part in ten million is not large for daily use, but in some scientific work, such an error is almost as large as the times being measured.

A further development came in 1914 when an alternating current was used to power the clock mechanism. A small electric motor, running in unison with the alternating current, operates the hands of the clock. Such a timepiece is very convenient because it requires no winding and produces no ticking sound; but it is no more accurate than the frequency of the alternating current.

For higher precision, we now have the quartz-crystal clocks. A quartz crystal, when subjected to an alternating electric field, vibrates at its own sharply defined rate. Such a crystal can be used to control the frequency of the current applied to the electric clock. These clocks are accurate to one part in a billion. A change in temperature slightly changes the frequency of the vibrating quartz crystal, thus introducing an error. The most accurate timing device we have today is the *atomic* clock. We have found that a cesium atom has a natural vibration of its own which does not fluctuate with changes in temperature or other external conditions. Through an electronic circuit, the vibration of a cesium atom can be made to control an electric clock. Such a clock is accurate to one part in 10 billion—which corresponds to an error of 1 second in 300 years.

Due to the rotation of the Earth, the Sun appears to move through 360 degrees in 24 hours; this is an apparent westward motion of 15 degrees per hour. Across the middle of the United States the Sun moves approximately 13 miles over the Earth's surface each minute. This means that every 13 miles one travels eastward or westward, he must change his watch 1 minute to achieve sundial time. This would be a nuisance in modern travel. Just imagine what it would be like traveling in a supersonic plane at speeds of 1,200 miles per hour relative to the ground, or 20 miles per minute, and having to change one's watch 1 minute every 13 miles. Until late in the nineteenth century, the time between different localities did vary in minutes and seconds as well as hours. For example, New York City was 11 minutes and 30 seconds behind Boston, and 12 minutes and 22 seconds ahead of Washington, D.C. After the advent of transcontinental railroads, such differences in local times led to utter confusion. In 1883, Charles F. Dowd, an American educator, suggested an hour-time-zone system which was immediately adpoted by the U.S. railroads, and a year later was adopted by many countries of the world. Today most countries use this scheme. It divides the world into time belts 1 hour wide with the longitude of the center of each time zone an exact multiple of 15 degrees, east and west of the Greenwich meridian. Each belt keeps the same time as that of the central meridian, and the time changes one whole hour at the edge of each time belt. In the original scheme, all time zones were to be equal widths, $7\frac{1}{2}$ degrees on each side of the standard meridian, but for various reasons, they have been modified and the edges through populated areas have become very irregular (see Fig. 3-5).

This system divides the mainland of the United States into four belts running north and south. The standard meridians are the 75th, 90th, 105th, and 120th, and the zones with these meridians at their centers are known as the Eastern, Central, Mountain, and Pacific time zones. Alaska, though smaller than the continental U.S., is so far north that it is also divided into four time belts: the Pacific, Yukon, Alaska, and Bering standard times. The Hawaiian Islands keep the same time as that of the 150th meridian, or the 10th time zone west of Greenwich. South America extends across three time zones, while Russia stretches across eleven zones. China cuts across four time zones, but prefers to have one time for the entire country, and they have selected the 8th eastern time zone, or that of Peking and Shanghai. India would normally be in the 5th and 6th time zones east, but has chosen the 5th time zone plus 30 minutes as their standard time. Saudi Arabia uses the Sun time as its standard. England has set its time 1 hour ahead to keep the same time as the Common Market countries. Many localities set their clocks

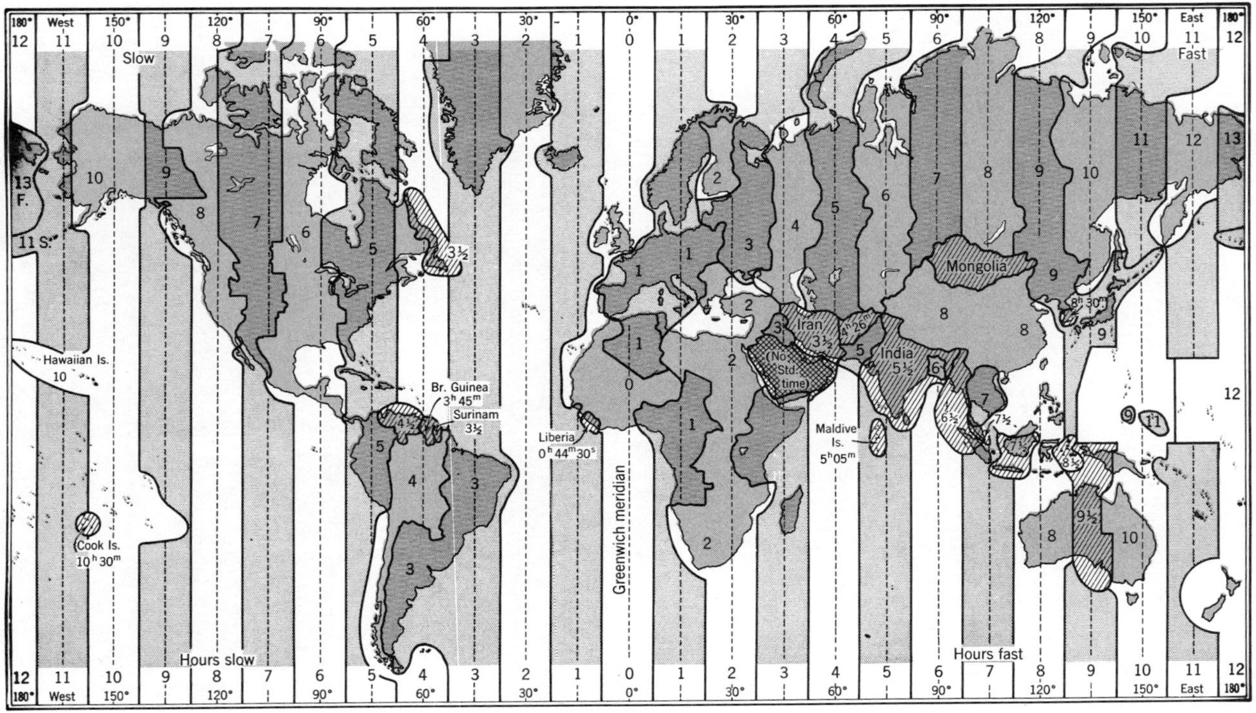

FIG. 3-5 World time zones.

1 hour ahead of the standard time for that zone to give the people more daylight after working hours. This is called *Daylight Saving Time*. Many areas use this "fast time" during the summer months only, while a few remain on it the year around.

3-5
Computing Time Differences

With supersonic planes crossing the Atlantic Ocean in approximately 2 hours, and foreign programs being televised by way of satellites, it is essential that we be able to determine the difference in times between various widely separated places on earth. For simplicity we will consider only standard times of locations for which the longitudes gives the correct time zone, or for which the correct time zone is known. If a person in Denver, Colorado, knows that a certain program is to be televised live from Bagdad, Iraq, at 3:00 p.m. (post meridian) Bagdad time, what time must he turn on his television set to receive the program? From Fig. 3-5, or a globe, he observes that Bagdad is in the 45° E time zone, and Denver is in the 105° W zone. This means that Bagdad is 45/15 or 3 hours *east* of Greenwich, while Denver is 105/15 or 7 hours *west*, therefore, Denver is 10 time belts *west* of Bagdad by way of Greenwich. The standard time in Denver is that of Bagdad (3:00 p.m.) *minus* 10 hours, or 5:00 a.m.

If it is 10:00 a.m. (ante meridian) Friday in Cedar Falls, Iowa, longitude 93° W, what time is it in Kobe, Japan, longitude 135° E? Cedar Falls is 93/15 or 6 time zones *west* of Greenwich, while Kobe is 135/15 or 9 time zones *east*; therefore, Kobe is 6 + 9 or 15 time zones *east* of Cedar Falls by way of Greenwich. Hence, the time in Kobe is the time in Cedar Falls (10:00 a.m. Friday) *plus* 15 hours, or 1:00 a.m. Saturday.

If it is 2:00 p.m. in Rio de Janeiro, Brazil, longitude 45° W, what is the standard time in Los Angeles, California, longitude 118° W, and in Bombay, India, 5 time zones east plus 30 minutes? Rio de Janeiro is 45/15 or 3 time zones west of Greenwich, and Los Angeles is 118/15 or 8 time zones west; therefore, Los Angeles is 8 − 3 or 5 hours *west* of Rio de Janeiro. The time in Los Angeles is that in Rio de Janeiro (2:00 p.m.) *minus* 5 hours, or 9:00 a.m. of the same day. Bombay is $3 + 5\frac{1}{2}$ or $8\frac{1}{2}$ hours *east* of Rio de Janeiro. Hence, the time in Bombay is that in Rio de Janeiro (2:00 p.m.) *plus* $8\frac{1}{2}$ hours, or 10:30 p.m. of the same day.

In summary, if we know the standard time in one locality and wish to determine what it is any other place on Earth, we proceed as follows:

1. Find the number of time zones, in hours, between the two places.

2. In going from the place where the time is known to where it is desired, if one goes *east* through the time belts, *add hours* to the known

time. If one goes *west*, then *subtract hours*. If, in the process one goes past midnight, *add or subtract a day*.

3-6
International Date Line

Let us suppose that a world traveler leaves New York and heads westward. When he enters the Central time zone, he sets his watch back 1 hour, and likewise when he enters the Mountain zone. He continues setting his watch back 1 hour for each 15 degrees of longitude. After he completes his journey around the Earth, he will have set his watch back 24 times, and will be 1 whole day behind the folks back home. If he returns on what he thought

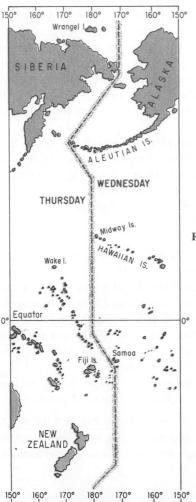

FIG. 3-6   The International Date Line.

was Saturday, he would discover that everyone there was observing Sunday. Someplace in his jouney he should have set his calendar forward 1 day. There is a place for such a change and it is in the middle of the Pacific Ocean, and is called the *International Date Line* (IDL). This line is near, but not always on, the 180th meridian (see Fig. 3-6). The International Data Line is halfway around the Earth from the prime or Greenwich meridian, and the two were located in these positions by international agreement. The calendar changes by one day when we pass the International Date Line (IDL). It also changes a day when we pass the midnight meridian, which is on the opposite side of the Earth from the Sun. The former remains in a fixed position, while the latter moves around the Earth with the Sun and passes us once every 24 hours. Very few of us have ever crossed the International Date Line, but we all have experienced the changing of a day at midnight. Our world traveler, in his westward journey, *subtracted* hours when going from one time zone to the next, but he must have failed to *add* the day when he crossed the International Date Line or he would have known that it was Sunday when he arrived back home. If he had been traveling eastward, he would have *added* hours when entering adjacent time zones, and *subtracted* a day at the Date Line. It might be interesting to note that as an eastbound traveler crosses the 180th meridian, he goes from the eastern into the western longitudes.

Let us now figure the difference in time by use of the International Date Line instead of the Greenwich meridian. We shall again attempt to find the time in Kobe, Japan, when it is 10:00 a.m. Friday in Cedar Falls, Iowa. Kobe is $(180 - 135)/15$ or 3 time belts *west* of the IDL while Cedar Falls is $(180 - 93)/15$ or 6 time zones *east* of the IDL. Therefore, Kobe is $6 + 3$ or 9 time zones *west* of Cedar Falls, and so the time in Kobe must be 10:00 a.m. Friday, *minus* 9 hours *plus* one day, or 1:00 a.m. Saturday.

3-7
Determination of Longitude

The longitude of any place on earth can be determined by taking the difference in hours between the local time and the Greenwich or universal time and multiplying this difference by 15. Universal time (UT) is the civil time for the Greenwich zone and is expressed on a 24-hour basis. Four figures are always used, with the first two indicating the number of hours since Greenwich midnight and the last two figures the number of minutes past the hour. For example, if the Greenwich civil time is 4:25 a.m., the universal time is 0425. If the Greenwich time is 5:35 p.m., the universal time is 1735. Greenwich noon is a universal time of 1200. If the local time of a certain locality is *ahead* of the universal time, the place in question must be *east* of Greenwich; if the local time is *behind* the universal time, it must be a *west* longitude. For example, if the local time of a certain place is noon when the universal time is 0920, we know that the local time is $2\frac{2}{3}$ hours *ahead* of the universal time. Hence, the longitude of that locality is $2\frac{2}{3} \times 15$, or $40°$ E. If the local time of another place is 10:00 a.m. when the universal time is 1620, we know that its local time is $6\frac{1}{3}$ hours *behind* the universal time. The longitude of this second position is $6\frac{1}{3} \times 15$, or $95°$ W.

Immediately the question arises as to how we, as individuals, can obtain these local and universal times since our clocks read zone times. True local noon occurs when the sun crosses the zenith meridian, or when a thin stick driven in the ground casts a shadow directly north. If at true noon we read the clock, which may not be exactly at 12:00, we can determine how much our local time deviates from the zone time, and consequently establish our local time. At sea, local times are secured by what the navigators call getting a "fix" on the Sun or a known star. The universal time can be obtained from our standard zone time by adding to our clock the number of hours that the zone is west of Greenwich or subtracting the hours if it is east of Greenwich. For example, Chicago is in the 90th meridian time belt; therefore, it is 90/15 or 6 hours west of Greenwich. At 3:05 p.m. Central Standard Time, the universal time, or the time it would be in Greenwich, England, is 1505 + 600 or 2105. Clocks aboard ships at sea usually keep correct universal time.

To clarify the problem of determining longitudes, let us say that in the Pacific time belt (8 hours west of Greenwich) a person's clock registers 11:30 at true local noon. Therefore, his true local time (not zone time) is 12 o'clock when the universal time is 1130 + 800 or 1930. Since his local time of 1200 is $7\frac{1}{2}$ hours *behind* the universal time of 1930, his longitude is $7\frac{1}{2} \times 15$, or $112.5°$ W.

3-8
The Seasons

One of the very important results of the Earth's revolution around the Sun is the seasons of the year. The Earth's orbit about the Sun is in the plane of the ecliptic, and, as we previously learned, its axis of rotation is not perpendicular to this plane, but is tilted $23\frac{1}{2}$ degrees. Except for its slight precession, the Earth's axis remains fixed with respect to the stars as it travels around the Sun (see Fig. 3-7). On the first day of spring, about March 21, the Sun is exactly above the Earth's equator, and each point on the Earth receives about 12 hours of sunlight (slightly more because of the bending of the light rays from the Sun toward the Earth as they enter our atmosphere). The position among the stars where the Sun appears to be located when it crosses the celestial equator is called the *vernal equinox*. Unfortunately, there is no star in this region of the sky by which we can visually locate the

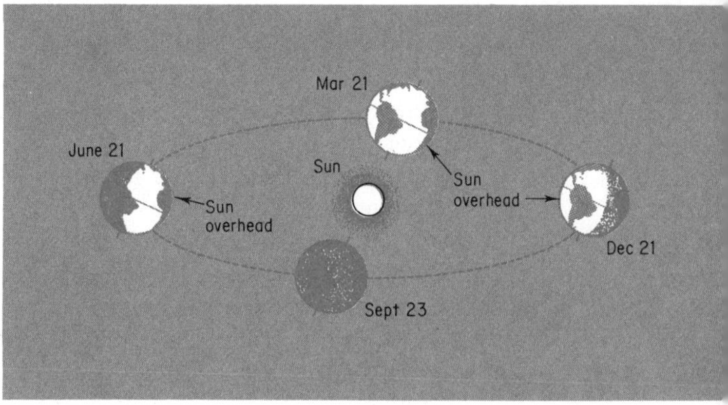

FIG. 3-7 Relative positions of the Earth and the Sun at the four seasons of the year.

equinox, as there is in the northern sky to locate the north celestial pole. Three months after spring, the northern end of the Earth's axis has a maximum tilt toward the Sun, producing our summer. Two effects are combined to provide the warm weather in the Northern Hemisphere. First, the Sun is higher than average in the sky, making its rays more nearly perpendicular to the ground. A given amount of sunlight and heat will spread over a smaller area, and the Earth will receive more heat per square mile. Second, in June the Sun shines for a longer period of time each day (see Fig. 2-12). About June 21, the Sun is above the horizon for about 16 hours in latitudes of 45° N, and for 24 hours in latitudes above 67° N. Three months later, the Sun is directly above the equator again, with days and nights approximately equal in length all over the world. The point in the sky where the Sun appears to be located when it crosses the celestial equator again on about September 23 is called the *autumnal equinox*. Three months later, in December, the northern end of the Earth's axis is at a maximum tilt away from the Sun. Thus the Northern Hemisphere receives less than its usual amount of heat because the rays strike the Earth more obliquely, spreading out over more square miles, and the daytime is much shorter. These two effects result in cold weather. Latitudes north of 67° N receive no sunshine for many days. Three months later we are back to spring again. The time from when the Sun passes the vernal equinox to the next time it passes the vernal equinox is one *tropical year* with its four wonderful but different seasons.

In the Southern Hemisphere, the seasons are reversed. There, winter is in June and summer is in December. People of the Southern Hemisphere thus have their warmest weather when closest to the Sun, and their coldest weather when farthest away. We in the northern latitudes have our summer when we are the farthest from the sun, and our winter when we are the nearest. This seems as if their summers ought to be warmer than ours, and their winters colder. Let us look at a few facts to see if this is true. The *average* temperature for the whole Southern Hemisphere is about 63° F for January and 49.5° F for July, while the average temperatures for the whole Northern Hemisphere are 46.5° F for January and 72° F for July. In the Southern Hemisphere, the preponderance of water and the closeness of the land masses to the equator temper the climate and mask out the effect of the distance from the Sun.

At the equator, daylight is slightly over 12 hours each day of the year, and the four seasons are very much the same.

One may also wonder why the warmest days in the Northern Hemisphere come in August instead of during the longest days of June. The answer lies in the fact that our temperature depends on the amount of heat the Earth keeps, rather than on how much it receives. The amount of heat gaind from the Sun varies with the seasons, while the loss to outer space is almost constant throughout the year. Starting on the first day of spring, the Earth gains more heat than it loses and gradually gets warmer, reaching its peak about two months after the longest day of the year. After September, the Earth loses more heat than it gains, and gradually cools off, reaching its lowest temperature in February instead of during the shortest days of December.

This may be illustrated by looking at the bank account of a worker who, during the year, spends as much as he earns. Because of his seasonal job, he earns more in June than in December but his expenses remain constant, as is shown in Table 3-1. Note that the bank balance, which is analogous to the earthly temperatures, is the highest between August and September and is the lowest between February and March.

TABLE 3-1
Bank Balance of Worker

Month	Income	Expenses	Bank Balance	
			$2,000	
Jan.	$300	$400	1,900	
Feb.	350	400	1,850	
Mar.	400	400	1,850	*Lowest*
Apr.	450	400	1,900	
May	500	400	2,000	
June	550	400	2,150	
July	500	400	2,250	
Aug.	450	400	2,300	*Highest*
Sept.	400	400	2,300	
Oct.	350	400	2,250	
Nov.	300	400	2,150	
Dec.	250	400	2,000	

3-9
The Calendar

The rotation of the Earth and the apparent motions of the Moon and Sun are various ways of reckoning time. A system that enables us to keep tally of the days, months, and years is the calendar, and most of us accept our present calendar without much inquiry or question. The truth is that it has had a long and stormy career, and may have more revisions in the future. Since the days, months, and years are not integral multiples of each other, any calendar will be only a compromise. There are 29.5306 days in a synodic month (full moon to full moon), and 365.24220 days in one tropical year. With such numbers it is rather difficult, if not impossible, to design a calendar to keep the days, months, and years in some kind of agreement and have spring arrive on the same date each year.

In ancient times the calendar was probably used to keep track of religious festivals and pagan rites. Primitive man regarded the Moon with awe and reverence, and so in the early calendars the month was based upon the interval between full moons. However, 12 lunar months equal 354 days, while 13 are 383.5 days, neither total being very close to the length of a tropical year. The early calendars used 12 lunar months for the year, and every 2 or 3 years an extra month, called an *intercalary month*, was added. This system fell into abuse and resulted in great confusion. No uniform agreement existed between various tribes or villages, and occasionally the extra month was used for political advantages.

The early Roman calendar had only 10 months with the year beginning in the spring—as indicated by the following names: March, April, May, June, Quintilis, Sextilis, September, October, November, and December. Later, two more months were added to keep the months in step with the phases of the Moon. They were placed at the beginning of the year, thus putting the other months out of the order indicated by their names. These early Romans also initiated the beginning of the day at midnight instead of at sunset. As with all lunisolar calendars, a lunar month was to be added occasionally to keep the calendar in phase with the seasons. When Julius Caesar came to power, he found the calendar in bad condition, with spring arriving in December. He was impressed by the solar calendar used in Egypt, and decided to abandon the idea of combining lunar and solar times. With the help of the astronomer Sosigines of Alexandria, he formulated a solar calendar with a common year of 365 days divided into 12 months; every fourth year an extra day was to be added, making that year 366 days in length. This made the average year 365.25 days long, which he knew was very close to the length of a tropical year. He assigned 31 days to the odd-numbered months and 30 days to the even-numbered ones, except February, which only had 30 every fourth year. Julius Caesar decreed that the year 46 B.C. be made 445 days long in order to have the first day of spring come on March 25 of the new calendar which started on January 1, 45 B.C. Julius's successor, Augustus Caesar, renamed Quintilis as July in honor of Julius. He also renamed Sextilis as August in his own honor, and to make his month as long as his predecessor's, he took a day from February, leaving it with only 28 days except on leap years. To keep from having too many long months in succession, the 31-day months were transferred from September and November to October and December. This new Julian calendar removed the confusion that had developed, and was adopted throughout the Roman Empire.

The average year under the Julian calendar was 365.25 days in length, instead of the exact length of 365.2422 days. Hence, the average Julian year was 11 minutes and 14 seconds too long. This amounted to one whole day in 128 years. In time, this introduced complications in the observance of certain Jewish and Christian religious festivals which were fixed by the Moon. In A.D. 325, the Christian Church Council met at Nicea in Asia Minor and fixed the date for Easter Sunday. It was officially set as the first Sunday after the fourteenth day of the Moon after the Sun crosses the vernal equinox. In other words, Easter is the first Sunday after the first full moon after the first day of spring. The council made no changes in the Julian calendar. The idea of recording dates before and after the approximate birth of Christ was introduced in about the sixth century. This did not replace the Roman calendar.

By 1582, however, the first day of spring had drifted back to March 11, and the calculated church holidays were becoming greatly confused. Pope Gregory XII, with the help of the astronomer Clavius, reformed the calendar again, and gave us the one we use today. First, he decreed that October 4, 1582, should be followed by October 15, 1582. This returned the Sun's crossing of the vernal equinox to March 21, and resolved the Easter difficulties that the March 11 date introduced. Then, to prevent a recurrence of this difficulty, he made a revision in the leap-year system. Every four years were to be leap years *except* the century years not divisible by 400. Since there are three such century years every 400 years, this corrects the calendar for 1 day every 133 years, which is very nearly the 128-year adjustment required by the Julian calendar. The Gregorian calendar is really in error of only 24 seconds in a year, which amounts to a day in 3,600 years. To correct for this, it has been proposed to skip leap years in A.D. 4000, 8000, and so on. However, the problem of gaining a day in 36 centuries is probably a good one to leave for a later generation to solve.

The Gregorian calendar was immediately adopted by all Roman Catholic countries, but the Protestant ones were slow in adopting the reform. When

FIRST QUARTER

JANUARY								FEBRUARY								MARCH					
S	M	T	W	T	F	S		S	M	T	W	T	F	S		S	M	T	W	T	F	S
1	2	3	4	5	6	7					1	2	3	4							1	2
8	9	10	11	12	13	14		5	6	7	8	9	10	11		3	4	5	6	7	8	9
15	16	17	18	19	20	21		12	13	14	15	16	17	18		10	11	12	13	14	15	16
22	23	24	25	26	27	28		19	20	21	22	23	24	25		17	18	19	20	21	22	23
29	30	31						26	27	28	29	30				24	25	26	27	28	29	30

SECOND QUARTER

		APRIL								MAY								JUNE			
S	M	T	W	T	F	S		S	M	T	W	T	F	S		S	M	T	W	T	F	S
1	2	3	4	5	6	7					1	2	3	4							1	2
8	9	10	11	12	13	14		5	6	7	8	9	10	11		3	4	5	6	7	8	9
15	16	17	18	19	20	21		12	13	14	15	16	17	18		10	11	12	13	14	15	16
22	23	24	25	26	27	28		19	20	21	22	23	24	25		17	18	19	20	21	22	23
29	30	31						26	27	28	29	30				24	25	26	27	28	29	30
																						** W

THIRD QUARTER

		JULY								AUGUST							SEPTEMBER				
S	M	T	W	T	F	S		S	M	T	W	T	F	S		S	M	T	W	T	F	S
1	2	3	4	5	6	7					1	2	3	4							1	2
8	9	10	11	12	13	14		5	6	7	8	9	10	11		3	4	5	6	7	8	9
15	16	17	18	19	20	21		12	13	14	15	16	17	18		10	11	12	13	14	15	16
22	23	24	25	26	27	28		19	20	21	22	23	24	25		17	18	19	20	21	22	23
29	30	31						26	27	28	29	30				24	25	26	27	28	29	30

FOURTH QUARTER

	OCTOBER								NOVEMBER								DECEMBER				
S	M	T	W	T	F	S		S	M	T	W	T	F	S		S	M	T	W	T	F	S
1	2	3	4	5	6	7					1	2	3	4							1	2
8	9	10	11	12	13	14		5	6	7	8	9	10	11		3	4	5	6	7	8	9
15	16	17	18	19	20	21		12	13	14	15	16	17	18		10	11	12	13	14	15	16
22	23	24	25	26	27	28		19	20	21	22	23	24	25		17	18	19	20	21	22	23
29	30	31						26	27	28	29	30				24	25	26	27	28	29	30
																					* W

* The Year-End World Holiday, W or 31 December (365th day), follows 30 December every year.
** The Leap-Year World Holiday, W or 31 June (an extra day), follows 30 June in leap year.

Fig. 3-8. World Reform Calendar.

Great Britain and its colonies adopted this calendar in 1752, a change of 11 days was required, and some Englishmen felt that they were being robbed of 11 days. An interesting calendar sidelight is that George Washington was really born on February 11 instead of February 22, which we now celebrate. When we purchased Alaska in 1867, Russia was still using the Julian calendar, and did not make the change until after the Revolution of 1918. Turkey did not adopt the new calendar until 1927.

The four business quarters of the Gregorian year are not equal in length but have 90, 91, 92, and 93 days. Furthermore, holidays and the beginning of business quarters move through the days of the week from year to year. Easter and the church holidays and festivals, which are associated with it, vary as much as a month. Therefore, there has been agitation for a reformed calendar. In 1923 the League of Nations examined 185 different plans, and narrowed the proposals down to two: the 12-month, equal-quarter World Calendar; and the 13-month plan with an extra month, called Sol, inserted between June and July. In 1953 the World Reform Calendar was presented to the United Nations. Each quarter of this calendar contains 91 days, consisting of 3 months of 31, 30, and 30 days (see Fig. 3-8). Each quarter would begin on a Sunday and end on a Saturday. Holidays and birthdays would always come on the same day of the week. For example, Christmas would always come on Monday, and the 4th of July on a Wednesday. These four quarters total only 364 days; therefore, an extra day is needed. This day would be inserted between Saturday, December 30, and Sunday, January 1. It would not be a day of the week and would be called Worldsday. Every fourth year a similar day would be inserted between June 30 and July 1, and would be called a Leap-year Day. All these extra days would be world holidays. The Gregorian leap-year system would be continued. An innovation of such a World Reform Calendar would certainly require unanimous international agreement.

QUESTIONS AND PROBLEMS

1. Why are solar days not equal in length? Why are sidereal days equal in length? Why is a solar day longer than a sidereal day?

2. If the Earth were spinning in the opposite direction (Sun rising in the west and setting in the east), but its rate of rotation and all the other motions of the solar system were the same, would our winters and summers be reversed, or would our afternoons come before our mornings, or would a sidereal day be longer than a solar day? Explain.

3. An electric clock is designed to keep correct time when operating on a 60-cycle-per-second alternating current source. If, however, the fre-

quency is 59.5 cycles per second, what is the approximate error in the clock in 24 hours? Would the clock be fast or slow?

4. If a star rises at 10:00 p.m. tonight, what time will it rise tomorrow night? Two months from now?

5. A person at a longitude of 93° W sees a certain star cross his zenith meridian at 9:00 p.m. (CST). At what time (PST) will a person in Los Angeles, longitude of 118° W, see the same star cross his zenith meridian?

6. A person notes that, according to his watch, it is exactly 12 o'clock, but the shadows cast by the Sun are not true north. How is this possible if his watch keeps accurate time?

7. How many degrees above the southern horizon is the Sun at noon on June 21 at a place of 93° W longitude and 40° N latitude?

8. If the standard time is 4:00 a.m. on February 12 in London, longitude 0°, what time and day is it in:
   (a) Chicago, Illinois, longitude 88° W?
   (b) Bagdad, 3 time zones east?
   (c) Kobe, Japan, 135° E?
   (d) Caracas, Venezuela, 4 time zones west + 30 minutes of time?
   (e) Hawaii, 150° W?

9. If it is 3:00 p.m. in China (8 time zones east) on May 25, what time and day is it in:
   (a) Los Angeles, 118° W?
   (b) Calcutta, India, 5 time zones east + 30 minutes of time?
   (c) Cairo, Egypt, 31° E?
   (d) New York City, 74° W?
   (e) Wellington, New Zealand, 175° E?

10. If it is 3:00 p.m. on June 15 in New York City, longitude 74° W, what time and day is it in:
    (a) Hawaii, 150° W?
    (b) Rio de Janeiro, 45° W?
    (c) India, $5\frac{1}{2}$ time zones east?
    (d) Moscow, 3rd time zone east?

11. Distinguish between standard and Daylight Saving time.

12. Where are the equinoxes located with respect to the ecliptic and the celestial equator?

13. At a certain locality the Sun crosses the zenith meridian at a universal time of 1500. What is the longitude of that locality?

14. At a certain place on Earth the local time is 4:00 a.m. when the Greenwich time is 1400. What is the longitude of that location?

15. If the local time is 2:30 p.m. when the Greenwich time is 0730, what is the longitude of the place in question?

16. While traveling from the United States to Japan one approaches the International Date Line at 2:30 p.m. on June 23. What is the time and day just after he crosses the Date Line?

17. If the Earth's axis were perpendicular to the Earth's plane of revolution or its ecliptic, what would the climate be like in the United States?

18. If the Earth's axis were inclined 45° instead of the present 23½°, how would this affect those who live at a latitude of 42° N? Explain.

19. What difference would you notice if the Earth revolved around the Sun as it does now, but did not rotate on its axis?

20. In the Northern Hemisphere, why doesn't the warmest weather come on June 21 instead of in August?

21. Why is it not possible to design a calendar which would never be in error?

22. If the tropical year were equal to 365.125 mean solar days, how often would we need a leap year?

23. If the Sun crosses the celestial equator on March 20, and the next full moon is not until Tuesday April 6, what is the date of Easter?

24. With our present leap-year system, which of the following years are leap years? 1976, 1988, 2000, 2017, 3000.

25. What is the main objection to our present calendar? What are the advantages of, and objections to, the proposed World Reform Calendar?

SUGGESTED REFERENCES

ABELL, GEORGE, *Exploration of the Universe*, 2nd ed., Chap. 8. Holt, Rinehart & Winston, New York, 1969.

BAKER, ROBERT, and LAURENCE FREDERICK, *An Introduction to Astronomy*, 7th ed., Chap. 4. D. Van Nostrand Co., Princeton, N. J., 1968.

PAYNE-CAPASCHKIN, CECILIA, and KATHERINE HARAMUNDANIS, *Introduction to Astronomy*, Chap. 2. Prentice-Hall, Englewood Cliffs, N.J., 1970.

WYATT, STANLEY P., *Principles of Astronomy*, Chap. 4. Allyn and Bacon, Boston, 1964.

4
The Moon

The Moon is the most conspicuous object in the evening sky, and its day-by-day change in shape and position among the stars adds variety to our celestial scenery. Sometimes it rises as a gorgeous, copper-colored ball in the eastern sky as the Sun sets in the west, and it appears as large as the Sun itself. At other times it is a beautiful, bright, shining sliver of light, called a "crescent moon," in the western sky shortly after sunset. Once each month it remains almost invisible for a couple of days. To the uninformed, such facts add an element of mystery which has produced many superstitions about the Moon and its behavior. To the informed, however, these few isolated facts are only part of a wonderful physical phenomenon.

4-1
Motions of the Moon

A casual observer notices that the Moon rises in the east and sets in the west, and each night it rises a little later with a slight change in shape. Closer observations show that it rises approximately 50 minutes later each night, and gradually moves eastward among the background of stars. The latter can be checked quite easily by watching the Moon when it is near a bright star, and in only a few hours, its eastward motion can be detected. If the Moon's position in the sky were observed for a whole month and plotted on a sky map, one would discover that the Moon moves *eastward* along a path almost the same as that followed by the Sun. The Moon moves in the same direction that the Earth is rotating. While the Earth turns through 1 solar day, about 361 degrees (see Section 3-2), the Moon moves some distance along its path in that same direction, and so the Earth must rotate a little farther to overtake the Moon. This accounts for the 50-minute delay in

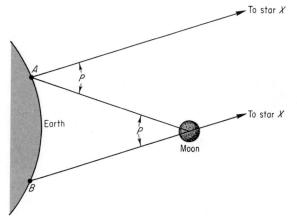

FIG. 4-1   Distance to the Moon.

the moonrise time. From one moonrise to the next takes an average of 24 hours and 50 minutes.

The Moon revolves around the Earth in approximately 1 month, just as the Earth revolves around the Sun in 1 year. To determine the type of path the Moon follows in its journey around us, we must measure its distance from the Earth at various intervals throughout a lunar month. This can be done by having two persons, at widely separated places on Earth, observe the apparent positions of the Moon with regard to the background of stars (see Fig. 4-1). Observer *B* signals *A* when the Moon is lined up with a certain star *X*, and then *A* measures the angle *P* between the Moon and the star *X*. Knowing the distance between *A* and *B*, and the angle *P*, the distance to the Moon can be computed. In this manner, we find that the Moon follows an elliptical path with the Earth at one focus. At the *perigee*, the Moon is a little more than 221,000 miles from the center of the Earth, and at the *apogee*, it is nearly 253,000 miles away, averaging about 239,000 miles (see Fig. 4-2). The plane in which it travels is close to the plane of the Earth's orbit around the Sun; they deviate only by an angle of about 5°9', or 5.15°. This means that the Moon follows a path through the stars very close to the path of the Sun, which is known as the ecliptic.

FIG. 4-2   Elliptical path of the Moon.

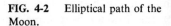
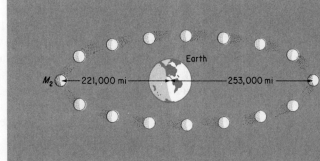

We also find that the Moon makes 1 complete revolution around the Earth with respect to the stars in 27.32 mean solar days. This is known as a *sidereal month.* That it makes one orbit in this time means that the Moon is traveling at an average speed of 2,300 miles per hour relative to the center of the Earth. To a person on Earth, the Moon appears to move eastward at an *average* rate of 360/27.32 or 13.2 degrees per solar day. For the Earth to rotate this extra 13.2 degrees each day in overtaking the Moon requires 13.2 × 24/360 or 0.88 hour, which is 52.8 minutes. This delay in moonrise varies considerably, depending on the location of the Moon along its elliptical path, and the arc it takes through the sky. Such complications arise because we observe the Moon's orbital motion superimposed upon the rotational motion of the Earth.

While the Moon is revolving around the Earth, the Earth is also revolving around the Sun. In one sidereal month, the Sun appears to move 27.32 degrees through the sky because of the motion of the Earth along its orbital path. Consequently, at the end of a sidereal month, the Moon is not in the same relative position with respect to the Sun and Earth that it was at the beginning. To get back into that same relationship, the Moon must travel a little farther to overtake the Sun. This requires slightly over 2 days. We find the interval between successive new moons is 29.53 solar days, which is called a *synodic month.* Hence, we have two kinds of months determined by the motions of the Moon: the one due to the revolution of the Moon with respect to the stars, and the other due to the revolution of the Moon with respect to the Sun (see Fig. 4-3). Early man kept track of time in terms of years and lunar months. He might have said, for example, that a certain event took place 15 summers and 5 moons ago.

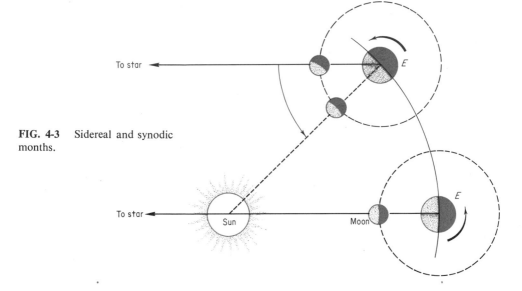

FIG. 4-3   Sidereal and synodic months.

There is another motion of the Moon which seldom comes to our attention, and that is its rotation about an axis. By direct observation we have never seen more than one side of the Moon; therefore, the Moon must make 1 rotation on its axis while revolving once around the Earth in order to keep its same side toward us at all times. (According to Mark Twain, some people are like the Moon because they have one side of their personality they never show to anyone.) Since the Moon makes 1 revolution in 27.32 days, it must also make 1 rotation in that same time. Hence, a sidereal day on the Moon is 27.32 of our solar days, but from sunrise to sunrise on the Moon is 29.53 solar days.

4-2

Phases of the Moon

The most striking aspects of the Moon are its phases. It changes appearance as it waxes from crescent through first quarter to full, and then wanes back through third quarter to crescent again. Since the Moon produces no light of its own, the light we see is reflected sunlight. The half that faces the Sun is always brilliantly illuminated while the other half is dark. The half

Fig. 4-4 The phases of the Moon.

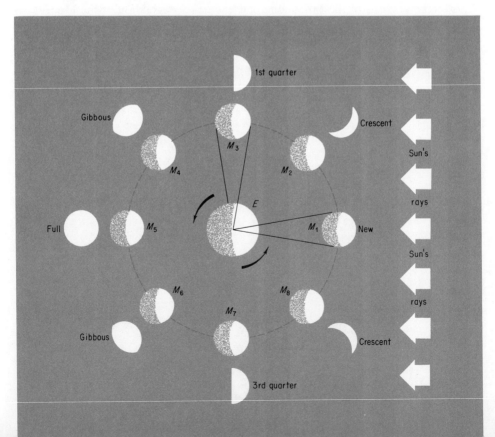

of the Moon we see from the Earth may be partly illuminated at certain times and fully illuminated at other times, causing the different phases.

Let us now see how the motion of the Moon results in these different phases. When it is in position M_1 in Fig. 4-4, the half we ought to see is dark, and therefore, not visible. This phase is called the *new moon*, and is usually taken as the beginning of the synodic month. In a couple of days, the Moon moves to position M_2. Now the half toward the Earth has only a small portion illuminated. The visible part looks like a thin sliver of light, and is called a *crescent moon*. Since the Moon revolves in the same direction that the Earth rotates, this crescent moon sets about 2 hours after the Sun. Therefore, shortly after sunset, one sees this beautiful crescent moon low in the western sky with its horns, or cusps, pointing away from the Sun. It can be seen trailing the Sun in the daytime, but does not come out in all its glory until dusk. Each night thereafter, the crescent moon is seen a little farther away from the Sun. It sets later and later and the crescent gets broader and broader. About 1 week after the new moon, exactly half of the half toward the Earth is illuminated, and we see a semicircle or a quarter of the Moon. This is called a *first-quarter moon* because it has completed one-quarter of its monthly journey, as indicated by position M_3. This Moon is near the zenith meridian at sunset, and will set 6 hours later. As the days go by, the Moon continues its eastward motion, and the dark side of the semicircle gradually fills in through the *gibbous* phase until the whole half we see is illuminated. This is the familiar *full moon*, and it reaches this phase about 15 days after the new moon. Since the full moon is on the opposite side of the earth from the Sun, it rises at sunset, and remains in the sky all night, being at the highest point in the sky about midnight. After a full moon, the phases are reversed. The Moon wanes through the gibbous moon, M_6, to the *third-quarter*, M_7, which rises about midnight. This quarter-moon wanes into a crescent, M_8, which is seen as a bright sliver of light in the eastern sky just before sunrise, and stays ahead of the Sun throughout the day with its horns pointing away from the Sun. After 29.53 days, the Moon is back to the new-moon phase and another lunar month is over.

There is a definite relationship between the phase of the Moon, its position in the sky, and the time of day. If any two of these facts are known, the third can be determined. For example, whenever we observe a moon on our zenith meridian at sunset, we know that it must be a first-quarter moon. Let us see how we arrived at this conclusion. An observer on the Earth directly below the Sun would be at position A in Fig. 4-5, and it would be his noon. By 6 p.m. the Earth has turned through 6 hours or 90 degrees, and the observer is at position B with the Sun on his western horizon, about ready to set. The Moon directly above the observer at this time, as seen from Fig. 4-5, would be a first-quarter moon. While the Earth makes one complete rotation,

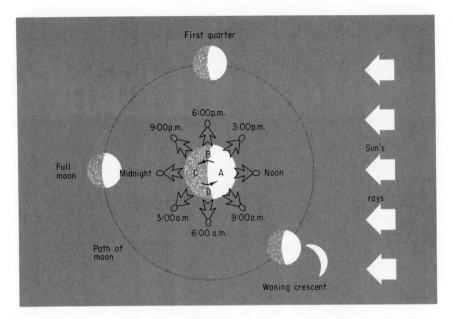

FIG. 4-5   The time of day, and the phases of the Moon as observed from the Earth.

the Moon also moves along its path around the Earth, and so the following night at 6 p.m., the Moon would not be directly over the observer's head, and it would not be exactly a first-quarter moon either. Hence, one can see the first-quarter moon directly overhead at 6 p.m. only once each month.

If the Moon is directly overhead at midnight, what is its phase? We see from Fig. 4-5 that at midnight the observer is on the side of the Earth opposite the Sun, at position *C*, and the Moon directly above would be a full moon. It would rise at sunset, and set at sunrise. If a Moon were directly over one's head at 9 a.m., what would its phase be? At 9 a.m. an observer on the rotating Earth would be halfway between 6 a.m. and noon, and a Moon directly above the observer would be a waning crescent.

Let us change the procedure slightly by saying that at 9 p.m. we see a first-quarter moon in the sky, where in the sky is it located? Turn the Earth in Fig. 4-5 until the observer is at the 9 p.m. position, halfway between 6 p.m. and midnight. Draw a line through the center of the Earth and perpendicular to the observer who is standing normal to the surface of the Earth. Draw in a first-quarter moon on the Moon's orbit and you will notice that it is about 45 degrees above the western horizon.

Let us change the conditions once more. If we see a third-quarter moon just above the eastern horizon, what time of day is it? On the Moon's orbit, draw in a third-quarter moon. Then through the center of the Earth draw a line so that the Moon will be slightly above the observer's eastern horizon. The direction of the observer's head points to the hour of the day, which in this case is about 1 a.m. What time is it when one sees a first-quarter moon setting? Draw in the first-quarter moon, and a line through the center of the Earth and the Moon. Place an observer perpendicular to this line such that the moon is on his western horizon. You will notice that the observer's head points toward midnight, which is the time desired.

Primitive man kept track of short periods of time by the different phases of the Moon. He took the week as the nearest whole number of days between new moon and the first quarter, or between the first quarter and the full moon. Since this interval is about 7.37 solar days, he took his week as 7 days, and we still continue the practice.

4-3
Earthshine

Shortly after and shortly before a new moon, we can often see the whole Moon partially illuminated with the bright, slender crescent along one edge. We call this "the old moon in the new moon's arms." Since the light from the Moon is reflected sunlight, how is it possible to have the side opposite the Sun partially illuminated? In Fig. 4-4, one notices that the Earth on the moon side during a crescent moon is brilliantly lighted. Since the Earth is a fairly good reflector, some of the sunlight striking the Earth is reflected to the Moon, and from there back to Earth again. The bright crescent is reflected sunlight, while the poorly illuminated surface is doubly reflected sunlight. This we call *earthshine* (see Fig. 4-6).

FIG. 4-6 Earthshine. Shows a slender crescent and the earth-lit portion of the Moon. (Yerkes Observatory photograph.)

Daily Paths of Sun and Moon through the Sky

It is common knowledge that in the winter the full moon follows an arc high in the sky while the Sun in the daytime follows a parallel arc that is much lower. In the summer, the conditions are reversed; the full moon passes low in the night sky while the Sun is much higher. Why should there be such a difference since the Moon and Sun follow paths through the stars that are within 5.15 degrees of each other? The answer lies in the fact that a full moon is always on the opposite side of the Earth from the Sun. It can be seen in Fig. 4-7 that in the winter, the full moon (M_2) is north of the celestial equator, the plane of the Earth's equator extended out to the stars, and the Sun is below the celestial equator. Therefore, as the Earth rotates, the Moon takes an arc through the sky north of the celestial equator, and the Sun follows a parallel arc south of the celestial equator. At a latitude of 42° N, the celestial equator is a circle through the sky from a point on the horizon due east, crossing the zenith meridian 48° above the southern horizon, and then to a point on the horizon due west. On December 21, the full moon follows an arc about $23\frac{1}{2}$ degrees north of this celestial equator; therefore, when it crosses the zenith meridian, it will be approximately $71\frac{1}{2}$ degrees above the southern horizon, while the Sun will be only $48 - 23\frac{1}{2}$ or $24\frac{1}{2}$ degrees above the ground.

In the summer, as seen in Fig. 4-7, the full moon (M_1) is south of the celestial equator and follows a path low in the sky while the Sun is north of

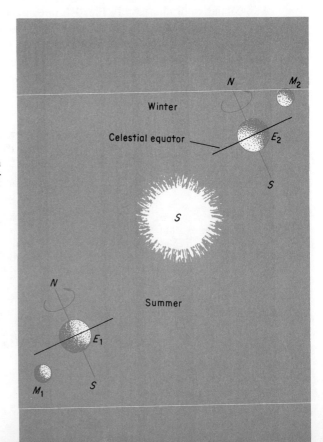

FIG. 4-7   Positions of the Sun S and the Moon M in the summer and winter sky.

the celestial equator and takes an arc high in the daytime sky. These effects are also true in the southern hemisphere, but with the north-south directions reversed.

4-5
Facts about the Moon

The Moon, our only natural satellite, is relatively large. It ranks fifth in diameter of all the planetary moons, and is more than two-thirds as large as Mercury. No other planet has a moon one-quarter its own size. Our Moon is 2,160 miles in diameter, has a volume of $\frac{1}{49}$ the volume of the Earth, and is about $\frac{1}{81}$ as massive. Its density is approximately $\frac{3}{5}$ that of the Earth, or close to the density of the rocks in the earth's crust. The gravitational attraction at the surface of the Moon is about $\frac{1}{6}$ of that on Earth. A 180-pound man would weigh only 30 pounds on the Moon, and with the same muscular effort could, by jumping, raise his center of gravity 6 times as high. This is where we ought to conduct our track meets!

During the daytime on the Moon, which is equal in length to 14.8 of our solar days, the temperature at the surface rises to about 212° F at midday, and drops to 14° F at sunset. During the lunar night, the surface cools off considerably, dropping to about −275° F by midnight. In the middle of the morning and afternoon, the temperatures might be tolerable, but during the rest of the time man would be miserable without air-conditioning units and heating systems.

The low surface gravity has made it impossible for the Moon to retain an atomsphere. The *Apollo XV* astronauts found this out when they landed on the Moon in July 1969. One astronaut, David R. Scott, through television gave us a visual proof that the Moon has no atmosphere when he dropped, a hammer and a falcon feather at the same time and they arrived at the surface of the Moon in a dead heat. If the Moon had an atmosphere, the feather would have fluttered through the air as it fell and would have hit the surface some time after the hammer. We might ask why it is that the Earth has been able to keep an atmosphere but the Moon has not. To escape from the Earth's gravitational attraction, an object has to be traveling at a speed of 7 miles per second away from the Earth, while to escape from the Moon, an object only needs a speed of 1.5 miles per second. During the hot summer days here on Earth, the air molecules cannot gain sufficient speeds to overcome gravity, while during the very hot lunar day, any molecule on the Moon can obtain thermal speeds in excess of escape velocity. Hence, throughout the ages, the Moon has gradually lost its atmosphere. As the astronauts found out, any person landing on the Moon must wear a pressurized suit with an air-tight helmet, a supply of oxygen, and some substance, such as charcoal, to absorb his exhaled carbon dioxide. The suit must be well insulated with built-in air-conditioning and heating systems to protect the person from the large variations in temperature he would experience. While in the direct sunlight it is extremely hot, but the minute he steps into the shadow of a mountain or crater wall, it becomes very cold. There is no breeze to transfer the heat from the sunny regions to the shaded ones. The spacesuit must also be able to reflect large amounts of the Sun's ultraviolet rays. Here on Earth our atmosphere protects us from the most powerful of these rays.

The absence of a layer of air around the Moon produces many strange effects. The sky appears black, and the stars can be seen in the daytime, providing the eyes are shaded from the intense sunlight. Meteors, experiencing no air resistance, leave no trails in the sky and strike the Moon's surface with extremely high speeds. From the near side of the Moon, the outstanding feature of the sky is the majestic Earth shining in all of its glory. It appears about 4 times as large as the Moon appears to us here on Earth. At full phase, the Earth lights up the lunar landscape about 80 times more than the full moon lights up the Earth. Our oceans and continents appear fuzzy through a blue haze caused by the scattering of the light in the Earth's atmosphere. Great white clouds float across the face of the Earth. Although the Earth changes phases, it always remains in about the same position in the sky during the lunar days and nights, since the Moon keeps one side toward the Earth at all times. If one were on the backside of the Moon, he would never have the pleasure of seeing the Earth shining in the sky. Since there are no clouds, winds, or storms on the Moon, the regularity of everything, but the meteorites, is indeed monotonous.

How did the astronauts of the Apollo flights converse with each other while on the Moon's surface since there is no atmosphere and sound requires some kind of medium for its transmission? To do this each astronaut had a built-in transmitter and receiver inside his helmet where there was a gas, mainly oxygen. The sound passed through the gas in the helmet from his mouth to the microphone of his transmitter where it was converted to electrical impulses, which were transmitted by radio waves through the Moon's vacuum to the antenna of the other astronaut and to us here on Earth. The waves were then converted back to sound in the other astronaut's and our receivers. Without the radio there would have been no audio communication.

As we have seen, living in the vacuum around the Moon not only introduces some spectacular sights, but it presents many problems for any air-dependent creature from Earth.

4-6
Surface Features

The surface of the Moon differs greatly from the surface of the Earth. With an unaided eye we observe dark and bright regions which make the full moon resemble a person's face, and so we speak of the "Man in the Moon." Through an ordinary telescope, we are able to see mountain ranges, dark areas called maria or "seas," thousands of craters of various sizes, and bright streaks radiating out from some of the larger craters (see Figs. 4-8 and 4-9). The mountains are scattered over much of the lunar landscape, but only three groups resemble our terrestrial mountain ranges. They are the Alps, Apennines, and Caucasus. These three ranges are along the western border of the dark region called the Mare Imbrium, and are quite comparable in height to some of our mountain ranges. Some of the peaks rise 20,000 feet above the neighboring "seas" or plains. Near the Moon's South Pole are the higher Leibnitz and Doerfel mountains, which have peaks rising to elevations of 26,000 feet. Heights on the Moon, however, are not as easily compared as they are here on Earth. Lunar elevations are measured with respect to the surrounding plains which are at different levels, whereas all of our moutain altitudes are expressed in terms of feet above sea level. Mount Everest, for example, is 29,140 feet above sea level and not above its surrounding foothills. A lunar height is determined from the length of the shadow a mountain casts along its surrounding plain for a known altitude of the Sun above the horizon of that plain. Because of the low gravitational attraction at the Moon's surface, the mountain-producing forces active in the past have had an easy task in forcing up large mountains. Its mountains are very rugged because they have experienced no erosion throughout the ages by the action of winds and weather since the Moon has no atmosphere.

FIG. 4-8   Moon, age 20 days. Photographed with 100-in telescope. (Photograph from Hale Observatories.)

FIG. 4-9   The Moon at the age of 16 days. The image in an astronomical telescope is inverted. (Yerkes Observatory photograph.)

Before the invention of the telescope, astronomers speculated on the nature of the dark areas, which are predominantly in the northern hemisphere, and concluded that they were large bodies of water like our seas. Hence, they used the word *mare* ("*sea*") to designate them. These regions bear such fanciful names as Mare Tranquilitatis (Sea of Tranquility), Mare Serenitatis (Sea of Serenity), and Mare Nubium (Sea of Clouds). The largest dark area is Oceanus Procellarum (Ocean of Sails). The lunar seas also have bays, such as Sinus Iridum (Bay of Rainbows). The maria form the features of the "Man in the Moon." We still call them seas, but they are really dry land. If there was ever any free water on the surface of the Moon, it has boiled into steam under the intense heat of the lunar day and escaped from the Moon long ago. From instruments left on the Moon, scientists claim that they have detected clouds of steam rising from the Moon, and believe that there is a good chance that liquid water might lie somewhere below the lunar surface. From the rocks brought back by our lunar explorers, we find that the surface material consists of dark grey rocks similar to terrestrial volcanic rocks known as basalt, but containing fine grains of material, while other rocks are composed of small rock fragments and minerals welded together in a mixture of pulverized material. These rocks are known as breccias, and are most likely the result of catastrophic events that took place long ago on the Moon. The soil covering the maria is enriched in nickel and volatile elements, and contains glassy fragments of interesting shapes and sizes. Some of the silicate material is clear and transparent. The soil and rocks of the maria absorb more sunlight than do the highlands and appear darker than the surrounding areas. The plains are covered with craters of various sizes, and rocks from a few inches in diameter to those the size of a house. *Apollo XV* astronauts found the surface rather rough for their lunar car, the Rover, but not impossible to travel across. The amazing thing about these rocks is that they are fairly smooth. Since there is no atmosphere, the weathering of the rocks must have been produced by the charged particles from the Sun, called solar winds, which have been striking the rocks for billions of years. From the amounts of uranium and lead in the samples of rock brought back by the Apollo astronauts, the age of the Moon, through radioactive dating, has been found to be about the same age as that of the Earth. In fact some of the rocks are older than the rocks on the Earth's surface. Hence, the Moon's surface must have solidified before the surface of the Earth did, or the older rocks on the Earth's surface have weathered and eroded away. The plains have valleys (see Fig. 4-10) and cliffs. One cliff in Mare Nubium is about 600 feet high and 80 miles long. From some pictures taken of the Moon, we have noticed tracks several hundred feet long on the Moon's surface left by some rocks rolling down a slope. This shows signs of movement in this eerie silent object. Some say that the rocks were dislodged by a

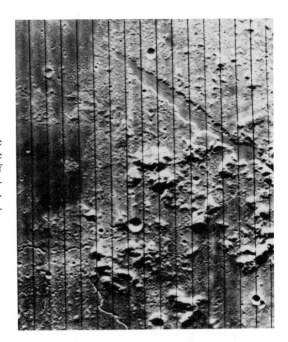

FIG. 4-10 The Alpine Valley in the mountainous region northeast of Mare Imbrium, aligned radially to the center of the mare and over 75 mi long. Photographed by *Lunar Orbiter IV* on its twenty-first orbit of the Moon. (National Aeronautics and Space Administration.)

moonquake. If this is the case, the Moon is a self-changing body like the Earth. Others say that the rocks were dislodged by a large meteorite impact someplace on the Moon.

The most remarkable characteristic of the Moon's surface is its abundance of craters, which range in size from Grimaldi, about 180 miles across, to small pits, a foot or so in diameter. More than 30,000 have been mapped on the visible side, and there are many more on the backside of the Moon. The larger ones have been named after philosophers and scientists. All craters are circular in shape with peripheral walls which, for the large craters, rise many feet above the surrounding plains (see Fig. 4-11). Most of them have

FIG. 4-11 The crater Copernicus. (Lick Observatory photograph.)

crater floors depressed below the outside plains, but a few, like Wargentin, seem to be filled to overflowing with solidified lava. Some have dark, smooth floors while others, like Aristarchus, have bright, rough floors. Many have low protrusions near the center of the crater, while some have small craters inside of the larger ones, craters in craters.

The origin of these craters is one of the major questions in lunar geology. There are two major hypotheses. Some scientists have the opinion that long ago the Moon underwent terrific volcanic action, producing the huge craters, and the resulting lava flowed out over large areas of the Moon's surface, forming the seas. Others believe that in the early history of the Moon, meteorites of all sizes collided with the Moon, while it was still in a more-or-less pliable state, forming the craters and throwing up the massive walls around them. Since we have both volcanic and meteoric craters on Earth, it seems possible that both kinds might exist on the Moon. Let us look a little closer at each kind.

The large craters look like *collapsed volcanoes*. These are volcanoes that have had a rapid expulsion and then a rapid suction and collapse. Crater Lake in Oregon is an example of this type. Crater Lake has the walls around it with a small cinder cone at its center. It is surrounded with a blanket of pumice and lava ejected from the crater. Geologists have found internal faults around the inner wall, the same as the astronauts saw on the Moon. The difference is that the Earth crater is filled with water to form the lake. Since the Moon's seas are basalt, the lava must have come from the interior through these craters. Some of the older craters have been filled without breaks in their walls and must have been filled through crevasses in the crater floors. Some believe that the rays extending out from some of the craters, such as Kepler and Copernicus (Figs. 4-8 and 4-9), were formed by lava flowing out through fissures like the ones in Hawaii. Why don't all craters have rays like this? These rays seem to fade with age, and so the ones with rays may be the ones most recently formed, maybe only 100,000 years ago. Both Soviet and American astronomers reported seeing reddish spots in the cones of a few of the craters which brighten up and then fade away. Some say that this indicates that volcanic activity is taking place on the Moon right now. There are also domes or mounds found on the Moon, the same as those we have on Earth. The domes here on Earth are pushed up by magma below. Magma is lava containing water. The presence of magma indicates that there could be volcanic action.

Those who believe in the impact theory claim that many of the craters on the Moon are too large for volcanoes; they are from 44 to 50 miles in diameter. We do have a crater in Africa formed by a meteorite that is 50 miles in diameter, but it has weathered and its outline can be detected only by flying at a high altitude. Most of our volcanoes are along a "fire ring," while those on the Moon are scattered at random. This randomness definitely indicates meteorite or comet impact. They would hit the surface at very high speeds because there is no atmosphere to slow them down. Upon impact they would explode, throwing meteoric material in all directions and forming a wall around the point of impact. We have a well-preserved impact crater near Winslow, Arizona, which is about $\frac{3}{4}$ mile in diameter and about 570 feet deep (see Fig. 5-7). Being in a desert, it has been preserved for the past 22,000 years. On the Moon the impact explosions produced the light-colored material radiating out from the craters which are called *rays*. The central peaks are due to the rebound of the liquid magma below the broken crust. Perhaps the impact of large comets or meteorites formed the circular maria, especially the Imbrium basin, and then they filled with lava. As for the reddish glow in some, we have produced a similar glow in the laboratory by bombarding achrondrite, meteorite material, with high-speed protons. Hence, if the craters were formed by impact, achrondrite material would be left in the crater, and when bombarded by protons from the Sun after a solar flare would make the material fluoresce with a pink glow without any lunar activity. Since the light-colored rays seem to have no thickness and fade with time, they must consist of material thrown out from a meteor impact. As these rays are continually bombarded by the charged particles from the Sun, they weather and eventually fade away. It seems possible that some of the craters are volcanic in nature, but most of them were undoubtedly formed by impact. The lunar terrain, visited so far, is made up essentially of lava flows that have been extensively fragmented by meteorite impacts over the ages. The main volcanic activity may have ended 3 billion years ago, and since then the lunar landscape has been altered by the solar winds and meteorite impacts. The latter would account for the rocks being scattered over the Moon's surface.

It has been mentioned that we can see only one side of the Moon, but since the Moon's axis is tilted to its orbit, we have been able to see slightly beyond the Moon's poles, when each pole is tilted toward us. Due to the fact that the Moon rotates at a constant rate but does not move along its elliptical path at a uniform speed, we have seen around the Moon's edges. Consequently, we have actually seen 59% of the Moon's surface, and for a long time have wondered what the remaining 41% is really like. This curiosity was first satisfied on October 7, 1959, when the Soviet space probe, *Lunik III*, passed within 40,000 miles of the backside of the Moon, while that side was almost fully illuminated. Since then American astronauts have seen the backside at fairly low altitudes. The other side seems to lack the large maria found on the Earth side, but in general the two sides are much alike. On the backside the mountains are not as high, and there are only two distinctive dark areas which the Soviet scientists called the Moscow Sea

FIG. 4-12   The southern half of the Moon's hidden side taken by NASA's *Lunar Orbiter II.* The Moon's equator runs roughly along the top of the photograph. (National Aeronautics and Space Administration.)

and the Sea of Dreams. There is also a prominent crater, which they called Tsiolkovsky, and a small crater with rays radiating from its center very much like Copernicus. The surface is practically covered with craters, both small and large (see Fig. 4-12).

FIG. 4-13   Lunar eclipse of December 31, 1963. The Earth's shadow began moving across the Moon about 3:30 a.m., and the Moon was totally eclipsed over Des Moines, Iowa, at about 4:28 a.m. (Photographed by Mr. Del Borer of the Des Moines Register and Tribune Company.)

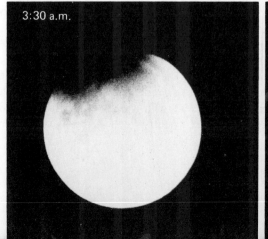

3:30 a.m.

3:45 a.m.

Eclipses of the Moon and Sun have frightened man throughout the ages. He has done everything imaginable, by shouting and pounding pans, to chase away whatever was trying to devour the Moon or Sun. This noisemaking always worked out quite well, for every time it was done, the eclipse disappeared. Of course, the eclipse would have disappeared without the commotion. Some people, because of superstition, are still afraid to let their children play out-of-doors during a solar eclipse. (There is a real danger, however, of damaging the retina of the eye if a person looks directly at the Sun at any time without using three layers of fully exposed film, and he is more likely to stare at the sun during a partial eclipse.) When we understand the causes of eclipses, of course, our fears vanish.

The *lunar eclipse* (Fig. 4-13) occurs when the Moon passes through the shadow of the Earth (see position M_1 in Fig. 4-14). This can happen only during a full moon. The dark conical shadow of the Earth is 859,000 miles long, and where the Moon, which is 239,000 miles away, crosses the shadow, the *umbra*, or dark region, is about 5,700 miles wide. Since the Moon is 2,160 miles in diameter and travels at an average speed of 2,300 miles per hour along its orbital path, it can remain at least partially in the Earth's shadow for over $3\frac{1}{2}$ hours and totally eclipsed for more than 1 hour, provided the Moon travels through the central portion of the shadow.

A lunar eclipse is interesting to watch, but yields no additional scientific information. It attracts wide publicity because all the people on the half of the world that faces the Moon can see nature's dramatic performance. Frequently the Moon does not completely disappear from sight during totality, but looks copper in color. This is due to the Earth's atmosphere, which bends the red rays of light in toward the Moon and scatters the blue light away, resulting in the orange or copper-colored effect. If the Earth had no atmosphere, the Moon would completely disappear during each total eclipse.

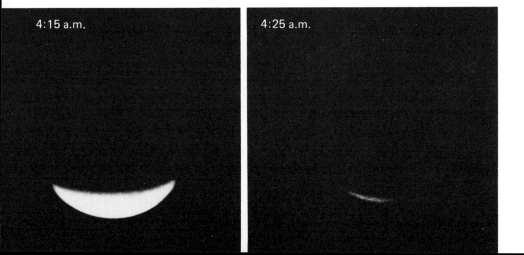

4:15 a.m.

4:25 a.m.

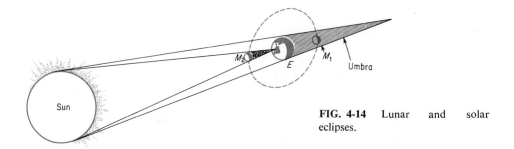

FIG. 4-14 Lunar and solar eclipses.

Now the question arises, why is there not a lunar eclipse each month during the full moon? Remember that the orbital path of the Moon makes an angle of about 5°9′ with the ecliptic, and out at a distance of 239,000 miles from the Earth, the Moon might be as much as 21,000 miles north or south of the plane of the ecliptic. Such a full moon would not go through the Earth's shadow—5,700 miles wide at that distance—and so no eclipse results. The Moon in its orbital motion has to cross the plane of the ecliptic at two points called the *nodes* (see Fig. 4-15). The Earth in its journey around the Sun carries the Moon with it, and twice a year the Sun, Earth, and nodes line up. If a full moon is near a node at this time, a lunar eclipse will be produced. Because of the precession of the Moon's orbit, there is slight westward movement of the nodes themselves, called *regression*, and the time between suc-

FIG. 4-15 Eclipses of the Sun and the Moon do not occur at every new or full moon. They occur only when the new or full moon is at a node: the intersection of the Moon's orbit with the plane of the Earth's orbit.

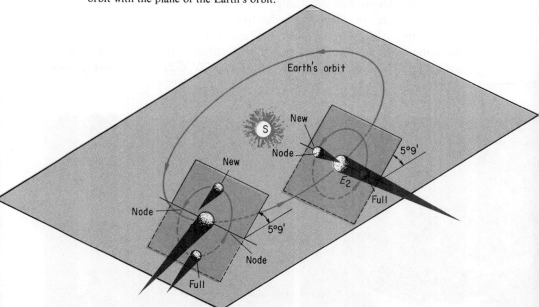

cessive possible eclipses is cut from 182.6 days (6 months) to 173.3 days when averaged over a period of 28.5 years. Hence, the eclipse seasons are less than 6 months apart, and occur progressively earlier from one year to the next. Table 4-1 gives the dates of the future total lunar eclipses to be seen from the Northern Hemisphere.

TABLE 4-1
Total Lunar Eclipses Visible in the Northern Hemisphere

Date	Duration of Totality
1975, May 25	90 min
1975, November 18	46
1979, September 6	52

A *solar eclipse* occurs whenever the shadow of the Moon passes across the surface of the Earth. This can happen only when a new moon is near the node at the time it is between the Sun and Earth. The conical shadows of other new moons completely miss the Earth. There are times, however, when a new moon appearing near the node does not produce a total eclipse for the simple reason that its shadow is not long enough to reach the Earth. The length of the Moon's shadow varies from 228,000 to 236,000 miles, depending on its distance from the Sun, and the distance from the Moon to the Earth's surface varies from 217,000 to 246,000 miles. Hence, there are times when a new moon at a node can cast its shadow on the Earth and other times it cannot. Under the most favorable conditions, the width of the shadow on the Earth is only 176 miles. Most of the time it is between 50 and 100 miles wide, and races eastward across the country at speeds of 1,060 to 5,000 miles per hour—about 1,060 miles per hour if it is traveling parallel to the equator at noon, and 5,000 miles per hour if the Sun is near the horizon. Because of these high speeds totality lasts a very short time. The maximum duration is $7\frac{1}{2}$ minutes, but the average is fewer minutes. Observers outside the path of the Moon's shadow can see, with proper devices, part of the Sun's surface covered by the Moon, leaving a crescent sun. This is known as a partial eclipse. In case the shadow is not long enough to reach the Earth, the Moon will appear smaller than the Sun. It will blot out only the central portion, leaving a narrow ring, or *annulus*, of the Sun's surface around the black disk of the Moon. Such an eclipse is only partial. The intensity of the sunlight diminishes, but does not fade out.

There have been instances where ancient eclipses have been used by historians to date certain important events. Total eclipses leave such a lasting impression on the minds of people that at some later date the eclipses can be recorded in great detail. From this information, the times and places of certain historical events have been well established. However, the greatest significance of a solar eclipse is the knowledge we gain about the Sun's atmosphere.

4-8
Viewing a Total Solar Eclipse

One of the most spectacular sights is the total solar eclipse. Not everyone has observed this celestial pageantry because the central shadow of the Moon follows a very narrow band across the Earth's surface. Within this limited region, as the Moon covers more and more of the disk of the Sun, its brilliance steadily diminishes. The light passing between the leaves of trees casts tiny crescents on the ground, each an image of the Sun, instead of the usual small round spots. This gives the shaded areas a weird, eerie appearance. When the Sun is nearly covered, the quality of its light changes because the light now comes from the edge of the Sun's disk. An unfamiliar paleness spreads over the landscape. Just before totality, shadow bands move like ripples across the lighted surfaces. Animals behave as though evening were approaching, and some flowers begin to close. Just before the Moon completely covers the Sun, bright spots, called "Bailey's beads," appear along the leading edge. This is the last bit of sunlight coming through the valleys between the mountains along the rim of the Moon.

At totality, the corona or the Sun's atmosphere bursts into view (see Fig. 4-16). It can be viewed without any protection to the eye and is an awe-

FIG. 4-16 Solar corona observed during total eclipse of June 8, 1918. (Photograph from the Hale observatories.)

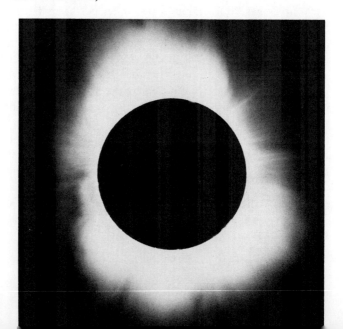

inspiring sight. The more dense inner corona is yellowish while the outer parts are pearly white. Streamers extend out for hundreds of thousands of miles from the Sun's equatorial regions, and short, curved streamers extend from the poles. Occasionally, flame-like prominences may be seen to stream out from the edges of the shadow into the corona. After a short time, but never more than $7\frac{1}{2}$ minutes, totality ends as abruptly as it began, and proper devices must again be used in viewing the remainder of the show. The corona disappears, Bailey's beads again flash at the trailing edges, and all the events follow the reverse order until the eclipse is over. Then one stands for a few moments in amazement over what he has just seen.

Although a total eclipse is visible at some place on Earth almost every year, the future opportunities for Americans to observe this wonderful sight are given in Table 4-2.

TABLE 4-2
Total Solar Eclipses in the Western Hemisphere

Date	Duration of Totality	Where Visible
1977, Oct 12	2.8 min	Northern South America
1979, Feb 26	2.7	Northwest U.S. & Canada
1991, July 11	7.1	Hawaii, Central America, Brazil
1992, June 30	5.4	South Atlantic
1994, Nov 3	4.6	South America
1998, Aug 11	2.6	Central America

QUESTIONS AND PROBLEMS

1. What motion of the Moon or the Earth is responsible for the Moon's apparent eastward motion among the stars? For its apparent westward movement across the heavens?

2. Why does the Moon rise approximately 50 minutes later each night instead of 50 minutes earlier? Under what conditions would the Moon rise earlier?

3. What ordinary visual observations lead us to believe that the Moon revolves around the Earth instead of around the Sun?

4. Describe a lunar day. How would the Earth change throughout the day?

5. Distinguish between sidereal and synodic months. Which is longer and why?

6. If the rate of the Earth's revolutionary motion around the Sun were increased, what would be its effect, if any, upon the length of the synodic month? Upon the sidereal month?

7. Under what conditions would the synodic month be equal in length to the sidereal month?

8. What is the phase of the Moon which
   (a) rises at noon?
   (b) crosses the zenith meridian at 3 p.m.?
   (c) rises at 3 a.m.?
   (d) sets at 9 a.m.?

9. What position in the sky is the Moon if it is a
   (a) full moon at 9 p.m.?
   (b) waxing crescent moon at 6 p.m.?
   (c) third-quarter moon at 11 a.m.?
   (d) first-quarter moon at 10 p.m.?

10. At approximately what time does a
    (a) first-quarter moon set?
    (b) a full moon cross the zenith meridian?
    (c) new moon rise?
    (d) a waxing-gibbous moon rise?

11. When the Moon appears slightly above the eastern horizon at sunset, what is its phase?

12. At 2 o'clock in the morning of April 19, 1775, Paul Revere was captured by a British patrol on the road between Lexington and Concord. They saw him coming by the light of the Moon in the eastern sky. What was the phase of the Moon?

13. If the Moon is full on May 15, what phase it on May 25?

14. If the Moon is a new moon on June 6, on approximately what date will it be full?

15. Why does the earthshine gradually decrease as the crescent moon waxes?

16. When the earthshine is the brightest, what is the phase of the Earth as seen from the Moon?

17. If a spaceship lands on the Moon on the earthside during a new moon, what would be the lighting conditions on the Moon around the spaceship?

18. If you took a trip to the Moon, what surface conditions would you find strikingly different from those here on Earth?

19. To a person on the Moon, how often would the Sun rise? How often would the Earth rise?

20. Why is a full moon seen high in the winter sky, whereas it appears low in the summer sky? Is this also true in the Southern Hemisphere?

21. How much would a 120-pound woman weigh on the Moon?

22. How would a person on the Moon prove that the Earth has an atmosphere?

23. How would a person on the Moon prove that the Earth is revolving around the Sun?

24. Is there any relationship between the phases of the Moon and the possibility of a solar eclipse?

25. Why don't we see a lunar and a solar eclipse every revolution of the Moon around the Earth?

26. Does the Moon enter the Earth's shadow from the west or from the east? Explain.

27. Why does a lunar eclipse last longer than a solar eclipse? Why is a lunar eclipse visible from half of the Earth while a total solar eclipse is seen from a very limited region?

28. To a person on the Moon, what does the Earth look like during a lunar eclipse? During a solar eclipse?

29. If the Moon's orbit were in the plane of the Earth's orbit instead of 5°9′ off, how would this affect the lunar and solar eclipses?

30. What determines the length of a total solar eclipse? What positions of the Earth and the Moon will give the longest duration of total solar eclipse?

SUGGESTED REFERENCES

ABELL, GEORGE, *Exploration of the Universe*, 2nd ed., Chap. 9. Holt, Rinehart & Winston, New York, 1969.

KROGDAHL, WASLEY S., *The Astronomical Universe*, Chap. 3. The Macmillan Co., New York, 1962.

PAYNE-GAPOSCHKIN, CECILIA, and KATHERINE HARAMUNDANIS, *Introduction to Astronomy*, Chap. 5. Prentice-Hall, Englewood Cliffs, N.J., 1970.

Science (Moon issue), 167, no. 3918 (Jan. 1970).

5
Our Solar Family

For thousand of years man knew that a number of star-like objects moved around in aimless motions among the background of seemingly fixed stars. The Greeks called them *planets*, meaning "wanderers," and they named them after Roman gods: Mercury, Venus, Mars, Jupiter, and Saturn. By 1846 two additional planets, Uranus and Neptune, were spotted, and in 1930 the ninth planet, Pluto, was discovered. The Babylonian astrologers assigned mystical qualities to the original five wandering celestial objects, and they thought that the planets and the Sun and Moon affected the destinies of men, of kings, and of nations. Astrology flourished for centuries and during that time man concentrated on the planets and the solar system. We have seen that the early astronomers believed that the Earth was at the center of the universe. In 1543 Copernicus shifted the center of the system from the Earth to the Sun. In 1640 Kepler showed that the orbits of the planets were elliptical, not circular, and he determined a relationship between the distances the planets are from the Sun and their periods of revolution. In 1703 Newton, with his law of gravitation, explained why the planets behave the way they do, and his calculated orbits agreed with Kepler's laws. The planets between the Sun and the Earth are known as the *inferior planets*, and those beyond the Earth's orbit are called the *superior planets*.

5-1
"Bode's Law"

In 1772 Johann Elert Bode introduced a very convenient way of obtaining the approximate distances of the planets from the Sun in astronomical units without going through the mathematics required by either Kepler's or Newton's laws. This relationship is known as *Bode's law*, but it was not discovered by Bode nor is it a physical law. Titus of Wittenberg discovered this relationship six years before Bode brought it into prominence. It is a neat way of remembering planetary distances. If we start with the figures 0, 3, 6, 12, 24, and so on, doubling each time after the zero figure, then adding 4 to each one, and finally dividing by 10, we obtain the distances from the planets to the Sun in astronomical units. Table 5-1 gives a comparison between the distances determined by Bode's law and their actual values.

TABLE 5-1
Mean Distance from the Sun

Planet		Bode's Law (a.u.)	Actual Distance (a.u.)	
Inferior Planets	Mercury	0.4	0.39	
	Venus	0.7	0.72	Inner
	Earth	1.0	1.00	Planets
	Mars	1.6	1.52	
	Asteroids	2.8	2.8 (Ceres)	
	Jupiter	5.2	5.20	
Superior Planets	Saturn	10.0	9.52	
	Uranus	19.6	19.16	Outer
	Neptune	38.8	30.00	Planets
	Pluto	77.2	39.37	

Actually, this scheme was more impressive before the discovery of Neptune in 1846 and, expecially, before the discovery of Pluto in 1930. How did Pluto get so far off unless it is a stray moon from some other planet?

5-2
Facts about the Solar System

The Sun, which is the dominating member of the solar system, contains about 99.86% of the system's mass. The remaining 0.14% is unevenly distributed among the other members—about half of it is concentrated in the planet Jupiter. Such a concentration of mass in the Sun really simplifies the mechanics of the system. The orbits of the planets lie nearly in a common plane instead of spread out in all directions. They all revolve around the Sun in the same direction along elliptical orbits that are almost circular. Except for Venus and Uranus, the axes of rotation are inclined only slightly to the orbital plane and the planets rotate in the same direction as their revolution. The moons of each planet revolve in that planet's equatorial plane. A few, however, revolve backward.

Another important fact about our solar system is that it is completely isolated in space. The light from our nearest star, Proxima, takes about 4.3 years to reach us, and so we say that Proxima is 4.3 light-years away. This

FIG. 5-1 The 200-in. Hale Reflector on Mount Palomar. For an idea of its size, note the chair near the bottom of the photograph. (Photograph by Hale Observatories.)

is a considerable distance when we realize that light travels 186,000 miles in 1 second; and in 1 year, light travels *5.88 million million miles.* If everything in the universe were proportionately diminished in size until the Sun were the size of a golf ball, the Earth would be the size of a grain of sand 15 feet away, and the nearest star would be 800 miles away. Hence, the stars in the Milky Way galaxy have very little effect upon our planetary motions.

The most important facts about the planets are listed in Table 5-2

In the last decade, man's attention has turned to the planets again. With all the present-day speculation about traveling in space, we might take a closer look at each of the planets to see if we wish to live, or take a vacation on any of them. From the data obtained from space probes and the 200-inch telescope (see Fig. 5-1), we know much more now about the planets.

5-3
Mercury

The planet closest to the Sun is the smallest of all of the planets. It is only 50% larger than our Moon. If it had been larger at one time, the scorching heat from the Sun has evaporated all of the lighter material away, leaving a cinder

TABLE 5-2
The Planets

Planet	Mean Distance from Sun, millions of miles	Period of Revolution (sidereal)	Period of Rotation (sidereal)	Equatorial Diameter, miles	Mass (Earth = 1)	Density, gm/cm³ (water = 1)	Highest Surface Temp., °F	Tilt of Axis from Normal to Orbit	Gravity at Surface Compared to Earth	Escape Vel., mi/sec	No. of Moons
Mercury	36.0	88 days	58.65 days	3,000	0.054	5.4	650°	30°	0.36	2.5	0
Venus	67.2	224.7 d	243 d ret.	7,600	0.815	5.1	800°	177°	0.85	6.4	0
Earth	92.9	365.2 d	23h56m	7,927	1.00	5.52	140°	23.5°	1.00	7.0	1
Mars	141.6	686.98 d	24h37m	4,200	0.11	3.97	80°	25°	0.38	3.1	2
Asteroids	260	—	—	1 to 480	—	—	—	—	—	—	—
Jupiter	483.3	11.86 yr	9h55m	88,600	318	1.3	−220°	3.1°	2.6	37.8	12
Saturn	886.2	29.46 yr	10h24m	74,000	95	0.72	−240°	26.7°	1.1	22.0	10
Uranus	1783.0	84.01 yr	10h40m ret.	29,400	14.5	1.6	−300°	98°	0.92	13.5	5
Neptune	2794.0	164.8 yr	15h48m	28,000	17.3	2.2	−330°	29°	1.42	15.0	2
Pluto	3671.0	248.4 yr	6.39 d	3,900	0.18	5 ?	−350°	?	0.4 ?	3 ?	0

of silicon and metal. It makes one complete trip around the Sun in 88 Earth's days. The early astronomers called it Mercury after the messenger of the Roman gods, because it moved so swiftly through the stars. Its orbit is more elliptical than any of the other planets. Its distance from the sun varies from about 28 million to 43 million miles during its 88-day revolution. At Mercury's perihelion (closest approach), the radiation it receives from the Sun is 10 times as great as that reaching the Earth. At aphelion (farthest from the Sun), the solar energy it receives is 5 times the amount we receive. The temperature at its surface varies from 650° F on its sunny side to about −300° F on its dark side. With such a high temperature on the sunny side, its atmosphere, if it ever had any, must have escaped the planet's gravitational pull long time ago. With no air there can be no winds to transfer any heat from the hot side to the cold side; therefore, the dark side gets extremely cold. Conditions do not look too favorable for life as we know it to exist on Mercury.

In many ways Mercury resembles the Moon more closely than it does any of the other planets. Each is a barren celestial object without an atmosphere, and has cratered surfaces of rock. These conclusions about Mercury are not certain since definite observations of the planet are difficult to make because Mercury is 50 million miles from the Earth at its closest approach, and its orbit never permits it to be any farther than 28 degrees from the Sun. At this elongation, it sets about 1 hour and 50 minutes after the Sun. Since the faintest stars are not visible until about an hour after sunset, Mercury, a faint "star," cannot be seen for very long periods of time. Records show that the Babylonians observed Mercury, but it is doubtful that Copernicus did. At its brightest, it only compares favorably with a medium bright star, but since it is so close to the horizon, its blue light is scattered by our atmosphere, and so it appears reddish in color, and is hard to see. Most of the time Mercury is not very spectacular and attracts very little, if any, attention.

For 80 years, we accepted G. Schiaparelli's hypothesis that Mercury's day was equal in length to its year, and the planet kept one side toward the Sun at all times. In 1965 radar echoes from Mercury indicated that it makes one rotation in 58.65 Earth days instead of the 88 days of its year, and that it rotates in the same direction as that of the Earth. The planet rotates 3 times in 2 revolutions. As seen from the Sun, Mercury makes one complete rotation in 176 Earth days ($1/58.65 - 1/88 = 1/176$). From sunrise to sunrise on Mercury is 176 Earth days. Hence, there are two seasons in 1 Mercury day. If the Sun rises when Mercury is in its orbit nearest the Sun, due to the orbit's great eccentricity the Sun could rise, hang above the horizon for a brief period of time, drop back below the surface, and then rise again.

Occasionally, as Mercury passes in front of the Sun, the alignment of the Sun, Mercury, and Earth is sufficiently good for us to see the tiny black dot of the planet silhouetted against the vast brilliant expanse of the solar disk.

The next planet in order from the Sun is Venus. Being twice as far from the Sun as Mercury, its angular distance at greatest elongation is enough to make it visible twice as long as Mercury. Venus is often the brightest star in the evening or morning sky. At times it is 15 times brighter than Sirius, the brightest star in the winter sky, and sometimes it can be seen in the day time, thereby attracting considerable attention. Because of its beauty it was given the name Venus after the Roman goddess of love and beauty. Its brightness is due to the reflection of sunlight off its surrounding layer of clouds that reflects about 60% of the sunlight in comparison to the 7% reflected by Mercury's surface. Through a telescope we can observe its phases like our Moon (see Fig. 5-2), but we have never detected any permanent markings on its dazzling, silvery cloud covering.

Venus is sometimes called the Earth's twin because its size and mass are 0.97 and 0.81 of that of the Earth, respectively, and a person on Venus would weigh 0.85 as much as on earth. These few characteristics of the two planets are approximately the same, but here the similarities seem to end. The data obtained from the space probe *Mariner II*, when it passed within 22,000 miles of Venus in 1962, and *Mariner V* in 1967 have given us a little clearer picture of the planet. Its surface temperature is about 800° F, which is higher than the melting point of lead, and is fairly uniform over Venus's entire surface. A "cold spot" was detected where the surface temperature is about 20° cooler than the surrounding region, perhaps indicating a mountain range. Its atmosphere is now thought to consist of 90% carbon dioxide, the gas we humans exhale, and very little, if any, water vapor. The atmospheric pressure is about 90 times that at sea level here on Earth. Our cloud cover, which only partially covers the Earth, never extends more than 10 miles high, while Venus's mysterious clouds, which completely cover the planet from pole to pole at all times, begin at an altitude of 45 miles and extend to

FIG. 5-2 Photograph of Venus in the crescent phase taken on July 18, 1927. (Lowell Observatory photograph.)

a height of 60 miles. The temperature at the bottom of the clouds is about 200° F and that at the top is −30° F.

Mariner II did not detect a magnetic field around Venus, indicating that the planet is either stationary or rotating very slowly. Past guesses varied from 1 month to 250 days for 1 rotation of the planet. We have never been quite sure because we cannot see its surface. Sensitive radar, however, has helped us penetrate the thick cloud that always covers the planet, and we find that Venus makes 1 rotation in 243 Earth days. Believe it or not, Venus turns backward, opposite that of the other planets, or a *retrograde* motion. This slow backward motion and the 225-day forward motion around the Sun means that the Sun rises in the west every 117 Earth days. There are 2 Venusian days in one season, which is due to the inclination of the planet's axis. Since Venus turns so slowly it seems as if the side toward the Sun should be extremely hot and the other side should be cold. Therefore, how does one account for the uniformity of the high surface temperature all the way around the planet? The solar energy that penetrates the dense clouds is absorbed by the material at the surface, and is then reradiated as infrared light and heat. These rays are absorbed by the atmosphere before they can escape into space. By this "greenhouse effect" the heat is trapped by the clouds, producing extremely high temperatures. The atmospheric winds transfer the heat from the sunny side to the dark side, keeping the temperature uniform over the entire surface. While passing the planet, *Mariner II* was pulled off its course, and from the exact amount the probe was deflected, the mass of Venus has been computed to be 0.81485 of that of the Earth.

Venus does not appear to be the glamorous vacation spot some have envisioned. It is a hostile planet broiling in 800-degree temperature in an atmosphere of carbon dioxide. Since the temperature of the clouds varies from 200° F at their bases to −30° F at their tops, there must be somewhere inside the clouds where the temperature is such that life can exist. It has been suggested that some forms of organisms may live at that level in the clouds, like plankton live in our seas. For us Venus is merely a beautiful morning or evening star.

Transits of Venus across the disk of the Sun are not as frequent as those of Mercury. None will occur in the twentieth century. They come singly, or in pairs, in December and June. The last were in 1874 and 1882, and the next will be in 2004 and 2012.

5-5
Earth

The next planet in order from the Sun is the Earth, and we have some indications that intelligent beings do exist there. The Earth is the Sun's nearest planet that possesses a moon. This planet was named after the ancient word *ear*, meaning "to plow." The Earth has about as much carbon dioxide as does Venus, but it is tied up in calcium carbonates, $CaCO_3$, such as seashells and limestone, leaving only a small amount in our atmosphere. Of course, we have an ample supply of oxygen and water, providing we do not continue to contaminate our air and the seas. The temperature on Earth is conducive to life, as we know it, of all sorts.

5-6 Mars

The fourth planet from the Sun, being reddish in color, was named Mars after the bloody Roman god of war. It is slightly over half the size of the Earth and a person on the surface of Mars would weigh about 0.4 of his weight here on Earth. This planet is not obscured by clouds as most of the others are; consequently, we are able to study its surface features in considerable detail. Since its orbit is outside the Earth's, we can observe it best when it is nearest us at opposition, on the side of the Earth opposite the Sun. While in this position, Mars rises as the Sun sets and remains in the sky all night, giving us ample opportunity to study its surface in full illumination. Due to the elliptical paths of both the Earth and Mars, the distance between them at opposition varies from 35 million to 63 million miles. At its closest opposition, Mars is brighter than any star or planet in the sky, except Venus. It is rather fortunate for astronomers that Mars rotates at about the same angular speed as that of the Earth; a Martian day is $24\frac{1}{2}$ Earth hours long. Since Mars turns through 1 rotation while the Earth turns around once, we can see the same area on Mars each night at the same time. At different times during the night, we can observe other regions of its surface, and repeat them again the next clear night.

Mars appears to us as a small red object in the night sky and is a rather unexciting sight to the average person, but to the astronomer it is a very interesting planet. When viewed through a large telescope at a favorable opposition, the disk of Mars is large enough for considerable surface detail to be evident (see Fig. 5-3). Three-fourths of the lateral area observed is a bright reddish color, indicating perhaps a desert covered with a dust of iron oxide. The rest of the surface consists of dark areas near the equator, and a white polar cap covering the pole that is tilted away from the Sun. Since Mars's axis is inclined to its orbital path about the same as that of the Earth (see Table 5-2), it has seasons very much like ours, but almost twice as long. As the seasons advance in either hemisphere, the dark areas change from brown to green as the polar cap recedes, and then back to brown as the polar cap reforms. The reddish areas remain about the same throughout the year.

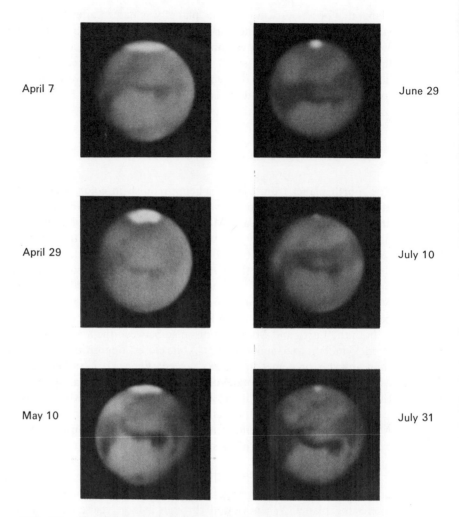

April 7

June 29

April 29

July 10

May 10

July 31

FIG. 5-3 Photograph of Mars during its spring and summer show the melting of the southern polar cap and the seasonal development of dark markings in the tropics. Dates like those of our Northern Hemisphere are assigned to the Marian Southern Hemisphere. (Lowell Observatory photograph.)

The change in color of the dark areas as the polar cap changes were thought by early astronomers to indicate that the dark areas consist of some kind of vegetation, and the polar cap of water in the form of snow or heavy frost. The layer of snow they thought to be rather thin, since most of it melts during the summer. The planet's southern polar cap practically covers half the hemisphere in the winter, and completely disappears in the summer.

The Italian astronomer Schiaparelli, at the favorable opposition of 1877, announced what proved to be one of the most controversial features of the surface of Mars. He saw what appeared to be fine straight lines radiating from points on the surface, forming a network of what he called *canali* (literally, "channels") that encompassed most of the planet. Subsequent work has verified his observations, but there is today considerable uncertainty as to the nature of the "canals." In order to be seen by us 35 million miles away, these canals must be 20 to 100 miles wide. Since they are straight instead of meandering as our rivers do, some astronomers suggested that they must be constructed by intelligent beings for the purpose of irrigation and preservation of the diminishing water supply. Percival Lowell regarded them as constituting an irrigation system.

From the close-up pictures relayed back to Earth from four *Mariners*, one in 1965, two in 1969, and one in 1972, we have mapped almost 100% of Mars's surface, and it appears as if Mars has a rather uninteresting landscape. In some regions, the surface is covered with many craters while in other regions the surface is featureless. The craters in depth and slope are much different than those on the Moon, indicating a different geological process was involved. The rims of the craters are smoothed off, and the bottoms are very flat. The featureless surfaces appear to be like the flat prairies on Earth, but on Mars they seem to be deserts which are much drier than our desert areas. Some scientists believe that Mars contains some water in the form of permafrost below the surface. The features in the equatorial regions might be due to water-ice fog or surface frost. The polar caps are most likely frozen carbon dioxide, or dry ice, which sublimate or evaporate in the summer. The straight lines we think we see might be rift valleys instead of irrigation canals.

The discussion of the possibility of life and, more particularly, of the existence of intelligent beings on Mars has led to considerable popular interest in the planet, but the photographs from the *Mariners* have cast gloom upon this idea. Certainly we would not be very comfortable there. The atmosphere is less than 1% of the density and pressure of that of the Earth. It is less dense than the air at an altitude of 20 miles above the Earth. It consists chiefly of carbon dioxide with very small percentages of oxygen and water vapor. Its small quantity of water vapor is also indicated by the scarcity of bluish clouds floating over its surface. Occasionally orange clouds have been observed moving across Mars's surface, but these are dust clouds originating from the dry desert regions. At one time the whole planet was covered with a dust storm. Being farther from the Sun, Mars receives only 43% as much heat per square mile as we do; therefore, its temperature is much lower than ours. Radiation measurements show that when it is nearest the Sun, noon temperatures at its equator are about 80° F, and night temperatures drop to about $-100°$ F. Like any desert area, the surface cools off rapidly at night. Since Mars has so little water vapor to act as a blanket to hold the heat in, the temperature drops lower than it does in our desert areas. Such extreme daily changes in temperature, the scarcity of water, the lack of oxygen, the abundance of carbon dioxide, and the low pressure seem to be too severe for the existence of any form of life as we know it, either animal or vegetable, except perhaps lichens or bacteria.

Mars has two known satellites. They can be seen only through the largest telescopes, but their behavior is rather interesting and worthy of mention. The inner is named *Phobos* "fear" and the outer *Deimos* "panic" after the chariot horses of the god of war. They are exceedingly small, 10 to 20 miles in diameter. Phobos is only 3,715 miles above the Martian surface, and it makes one complete revolution around Mars in slightly less than 8 Earth hours. Since it travels eastward three times as fast as the planet, it rises in the west and sets in the east as it moves over the surface. It rises every 11 hours and 7 minutes, and so it might rise twice in 1 night. Phobos is the only natural satellite in the solar system with this peculiarity. Deimos is approximately 12,000 miles high and makes 1 revolution in a little over 30 hours, which is only slightly slower than the planet itself rotates. Consequently, it slowly rises in the east and reluctantly sets in the west, going through all of its phases between rising and setting times.

5-7
Asteroids

The next known planet is Jupiter; but between Mars and Jupiter there are thousands of little irregularly shaped planet-like objects called *asteroids* revolving around the Sun in the vicinity where Bode predicted a planet to be. The largest of these is Ceres, which is about 480 miles in diameter and has a mean distance from the Sun of 2.8 astronomical units. Most of the asteroids, however, are considerably smaller than Ceres. The majority are about 50 miles in diameter, while a few are only about 1 mile across. Such small objects have very weak gravitational attractions, and can hold no atmospheres. We judge that they are irregular in shape because their brightness fluctuates as they rotate on their axes.

Presently more than 100,000 asteroids have been observed through the 200-inch telescope. Most of them are in the region of the zodiac, but a few have orbits that deviate considerably from this zone. Some come within the orbit of Mars and at times pass near the Earth. Eros, which is shaped somewhat like a brick 15 miles long and 5 miles wide on each side, comes within 14 million miles of the Earth at its closest approach. The closer an asteroid comes to the Earth, the more accurately its distance away can be measured, and, by applying Kepler's laws, the more precisely can the dimensions of our solar system be determined. Hence, we use the asteroids to check on the accuracy of the astronomical unit.

Some astronomers suggest that perhaps at one time a planet orbited the Sun in this region and broke up into the irregularly shaped asteroids. Others think that for some unknown reason a planet failed to form from the existing material in this region, and through the ages these substances became irregular in shape through repeated collisions with each other. The total mass of all the known asteroids is quite small, probably less than 0.1 % of the Earth's mass. Maybe it was the smallness that kept the pieces from being attracted together and forming a planet.

5-8
Jupiter

The planets beyond the asteroids are called the "outer planets" and form a group considerably different from the inner planets that we have been discussing. Except for Pluto, they are all much larger and have atmospheres consisting mainly of methane gas.

Jupiter, the first of the outer group, is by far the largest of all the planets. In fact, it is more massive than all the other planets combined. Its equatorial diameter of 88,600 miles is 11 times that of the Earth, and it is 318 times as massive. An object at its outer surface would weigh 2.6 times as much as it does on Earth. Jupiter's volume is 1,300 times as large as the volume of the Earth. It is truly a giant among its fellow planets. It shows up as a bright star in the night sky, surpassed only by Venus and occasionally by Mars. Because of its kingly size and brilliancy, it was named jupiter after the ruler of the Roman gods.

Through a telescope, we can see a flattening at the planet's poles, indicating a rapid rotational motion. A day on Jupiter has been observed to be 9 Earth hours and 55 minutes long, the shortest of any of the planets. Jupiter may spin faster than the Earth, but it revolves slower around the Sun. One year on Jupiter is equal to about 12 of our years. Since its axis of rotation is almost perpendicular to its orbital plane, its climate must remain practically the same throughout the year. It has been calculated that if the density (mass per unit volume) of Jupiter were uniform throughout the planet, its polar flattening would be considerably greater than it actually is. Therefore, we believe that Jupiter has a dense core with lighter material over the core, and a fairly dense atmosphere above that. To account for the observed degree of flattening, the astronomer Rupert Wildt has theorized that Jupiter has a metallic, rocky core which is about 6 times as dense as water with a radius of about 18,500 miles. Above that is a layer of ice 17,000 miles thick and about 1.5 times as dense as water. Over the ice is an atmosphere 8,000 miles

FIG. 5-4 Jupiter, in blue light, showing the cloud bands and the large red spot. The third satellite and its shadow appear near the top of the disk. (Photograph from the Hale Observatories.)

thick. From reflected sunlight, we know that Jupiter's atmosphere consists of methane and ammonia. It must also have an abundance of hydrogen to have combined with all the available carbon and nitrogen to form the methane and ammonia. At Jupiter's temperature of about $-220°$ F, the methane and hydrogen are still in the gaseous state while most of the ammonia has solidified. Therefore, its atmosphere consists of ammonia crystals floating in a mixture of methane and hydrogen gases. What we see, of course, is the outer layer of this cloudy atmosphere. Life as we know it could not adjust to such conditions.

The most striking feature of the planet itself is the orange, red, brown, and sometimes green cloud bands encircling the planet parallel to its equator (see Fig. 5-4). These bands are similar to the wind belts here on earth, but are much more extreme. The dark stripes are clearer, more transparent clouds, and the bright belts are the regions were the clouds are reflecting a larger percentage of the sunlight. Another interesting planet feature is the Great Red Spot. It first appeared in the early part of the nineteenth century. By 1878 it became a deep red spot 31,000 miles long and 7,000 miles wide. The redness of the spot varies from time to time. Some astronomers believe that this red spot is produced by tremendous eruptions taking place at the planet's surface; Jupiter emits radio waves which come in bursts like those associated with our thunderstorms. Some say that this might be due to electrical discharges in Jupiter's clouds while still others say that they come from the eruptions in the Great Red Spot. Observations, however, show that the Great Red Spot does not remain fixed but wanders about, as much as 44,000 miles. If it is produced by eruptions at the surface, how could eruptions of this magnitude move about? Hence, some believe that the spot might be a great mass of frozen ammonia in Jupiter's atmosphere.

The most interesting thing about Jupiter is its system of twelve moons. Through any telescope, one can see four of them all in a row along the planet's equatorial plane. Their orbital planes are seen nearly edgewise from the Earth, causing them to shuttle back and forth as they travel around Jupiter. Frequently they pass in front of the planet or are eclipsed as they pass behind it. Two of the visible satellites are as large as our Moon, and two are larger, exceeding the diameter of Mercury. The other eight are fairly small and quite faint. Four of the outer satellites revolve in directions opposite to the rotation of the planet. These moons rise in the east and set in the west as usual, but they rise a little earlier each night instead of later.

An extremely interesting feature of the planet is that it releases more energy than it receives from the Sun, in fact about twice as much. This brings up an intriguing idea—Jupiter the giant is almost a star. If it had been slightly more massive, gravitational attraction could have released much more energy and turned the planet into a nuclear furnace, or a star. Then the Sun would have been part of a double-star system with a much different solar family than we now have.

5-9
Saturn

Saturn, when it is visible, appears as a fairly bright, yellowish star. Because of its great distance from the Sun, it takes 29.5 Earth years to make one trip around the Sun; therefore, it progresses through the stars about 1 degree per month. On account of its slow, deliberate pace, the ancients called it Saturn after the father of the ruler of the Roman gods. Through a telescope,

FIG. 5-5 Saturn and ring system. (Photograph from the Hale Observatories.)

it is one of the most spectacular of all the celestial objects. It has a most interesting set of four very thin concentric rings, which lie in the planet's equatorial plane and most of the time appear to be halos around the planet (see Fig. 5-5). Each 15 years we see them edgewise. The rings are not solid flat disks, but consist of independent particles. We know this to be the case because the inner section of each ring revolves faster than the outer part, and a solid could not do this. In addition, we have seen stars through the rings. The innermost ring, which is extremely faint, was observed recently by Pierre Guerin of France, and almost touches the surface. The next disk, or "Crape" ring, is about 7,000 miles above Saturn. It is rather faint and can be seen only through a large telescope. The next ring is the brightest and is separated from the outer or fourth ring by a 2,500-mile gap, called the "Cassini division." These rings extend out almost 50,000 miles from the planet's surface. Some astronomers believe that these rings are about 10 miles thick. Some think that they are only 10 inches thick, but since we can see them edgewise, they must be at least a half-mile thick. Their origin is a mystery. They represent particles that never did condense into a satellite, or maybe a satellite that came too close to Saturn and broke up under its gravitational pull. However, all of the rings put together contain far less matter than that of a small-sized moon.

In addition to the rings, Saturn has ten moons. One is larger than our Moon, and all evidence indicates that this particular moon has an atmosphere of methane gas. The other satellites are fairly small, and the outer one revolves backward, like four of Jupiter's moons.

Saturn is the second largest planet in both size and mass. It has an equatorial diameter of 74,000 miles and a mass 95 times that of the Earth. A person on Saturn would weigh 1.1 times his weight on Earth. This planet is the least dense and the most flattened of any of the planets. It is about 0.7 as dense as water. Hence, Saturn would float in water, provided one could find enough water. Its oblateness is striking to the casual observer, for its polar diameter is only about 90% of its equatorial. Its structure must be similar to that of Jupiter, but with a smaller core and a thicker layer of atmosphere. Its cloud bands are much more uniform and less prominent than Jupiter's. At its temperature of −240° F, all of the ammonia has crystallized, and so its atmosphere has a greater concentration of methane than Jupiter's. Saturn appears to be a very undesirable place to live.

5-10
Uranus

For centuries Saturn represented the outer edge of our solar system. Beyond it were space and stars. In 1781, William Herschel observed through his telescope a star that appeared disk-shaped instead of a little spot of light.

Searching through old star charts, he observed that this particular object had been plotted as a star for over a century. He wished to name the new planet in honor of King George III of England, but the name Uranus, grandfather of the ruler Jupiter, was selected because it fit into the pattern of the other planets' names.

The planet is greenish in color and occasionally shows faint markings of cloud belts. Its atmosphere is basically methane with very slight traces of ammonia. It is impossible to determine its period of rotation, but we believe it to be about 10.7 hours because of its large equatorial bulge. It has an equatorial diameter of 29,400 miles and is 14.5 times as massive as the Earth; a person on Uranus would weigh about $\frac{9}{10}$ his weight on Earth. Its temperature is a cool $-300°$ F.

The most interesting aspects of Uranus are: first that it rotates from east to west like Venus; and, second, its equator is inclined 82 degrees with its orbit, meaning that its axis is almost lying in its orbital plane. Consequently, the seasons are much different from ours. Let us assume that we could visit some northern latitude of Uranus to see what the seasons would be like. On the first day of spring, when the Sun crossed the vernal equinox, the days and nights would be of equal lengths—about 5 Earth hours each. After that, the days would gradually get longer and the nights get shorter. Eventually, the Sun would stay in the sky all the time for thousands of Uranusian days. After midsummer, the Sun would swing closer and closer to the horizon, and eventually we would have a few minutes of night again. The daytimes would gradually decrease until at the autumnal equinox the days and nights would be equal again. Then the nights would gradually get longer and longer and eventually it would be continuous nighttime for thousands of days. Finally, upon seeing a glimpse of the Sun again, we would know that spring and the sunshine were returning. This is what a year would be like on Uranus.

Uranus has five satellites which revolve around the planet in its equatorial plane, and in the direction the planet rotates. Sometimes we see them fully open in circular paths, and at other times edgewise. They are very faint because they are only 400 to 1,000 miles in diameter.

5-11
Neptune

As soon as Uranus was discovered, mathematicians calculated its exact orbital path, but within 60 years the planet had strayed a considerable distance off the computed path. It was finally decided that another planet, as yet unknown, was responsible for this deviation. Two mathematicians, Leverrier and Adams, working independently, calculated the size and position of such a planet. Leverrier gave his results to a German astronomer in 1846, and after only a half-hour of searching, he found the new planet within

1 degree of the predicted spot. It was named Neptune after the god of the seas. This was a great triumph for the Newtonian gravitational theory, and for the ability of man to spot an object 350 million miles out in space.

Neptune is Uranus's twin in all respects, except in its rotational motion. It is 28,000 miles in diameter and has a mass 17.3 times that of the Earth; an object on Neptune would weigh 1.4 times as much as on earth. Its greenish color indicates that methane is the only gas left in bundance in its atmosphere, which is at a temperature of $-330°$ F. It rotates in the same direction and has its axis inclined about the same amount as most of the planets. Neptune has two satellites. One is the size of our Moon, but the other is so faint it must be located by long-exposure photography.

5-12
Pluto

The exact path of Uranus was not fully explained by Neptune, and besides that, deviations in Neptune's path were soon noticed. To account for these perturbations, the existence of another planet was assumed. Lowell and Pickering attempted the difficult task of predicting its position. After decades of searching for this planet, Lowell's efforts were rewarded in 1930 when the new planet was discovered on a photographic plate by Clyde Tombaugh. It was named Pluto after the god of the underworld. This particular god's name was selected because the first two letters are Perceval Lowell's initials. This planet is about half the size of the Earth, and it is so cold its atmosphere is frozen. Table 5-2 gives most of our knowledge about Pluto.

5-13
Comets

Other objects closely associated with our solar system are the beautiful *comets* with their luminous tails fanning out across the sky. From ancient times to the seventeenth century, they were considered forerunners of terrible disasters such as wars, famines, and epidemics. After the invention of the telescope, many comets were observed every year, and since man did not experience a ceaseless flow of major calamities, the superstitions about such celestial bodies vanished. When a comet is first observed through a telescope as it approaches the Sun, it appears as a fuzzy spot in the sky. Night after night it moves through the background of stars, and as it gets closer to the Sun a majestic tail develops. This luminous tail extends from the head of the comet and away from the Sun, and is most prominent when the comet is nearest the Sun. Only a few of the larger comets are actually visible to the unaided eye at the perihelion passage. Those that are visible remain in sight from a few days to a few months. After the comet passes the Sun, it gradually fades away and is soon lost from sight, even through a telescope.

A given comet has no individual feature by which it can be differentiated from other comets. Its only differentiation is the path it takes around the Sun. Some have orbits that extend far beyond the extremities of our solar system, and travel so slowly out there that they have appeared only once in recorded history. Comets appear at unpredictable times, and most of their orbits are greatly inclined to the ecliptic. Some move eastward among the stars the same as the planets, but many have been observed to move westward. Other comets have orbits within our solar system, and return periodically. The most famous of these is Halley's comet (see Fig. 5-6). According to historical records, this comet has reappeared every 75 to 76 years since 240 B.C. It follows an elliptical path around the Sun. Its path extends beyond the planet Neptune and its perihelion is within the Earth's orbit. It was named in honor of Sir Edmund Halley, an English astronomer, who predicted that it would return in 1758,

FIG. 5-6 Halley's Comet, May 12 and 15, 1910. The tails are 30° and 40° long. (Photographs from the Hale Observatories.)

which was the exact year of its arrival, but Halley did not live to see his prediction come true. The comet appeared again in 1835 and 1910, the years of the birth and death of Mark Twain. The next spectacular showing of this comet will be 1986. There is a family of periodic comets which follow elliptical paths around the Sun and out to the region of Jupiter. In this family there are about seventy known comets, and they have periods of revolution of 5 to 9 years. When comets pass too near some of our planets, especially the larger ones, they are either pulled into a smaller orbit or turned outward into outer space, never to return.

Each well-formed comet consist of a solid nucleus embedded in a brightly luminiferous *coma*, or "head," which is several thousand miles in diameter, and a long, magnificent, glowing tail. The comet's nucleus, according to F.L. Whipple, is a porous mixture of frozen methane, ammonia, and water, with metallic and stony pieces of material embedded in it. When the comet approaches the Sun, the ices evaporate, causing the gas to be ejected in all directions. This exploding gas carries some of the solid material with it. The material ejected toward the Sun is turned back by streams of charged particles radiating out from the Sun. This "solar wind" pushes the material back into a shell, or coma around the comet's nucleus on its sunward side, and forces the material away from the head on the opposite side of the Sun, forming a tail 5 to 50 million miles long. From a study of the light emitted by a comet, we learn that some of the radiation is reflected sunlight, although most of it is fluorescent light; ultraviolet rays from the Sun are absorbed by the material and then reradiated as visible light. Each time a comet passes near the Sun, it loses to its long tail some of its mass which it never regains. Therefore, a comet gradually decreases in mass as it repeats its cycle, and after a number of returns, the comet disappears. The ejected material, however, continues to revolve around the Sun.

5-14
Meteors

Some of this comet material, and other solid celestial debris, which may be caused by colliding asteroids, are attracted to the Earth and plunge into our atmosphere at very high speeds. Due to the air resistance, they are heated to incandescence, and glow as they streak through the heavens. These glowing objects are the "shooting stars," or *meteors*, that we frequently see in the night sky. Those which survive the journey through our atmosphere and strike the Earth are called *meteorites*. Those recovered are irregular in shape with many pits in their surface where the softer material was melted and swept away faster than the hard substance. A glassy coating usually covers the meteorite, indicating that the terrific heat it experienced fused its surface material together. There are two kinds of meteors, the metallic and the stony, with all gradations between the two. An iron meteorite may be identified by etching its surfaces with acid and observing the crystalline patterns. The pure stones, on the other hand, are more difficult to identify with certainty. To the inexperienced eye, some stones may have the appearance of meteoric origin, but have always been here on Earth.

To a casual observer, "shooting stars" seem to appear at almost any time and shoot across the sky in random directions. If careful records are kept, we notice that at certain times of the year showers of these meteor trails seem to radiate from certain constellations. Such showers are named after the constellation in which they appear, but that constellation is in no way responsible for their existence. Swarms of meteors revolve around the Sun in certain orbits, and if the Earth moves through such a swarm, meteoric showers are produced. At the peak of such a shower, as many as one hundred meteors per hour have been counted.

Of the thousands of meteorites that penetrate our atmosphere, only about once a century is a meteorite large enough to produce a noticeable crater in the Earth's surface. The best known of these is the meteor crater near Winslow, Arizona (see Fig. 5-7). This meteorite hit the Earth about 22,000 years ago, and left a circular hole in the ground 570 feet deep and about 4,000 feet across, with a rim that rises 100 feet above the surrounding desert. Tons of meteoric material have been picked up around the crater. Due to the dry conditions in that region, this crater has remained intact for centuries.

The greatest meteoric impact so far in the twentieth century was the one that struck a remote region in Siberia on June 30, 1908. This meter exploded before striking the ground and formed hundreds of craters within a mile radius. The explosion was heard hundreds of miles away. Trees were leveled for miles around with their trunks pointing outward from the center. A herd

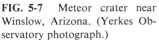
FIG. 5-7 Meteor crater near Winslow, Arizona. (Yerkes Observatory photograph.)

of reindeer, known to be in that area, completely disappeared. If such a meteorite were to explode near the ground in a metropolitan area, the casualties would be enormous.

QUESTIONS AND PROBLEMS

1. What is "Bode's law"? According to this relationship, how far from the Sun would a tenth planet be located?

2. How large would a building have to be to house a scale model of the solar system if the Earth were represented by a sphere 1 inch in diameter?

3. How many solar systems laid diameter-to-diameter would be required to reach from the Earth to the nearest star, which is 4.3 light-years away?

4. Is it true that the farther a planet is from the Sun, the faster it rotates on its axis? The faster it revolves around the Sun?

5. Why is it so difficult to see Mercury as either a morning or evening star?

6. How long is a day, sunrise to sunrise, on Mercury? Does Mercury have seasons? Explain.

7. Why is Venus called the Earth's twin? Are there any differences between the two?

8. What are the main factors contributing to the high temperature on Venus? Why is Venus uniformly hot all the way around the planet?

9. Explain why Venus takes 440 days to go from its greatest elongation as a morning star to its greatest elongation as an evening star, and only 144 days to get back to its greatest elongation as the morning star again?

10. To a person on Venus, if there is such a person, what would the Earth look like with the naked eye? With a powerful telescope?

11. Does Mars have an atmosphere? If you were an astronomer, how would you go about determining whether or not it has an atmosphere?

12. What are the features of the surface of Mars? Does it have seasons? Explain how you know. Are the polar caps really snow or ice?

13. How do you account for the irregular shapes of the asteroids?

14. What are the most interesting things about Jupiter? How do we know that it was almost the Sun's double star?

15. What are the interesting things about Saturn? What evidence indicates that the rings are not continuous solids? How do you think the rings were formed?

16. Table 5-2 indicates that Uranus's axis is tilted 98° from the normal to its orbit while in the discussion it was stated that the planet rotates

opposite to the direction of the other planets and its equator is inclined 82° to its orbital plane. Is this a contradiction? Explain.

17. Name all of the planets in order from the Sun, and give one interesting feature of each.

18. What is the most pronounced difference between the structure of a comet and other celestial objects? Describe the three main parts of a comet. How can one comet be distinguished from another?

19. What is a "solar wind"? How does a "solar wind" affect the appearance of a comet? What is the nature of a comet's light?

20. What is the composition of a meteor? Why do meteors look like shooting stars? Why do shooting stars last for such a short period of time?

21. Large meteorites are likely to explode before striking the surface of the Earth. What might cause such an explosion?

22. Would the danger of being struck by a meteorite be greater on the Moon or on the Earth? Explain.

SUGGESTED REFERENCES

ABELL, GEORGE, *Exploring the Universe*, Chaps. 14, 15, 16, and 17. Holt, Rinehart & Winston, New York, 1969.

PAYNE-GAPOSCHKIN, CECILIA, and KATHERINE HARAMUNDANIS, *Introduction to Astronomy*, 2nd ed., Chaps. 8 and 9. Prentice-Hall, Englewood Cliffs, N.J., 1970.

WEAVER, KENNETH F., "Voyage to the Planets," *National Geographic*, 138, no. 2 (August 1970), 147–93.

WYATT, STANLEY P., *Principles of Astronomy*, Chaps. 8, 9, and 10. Allyn and Bacon, Boston, 1964.

ZIM, HERBERT, and ROBERT H. BAKER, *Stars*. Simon & Schuster, New York, 1956.

6

The Sun and the Stars

The Sun is the master of our solar system, and controls the motions of everything within its domain. It is our main source of energy; without it, the Earth would be a barren wanderer of eternal coldness and darkness. The Sun has been pouring out this life-sustaining energy with undiminished vigor for billions of years, and it is expected to continue to do so for billions more. Compared with other stars in the universe, it is about average in many respects, but to us here on Earth it is by far the greatest star of them all, for we could not exist without it. As we have previously learned, (see Section 5-2), our solar system is somewhat isolated in space, despite the fact that the Sun is a member of a group or galaxy of about 100 billion stars. Even the closest star is so far away it appears to be only a point source of light. A thorough study of the Sun will reveal what effect it has upon our lives, and in addition will give us worthwhile information about the other stars.

The only way astronomers are able to gain any knowledge about the Sun is through the light, heat, and other electromagnetic waves received from it. A piece of the Sun cannot be taken into the laboratory to be analyzed. But a little beam of sunlight can, and does reveal many of the Sun's secrets. Sunlight consists of an array of colors which we have seen many times in the form of rainbows after refreshing summer showers. As the light passes through the droplets of water, it is dispersed into its colors, with one blending into the next, giving a beautiful continuous spectrum from red to violet. Such a spectrum can be produced at will rather easily by sending a small beam of sunlight through a glass prism (see Fig. 6-1). The resulting spectrum can be carefully analyzed with an instrument called a spectrometer. In 1814, Joseph Fraunhofer, a German optician, made a very important discovery while closely examining such a spectrum; he noticed that a great number of fine, dark vertical lines were spread throughout the entire color band. It is from

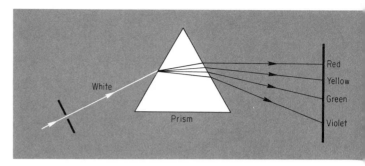

FIG. 6-1 Sun's spectrum.

the positions of these dark lines, rather than from the colors themselves, that we are able to learn so much about our Sun. These "Fraunhofer lines" appear in the spectrum because the light from the inner, intensely heated portions of the Sun has some of its frequencies removed by absorption while passing through the Sun's atmosphere. By studying these absorption lines, a great amount of information about the chemical composition, rotational motion, atmosphere, and magnetic field of our solar furnace can be acquired. We shall not discuss the techniques used to determine these characteristics, but shall give only the results obtained.

6-1
Physical Characteristics of the Sun

The Sun is a glowing ball of hot gaseous material called *plasma*. It has a diameter of 864,000 miles, or about 109 times as large as the Earth. If the Earth were placed at the center of the Sun, the Moon in its present orbit would be only halfway to the Sun's surface. Although gas-like in nature, it is rather massive, about 332,500 times the mass of the Earth. Hence, the Sun has an average density 1.4 times that of water. This seems rather dense for anything that behaves like a gas, but the enormous compression that must exist at the center due to the amount of material above it, accounts for the high density. The surface gravity is not as large as one might expect for an object of such magnitude. It is only 28 times as much as that at the Earth's surface. Spectral analysis reveals that more than sixty of the naturally occurring elements on the Earth exist on the Sun, hydrogen being the most abundant. About 90% of the material at the solar surface is hydrogen and most of the remaining 10% is helium, an element discovered in the atmosphere of the Sun nearly 30 years before it was detected here on Earth.

Although the Sun is gaseous in nature and shows no exact boundaries between the different layers, there are nevertheless distinctive regions. The visible surface is called the *photosphere* (see Fig. 6-2). This is the lowest level

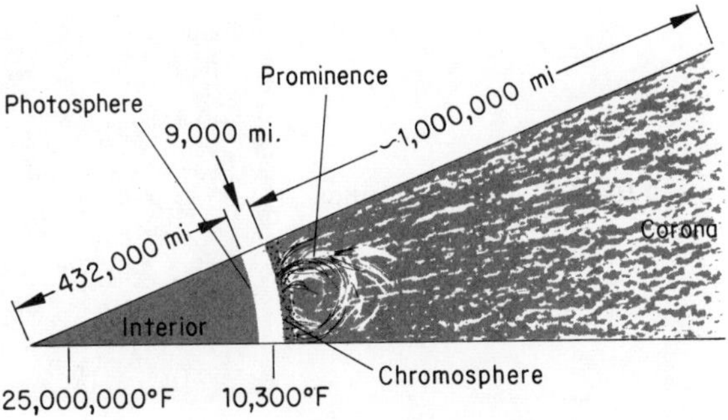

FIG. 6-2 Cross section of the Sun.

we can see. It is the surface scientists photograph and use for measuring the Sun's diameter. This surface is not uniform in brightness; it is granulated and looks like oatmeal. The granulated regions appear bright and are surrounded by narrow dark regions. The bright areas vary in size, having diameters from 150 to 2,000 miles. The surface pattern is constantly changing, indicating that some kind of turmoil must be taking place inside the Sun. The intensity of the light in each of the various colors of the Sun's spectrum compares favorably with the light emitted from a solid material heated to a temperature of 10,300° F. The structure of the Sun below this surface is truly speculative, but astrophysicists have estimated the temperature at the center to be on the order of 25,000,000° F.

The gases above the visible surface constitute the Sun's atmosphere and can be separated into two regions. Immediately above the photosphere and extending for several thousand miles is the *chromosphere*, so named because of its red color due to the glow of the hydrogen present. Normally this layer of atmosphere is not visible, but appears as a red crescent just as the Moon covers the photosphere during an eclipse, and then disappears during totality. The lower portion of the chromosphere is called the *reversing layer*. This is dense enough to absorb certain frequencies of the light radiated from the photosphere, thus producing the Fraunhofer lines observed in the Sun's spectrum.

The chromosphere blends into the outer atmosphere called the *corona*, which extends from the Sun for millions of miles. The corona is not visible under ordinary circumstances, but appears as a pearly white region around the Sun during a total eclipse (see Fig. 4-16). Until 1930, astronomers had to wait for solar eclipses to study the corona. Now anytime the Sun is visible, the Sun's atmosphere can be studied by using a *coronagraph*, a telescope with a black disk placed at its focal plane, thus blocking out the photosphere and producing an artificial eclipse. The density of the outer corona has been found to be extremely low, considered by scientists to be about the same as that of a good vacuum produced in the laboratory. Theory leads us to believe that the temperature of the gases in the corona is at least a million degrees Fahrenheit. This is considerably higher than that of the photosphere, but because of the low density its heat content is extremely small. Why the corona has such a high temperature is another of the many mysteries of nature still puzzling Man.

6-2
Solar Activities

The Sun does not always pour out energy at exactly the same rate, but fluctuates with the activities that take place in and on the Sun. All natural phenomena here on Earth are influenced by the rhythm of these activities. Some of the solar eruptions may also introduce hazards to those venturing outside the Earth's protective atmosphere.

Sunspots

When the sun is examined with proper equipment, black spots are frequently seen on its face. A word of warning must be given here. *The Sun should never be viewed directly, or through a telescope or binoculars, without an adequate darkening or filtering device, lest there be serious and probably permanent damage to the eye.* The surface of the Sun can be viewed safely by placing a piece of white paper about a foot from the eyepiece of a telescope and focusing the Sun's image on this paper. The black spots detected by this method are called *sunspots*. Each consists of a dark central region called the *umbra*, and a lighter surrounding area called the *penumbra* (see Fig. 6-3). Sun spots are somewhat circular in shape with jagged edges, and usually come in groups that have a *leader* and a *follower*, sometimes with smaller

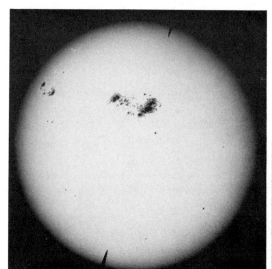

FIG. 6-3 A white-light photograph of the Sun, and an enlargement of the large sunspot group. (Photograph from the Hale Observatories.)

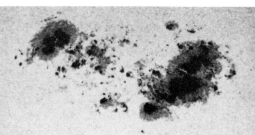

spots between them. They vary in size from a mere speck to 90,000 miles in diameter. Sunspots look dark because they are cooler than the photosphere around them; they are at temperatures of about 8,600° F while the regions around them are at 10,300° F. If isolated and viewed by themselves, they appear orange. These spots indicate that eruptions must be taking place inside the Sun. Evidently, as the hot, compressed gas of the interior rises to the surface, it expands and cools to temperatures below that at the surface.

Sunspots are not permanent features on the Sun's surface as are the continents on the Earth. A group of sunspots start as a couple of small spots and rapidly develop into a group of spots with a leader and a follower, which have opposite magnetic polarities. The follower spot breaks up into smaller spots, and gradually all but the leader vanish. Finally, after weeks or months, this remaining spot disappears as new groups are formed in different areas. They start out in latitudes of about 30 degrees north and south, and the new ones are formed closer and closer to the Sun's equator. When they have been formed within 5 degrees of the equator and have vanished, no new ones or very few new ones are formed for a couple of years. These are called the years of the quiet Sun. Then the sunspots start forming in abundance again at the higher latitudes. This process is repeated approximately every 11 years, the time used to progress from maximum activity to minimum and back to maximum again (see Fig. 6-4). During maximum activity, more than 100 spots have been observed at one time, and sometimes during the minimum, no spots are sighted.

FIG. 6-4 Sunspot cycle, 1870–1970.

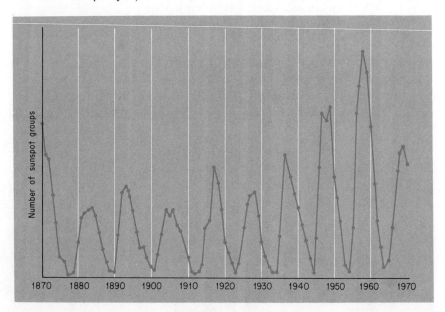

Sunspots appear to move across the face of the Sun, but this must be due to the rotational motion of the Sun because they move across the disk of the Sun, disappear from sight at the eastern edge, and after 12 or more days a few that survive reappear at the western edge. From this motion we observe that the Sun, like most of its planetary members, is rotating from west to east. From the directions in which the spots move, we know that the Sun's equator is inclined $7\frac{1}{4}$ degrees to the plane of the ecliptic. From the time it takes a long-lived sunspot to complete a trip around the Sun, we also know that the Sun at the equator makes 1 rotation in 24.9 Earth days, and that at a latitude of 30 degrees it makes a rotation in 25.9 days. Since no sunspots appear at latitudes greater than 40 degrees, the rotation near the poles has been determined by spectroscopic means. At a latitude of 85 degrees, it has been found that the Sun makes 1 rotation in 34 days. From this limited data we see that the Sun rotates more slowly at higher latitudes than at the equator. In fact, it gradually turns more and more slowly as the latitudes get larger and larger. Since the various layers must slide by each other, the Sun cannot be a solid, but must be fluid in nature. At the temperature of the Sun, no known substance could exist as a liquid. Hence, the Sun must be a glowing ball of gaseous material.

Prominences

Along the outer edge of the chromosphere numerous tiny jets of gas shoot out distances of about 4,500 miles and, after a few minutes, disappear. They seem to be associated with the bright, granulated areas of the photosphere, because they give the entire outer surface of the chromosphere a grass-like appearance. Larger than these *spicules* are the more spectacular *prominences*, which at times extend several hundred thousand miles into the corona. These great flame-like projections of solar material are most dramatic when viewed at the edge of the Sun against the dark background of space (see Fig. 6-5).

FIG. 6-5 Solar prominences. The white dot represents the size of the Earth. (Yerkes Observatory Photograph.)

FIG. 6-6 A hydrogen filtro-heliogram showing the granulated photosphere, sunspots, plages, filaments, and a flare in progress in the lower left-hand quadrant of the solar disk. (Courtesy of McMath-Hulbert Observatory of the University of Michigan.)

At first they were observed only at the time of solar eclipses, but with present-day instruments, such as the spectroheliograph, they can be studied whenever the Sun is visible. Because the gases may be cooler than the photosphere due to their expansion, they often appear as long, dark *filaments* when seen against the Sun's disk (see Fig. 6-6). Prominences vary in size and complexity. Some appear as sheets of flame, others look like great arcs above the chromosphere (Fig. 6-5), and many only appear to be moving downward into the chromosphere from the corona. By means of special motion-picture equipment pioneered at the McMath-Hulbert Observatory of the University of Michigan, excellent movies of the Sun's surface have been taken and show the action of the various prominences. There seems to be a relationship between the prominences and the sunspot cycle because prominences are more numerous when there are many sunspots, and the latitudes of many of the prominences vary systematically with the spot cycle.

Plages and Flares

All active sunspots are surrounded by bright "clouds" in the chromosphere called plages (pronounced *plahzhes*; see Fig. 6-6). Occasionally an intense brightening of hydrogen light appears near the center of a group of sunspots. It usually becomes intensely bright within a few minutes and fades away in an hour or so. Such a sudden brightening is called a solar *flare* (see Fig. 6-6). Flares have been observed to vary in duration from 4 minutes to 7 hours. They usually are not visible in white light, but are very prominent when photographed by using only the hydrogen light which they emit. Each spot group has a number of flares during its lifetime. A really active group produces from 30 to 50 flares while moving with the Sun across its disk. During maximum activity, flares average about 1 every 2 hours.

6-3
Terrestrial Effects of Solar Activities

We have noticed that radio fadeout, terrestrial magnetic storms, and the polar auroras are very closely associated with the activities on the Sun, especially the solar flares. In addition to the bright hydrogen light produced by the flares, they emit intense X rays, ultraviolet, and infrared radiations, bursts of short radio waves, and streams of high-speed charged particles. The X rays and ultraviolet light, upon reaching the Earth (after about 8 minutes and 20 seconds), disturb the ionization layer in our atmosphere from which radio waves are normally reflected. This interrupts our long-range radio communications by producing fadeouts. Such disturbances may last for several hours. The bursts of short wave radio radiations emitted by the flare may appear as "static" on radio, and interfere with its use. The charged particles that strike the Earth reach us in a little over a day and produce magnetic storms and the auroras. Magnetic storms are not related to our electrical storms. They are merely fluctuations in the Earth's magnetic field and can be detected by observing the variations in the direction of a sensitive compass needle. Such magnetic storms may disrupt telegraphic and teletypewriter communications. The entering charged particles are deflected by the Earth's magnetic field and pile up at the terrestrial magnetic poles, producing the beautiful auroras. Those we see in the Northern Hemisphere are called *aurora borealis*, or "northern lights." They are drapery-like lights arching across the northern sky, changing in shape like curtains fluttering in a gentle breeze. Usually auroras are yellow-green in color, but occasionally they are red and sometimes blue. Some solar flares have been strong enough to produce auroras that have been seen as far south as Mexico City.

The X rays, ultraviolet light, and high-speed charged particles which have such pronounced effects upon our atmosphere would be extremely harmful to life on Earth if it were not for the protective layer of air. The major question yet unanswered is how they will affect an astronaut traveling in outer space. Also, will the short-wave radio outbursts produced by flares decrease the effectiveness of our radar defense, and disrupt our radar detection of approaching rockets?

6-4
Beyond the Solar System

Beyond the solar system there are billions of brightly glowing celestial objects similar in nature to our Sun. On a clear moonless night the sky seems to be filled with these twinkling point sources of light. About 6,000 stars can be seen with the unaided eye, but with a large telescope billions can be observed. Whether viewed with the naked eye or the telescope, all appear to be the same size, and the same distance away, but differ in brightness and color. Some, like Sirius, are extremely bright while many others are barely visible. Some stars, like Arcturus, are reddish in color, many are yellow like our Sun, a number are as white as Vega, and others are blue-white like Spica. They are not evenly distributed in space. Through one section of the sky the stars appear so close together that they give the illusion of an irregular luminous cloud across the heavens. This we call the *Milky Way*. Many others seem to form patterns in the nightly sky, and such an array of stars is called a constellation. The most obvious of these is Ursa Major, or the "Big Dipper." The names of at least 60 constellations have come down to us from the Greeks and other ancient astronomers who named them after animals, birds, fish, serpents, and gods. Some of the configurations are rather difficult to visualize, but with a bit of imagination one can see a skeleton outline of what the constellation is supposed to resemble. Orion (the hunter), for example, appears in the southern sky in the early evenings during the winter months. Three fairly bright stars are lined up in a row. They represent Orion's belt. Three fainter stars in a row below the belt and approximately perpendicular to it represent his sword. A bright red star some distance above the belt is his shoulder, and the blue-white one below the sword is his knee. With a little stretching of the imagination one can see the figure of Orion facing Taurus (the bull). After locating Orion, we should have no difficulty in finding it again. It is rather intriguing and challenging to try to locate the constellations shown on star charts. Try it some clear night.

Our knowledge of stars, regardless of their remote distances and apparent pinpoint sizes, has been gained by analyzing the extremely small amount of light received from them. From their spectra we have learned about their distances from the Earth, their brightnesses, temperatures, sizes, masses, compositions, and motions in space.

6-5
Stellar Distances

Since the stars appear to form a hemisphere in the sky, early astronomers assumed that all stars were equal distances from the Earth. Isaac Newton made the first attempt to determine the distances to the stars. He assumed that all stars emitted the same amount of light as that of the Sun, and their apparent difference in brightness was due to their difference in distances from the Earth. He reasoned: the brighter the star, the closer it is to us; the dimmer, the farther away. Knowing that the intensity of light falls off inversely as the distance squared, he was able to calculate the distances to many of the stars. Since his assumption was false, for all stars do not have the same intrinsic brightness, he arrived at the correct distances for only those stars which have the same light output as the Sun. The astronomer Bessel was the first to measure the distances to the nearer stars. In 1838 he observed a star's position with respect to the background of stars in the autumn and again in the spring. From the angle the star shifted, he was able to make a trigonometric calculation of the distance from the Sun to the nearest star. Present-day astronomers use the same method for measuring the distance to stars which are less than 300 light-years (300 years for their light to reach us, or 1.8×10^{15} miles) away. Photographs are taken of the stars 6 months apart, and the parallax angles are obtained from the photographic prints. Distances are computed from these angles. For stars in our galaxy or group of stars beyond 300 light-years, indirect methods have to be employed by using data obtained from pulsating stars called *Cepheid variables*. It has been determined that our nearest star, Proxima, is 4.3 light-years from the Earth, while the most distant galaxies are between 6 and 7 billion light-years away. In the future, with refined instruments, man may push the horizons millions of more light-years into space.

6-6
Brightness

The *apparent brightness* of a star is its brightness in comparison to other stars as seen from the Earth. Hipparchus classified stars in six categories according to their observed brightness. The twenty brightest stars in the sky were called *first-magnitude* stars, the next fainter group were the *second-magnitude*, and so on to the *sixth-magnitude* which were those stars barely visible to the naked eye. Later it was found that those considered as the brightest stars were about 100 times as bright as the ones just visible. Now we define a first-magnitude star as that star which is exactly 100 times as bright as a sixth-magnitude. On this basis, each magnitude is $\sqrt[5]{100}$ or 2.512 times as bright as the next magnitude. For example, a second-magnitude star is 2.512 times as bright as a third-magnitude, and a fifth-magnitude is 2.512 times as bright as a sixth. Using this factor and taking a star just visible to the naked eye as magnitude 6, Spica, which is 100 times as bright, has a magnitude of 1.0, Sirius a magnitude of -1.43, and the Sun a magnitude of -26.5. The apparent brightness of a star can be determined by taking a picture of that star through a telescope, and measuring the amount of darkening of the film for a specific exposure time and opening of the camera; the brighter the star, the darker the image is on the negative. By photographic means, very faint stars up to the twenty-third magnitude can be detected.

We receive billions of times more light from the Sun than we do from any other star because the Sun is so much closer. This does not mean that the Sun emits more light per second than any other star. If the Sun and another star were placed the same distance away we could then compare their energy outputs, or *luminosities*, by comparing their brightnesses. Astronomers have agreed that this distance shall be 32.6 light-years. The magnitude at this distance from the Earth is called its *absolute magnitude*. Luminous outputs of stars can be determined accurately by comparing their absolute magnitudes with that of the Sun. If our Sun were taken 32.6 light-years away, it would have a magnitude of 4.3. If Alpha Centauri were taken from its present position of 4.3 light-years to 32.6, it would have a magnitude of 4.2. Hence, Alpha Centauri and the Sun are almost identical stars; they emit about the same amount of light per second. The luminosity of many of the stars is greater than the Sun. For example, Canopus emits 5,000 times the amount of light the Sun emits. On the other hand, there are dwarf stars that are about 1/10,000 as luminous.

6-7
Temperatures, Sizes, and Masses of Stars

The temperature of a star can be accurately determined from its spectrum, but a fairly close estimate can be obtained from its color. A red star like Antares is relatively cool, about 5,000° F; yellow stars have temperatures approximately that of the Sun, 10,300° F; white-hot stars like Vega are at about 18,000° F; and blue-white stars like Spica are extremely hot, 36,000° F.

From the temperature and the absolute magnitude of a star, its size can be computed. Antares, in the constellation Scorpius, is 428 million miles in diameter, about 500 times as large as the Sun. If the Sun were placed at the center of Antares, the planet Mars would extend out one-third of the distance to Antares's surface, and Jupiter would be slightly above its surface. At the other extreme, the white dwarf companion of Sirius is only 25,000 miles in diameter, about the size of the planet Neptune. Some dwarf stars are not much larger than the Earth.

Despite the large differences in diameter, the masses differ only by a relatively small amount. The masses of most stars are between $\frac{1}{10}$ and 30 times the mass of the Sun. There are, however, exceptionally massive stars, about 100 times that of the Sun, but these stars are very rare indeed.

Spectral analysis indicates that all the stars consist of the same materials as our Sun, mainly hydrogen, with a small percentage of helium and only traces of the other elements. The basic element of the whole universe seems to be hydrogen.

In 1911, Ejnar Hertzsprung of Denmark and, in 1913, Norris Russell of the United States independently plotted the absolute magnitudes of a great number of stars against their spectral class or color, and made a very important discovery between the intrinsic brightness of the stars and their surface temperatures. This plot is known as the *H-R* (Hertzsprung-Russell) *diagram*. It shows that most of the stars fall along a narrow region running diagonally from the bright, hot stars to the dim, cool ones (see Fig. 6-7). This is called the *main sequence of stars*. Our Sun is located on this main sequence in the yellow region. Therefore, our Sun is one of the regular stable stars. It has enough hydrogen to remain there for about 6 billion years more. Off the main sequence and in the bright, cool region are the red giants such as Arcturus in the constellation Bootes, and the supergiants such as Antares. Below the main sequence and in the dim, hot region are the dwarf stars. The H-R diagram shows that 90% of the stars bright enough to produce spectra observable on photographic plates lie on the main sequence. This indicates that the universe of stars is not chaotic in nature, but follows some rhyme and reason in its structure. Many questions are still unanswered, but a pattern is beginning to evolve (see Section 18-10). For man to conceive of such a pattern is remarkable since he has seen the surface of only one of these stars, namely, the Sun.

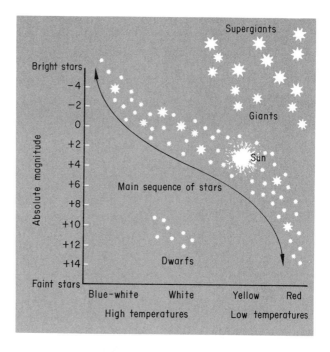

FIG. 6-7 The Hertzsprung-Russell diagram.

Looking into space through a large telescope, we not only see billions of stars, but we see them clustered together in groups. With the naked eye, we can see a hazy patch of light in the constellation of Andromeda. When viewed through binoculars, it looks like a luminous cloud. When photographed with a large telescope and for an exposure time of several hours, the object takes on the details shown in Fig. 6-8. It consists of about 100 billion stars that remain confined to the system. Such a group of stars is called a *galaxy*. The Andromeda galaxy contains a spherical group of stars distributed rather uniformly at its center, and from this central region spiral arms extend outward like those of a giant pinwheel often seen during a display of fireworks. Such a system of stars is known as a *spiral galaxy*. The Great Spiral Galaxy of Andromeda is about 1.5 million light-years from us, and it is approximately 140,000 light-years in diameter.

Of course, we cannot photograph our own galaxy, but from star counts and distance measurements, we believe that our family of stars, called the Milky Way galaxy, is a flat disk with a huge central ball of stars and spiral arms very much like those of the Andromeda galaxy. As we look through our galaxy edgewise, we see thousands of stars so close together they appear as the Milky Way through the sky. Our galaxy is much smaller than the Great Andromeda galaxy. It is about 98,000 light-years in diameter and 10,000 light-years thick. It includes about 100 billion stars, one of which is the Sun. Early astronomers thought that the Earth was at the center of the universe. Later Copernicus introduced the heliocentric system, and then it was thought that the Sun was at the center of the universe. Now we find out that the Sun is not even at the center of our galaxy, but is in one of the spiral arms about 30,000 light-years from the center, or about three-fifths of the way to the

FIG. 6-8 The great spiral Andromeda galaxy. Its two companions, one above and the other below, are elliptical galaxies. (Photograph from the Hale Observatories.)

FIG. 6-9   Barred spiral galaxy in Eridanus. 200-in. photograph. (Photograph from the Hale Observatories.)

FIG. 6-10   Spiral galaxy in Coma Berenices seen edgewise. (Photograph from the Hale Observatories.)

edge. The disk shape of the Milky Way galaxy indicates that it is rotating, and from spectral data, we believe that the Sun makes 1 revolution around the galaxy in 200 million years. Therefore, the Sun must be traveling at a speed of 180 miles per second relative to the center of our galaxy. The spiral arms contain vast amounts of hydrogen and cosmic dust, the raw material for building stars. Since the sun is on a spiral arm and near such gas clouds, we think that it is a middle-aged star.

The Milky Way and Andromeda galaxies are by no means the only two systems of stars in the universe, for we can observe other galaxies scattered in all directions throughout space. There are probably 10 billion galaxies within the range of the 200-inch telescope, and this may be only a small fractional part of the number in existence. These billions of galaxies can be grouped into three categories; the *spiral*, the *elliptical*, and the *irregular*. About 75 % of all the galaxies observed are the spiral type. Two thirds of these have their spiral arms extending out from a spherical hub of stars, and one-third have spiral arms extending out from the ends of a broad band, or bar, of stars which passes through the center of the galaxy. The latter group are called *barred spiral galaxies* (see Fig. 6-9). These spiral groups differ only in the number of stars in the central sphere or bar, and in the positions of the arms. Some of them we view flat, others we see edgewise (Fig. 6-10), and many we find between these two positions.

FIG. 6-11   Elliptical galaxy. (Photograph from the Hale Observatories.)

FIG. 6-12   An irregular galaxy taken with the 200-in. telescope. (Photograph from the Hale Observatories.)

Over one-fifth of the observed galaxies have neither arms nor surrounding clouds of gas and dust. They are merely spherical groups of stars. Some are slightly flattened due to their rotational motion. These are called *elliptical galaxies* because those first observed appeared as elliptical disks (see Fig. 6-11). These galaxies have all their stars concentrated near the center without any building gas and dust visible.

The third type, which constitutes about 5% of the galaxies, show no trace of any rotational motion, and appear very irregular in shape (see Fig. 6-12). These are called *irregular galaxies* as their shapes indicate. In the Southern Hemisphere two such galaxies can be viewed with the naked eye. They are the Magellanic clouds, so named in honor of the navigator Magellan. They are our nearest galaxian neighbors, about 150,000 light-years away, They consist of star clusters, variable stars, supergiants, and gaseous nebulae, but with no rotational pattern. The smaller cloud is lacking in cosmic dust but contains interstellar gas. Some irregular galaxies consist of stars too faint to be resolved as separate stars, and so the whole galaxy looks like a luminous, irregular-shaped object.

A count of the galaxies in all directions indicates that even the galaxies occur in groups instead of being uniformly spread throughout space. Between forty and fifty clusters have been recognized with between 10 and 100 galaxies in each group. Our Milky Way galaxy is one of a family of nineteen galaxies all within 4 million light-years from us. This is close on the intergallactic distance scale. The Great Galaxy of Andromeda and the two Magellanic clouds are other members of the system. In 1968 two new neighbor galaxies were detected through the obscuring interstellar dust of our Milky Way. They are called Maffei 1 and Maffei 2 after the Italian astronomer, Paolo Maffei, who first reported them. Maffei 1 is 3.3 million light-years away, and at the outer edge of our local group. In the Milky Way family there are at least ten elliptical galaxies, and so it seems that our galaxy family received more than its share of elliptical galaxies and far below average of spiral galaxies.

In 1960 Allen Sandage discovered, with the use of a radio telescope, an extremely bright object in the sky, which was about 100 times as bright as any known galaxy. Shortly afterward, others were found, and it was established that these were smaller than regular galaxies and were not stars in the usual sense. They were called *quasi-stellar radio sources* (*quasi* meaning "seemingly") and were later abbreviated to *quasars*. Since then many more quasars have been identified. From their spectra, we know that they are receding from us at very high velocities, over 100,000 miles per second, and they must be very far away, 3C147 being about 8.7 billion light-years away. What are these quasars? Some say that they might be large masses, probably hundreds of solar masses, in gravitational collapse. The energy they radiate comes from the loss of gravitational potential energy as they collapse. Others say that they might be galaxies in the process of formation, and still others suggest that they are old galaxies in which the central regions have evolved to a high density of stars. As yet no scientific model has been formed that answers all of the questions.

6-10
What Keeps the Stars Shining?

The Sun and stars emit unbelievable amounts of heat and light. We may wonder how they can produce such tremendous amounts of energy and continue to shine for billions of years. They cannot continue shining just because they are hot. Neither can the heat be furnished by a burning process because they possess very little, if any, oxygen. The German scientist, Hermann von Helmholtz, tried to explain their heat output by the contraction of their gaseous materials. He argued that the gravitational attraction caused the material to be compressed, which produced the heat. A yearly contraction of 140 feet of the Sun's radius would produce the amount of heat the Sun delivers. If in the past it had radiated heat at its present rate, the Sun would have shrunk from the size of a solar system to its present diameter in about 50 million years, but according to the geologists the age of the Earth as obtained from rock formations must be at least 4.5 billion years. Hence, the contraction theory is not the answer. After the discovery of radioactivity, it was suggested that the stars obtain their heat from radioactive sources at their centers, but this proved unsatisfactory.

The currently accepted idea is based upon the theory, introduced by Einstein, that mass is a form of energy and can be converted to heat. Spectral analysis shows that all the stars have an abundance of hydrogen with a small amount of helium. At the temperatures of the stars, the hydrogen nuclei run into and react with other hydrogen nuclei, forming helium nuclei, and in the process mass is lost. This lost mass is converted to heat and light. Before we can fully understand such a process, we must learn more about the various forms of energy and the true structure of all matter.

QUESTIONS AND PROBLEMS

1. If a model of the solar system were made to scale with the center of the Earth 1 foot from the center of the Sun, what would be the diameter of the Sun? How far would Pluto be from the Sun?

2. Since light travels at a speed of 186,000 miles per second, how long does it take the light emitted from the Sun to reach the Earth? To reach Pluto?

3. What is the most abundant element in the Sun? What other element is rather plentiful?

4. Make a diagram of the cross section of the Sun, and name the various layers and their temperatures.

5. What reason have we for saying that the Sun is a gas, although its density on the average is greater than that of water?

6. At the high temperature of the Sun, why has not the gas-like material acquired high enough speeds to escape from the Sun, causing it to lose a large amount of material each day and gradually disappear?

7. What conclusion can be drawn from the fact that a photograph of the Sun is almost a perfect disk?

8. What are the structure and temperature of the corona? When is it possible to see the corona with an unaided eye? With a coronograph? Why isn't the corona visible whenever we can see the Sun?

9. What are sunspots? Name the various parts and describe each. In what latitudes of the Sun are they usually found?

10. What is meant by the sunspot cycle? During what part of this cycle are the years of the quiet Sun?

11. What are prominences, filaments, plages, solar flares, and solar granules?

12. How do solar spicules differ from prominences? What is the difference between a prominence and a filament?

13. What is a star? How do we know that the Sun is really a star?

14. What is the meaning of a first-magnitude star? A zero-magnitude star?

15. How much brighter is a second-magnitude star than a third-magnitude? Than a fourth-magnitude? Than a sixth-magnitude?

16. What is meant by the absolute magnitude of a star? What is the absolute magnitude of the Sun? Why does the Sun appear so bright since it is only as luminous as Alpha Centauri, a fairly dim star?

17. How do we know that the Sun and Alpha Centauri are identical stars?

18. What is meant by the *main sequence* of stars? Where is the Sun located on the main sequence? What are giants and supergiants? What are white dwarfs?

19. Where would a hot, bright star be located on the H-R diagram? Where would a cool, dim star be located? A dim, hot star? A bright, cool star?

20. Stars X and Y are equal in size and are approximately the same distance from the Earth. Star X is a red star, while star Y is a blue-white one. What else do we know about the two stars?

21. What are galaxies? What type of galaxies are there? Which type is the most abundant in the universe? In our family of galaxies?

22. What is the shape and size of our Milky Way galaxy, and where is the Sun located in it?

23. Are the Magellanic clouds in our galaxy?

24. Are the galaxies evenly distributed in space? Explain.

SUGGESTED REFERENCES

ABELL, GEORGE, *Exploration of the Universe*, 2nd ed., Chaps. 27, 29, and 30. Holt, Rinehart & Winston, New York, 1969.

GAMOW, GEORGE, *The Birth and Death of the Sun*. Viking Press, New York, 1952.

MEHLIN, THEODORE G., *Astronomy*, Chaps. 2, 3, 4, 7, and 8. John Wiley & Sons, New York, 1959.

RUDAUX, LUCIEN, and G. DEVAUCOULEURS, *Larousse Encyclopedia of Astronomy*. Prometheus Press, New York, 1959.

2

Energy

Science is not just a collection of laws, a catalogue of unrelated facts. It is a creation of the human mind, with its freely invented ideas and concepts.

—From The Evolution of Physics *by Albert Einstein and Leopold Infeld*

Saturn SA-5 lifting off launching pad. During launching, tons of water are poured on the pad to keep it from being damaged by the intense heat of the rocket exhaust. (National Aeronautics and Space Administration.)

7

Units of Measurement

In the development of the physical sciences, a rapid increase in scientific achievements came after man began basing his conclusions upon experimental facts instead of upon inferences and personal opinions. Experimentation, however, indicates a quantitative investigation of some aspect of nature, and the important phase of such an inquiry is the measurement of the things with which it deals. Measuring any quantity means comparing it with an accepted, arbitrarily chosen unit as a standard, and finding out how many times larger or smaller it is than the standard unit. The length of an object is measured by finding how many times longer it is than some standard unit of length. For example, if this book were taken as a standard, and laid end to end five times along a desk top, we know that the desk is 5 book-lengths long. If by laying the book down end to end five times does not quite reach the other end of the desk, we say that its length is a little over 5 books. In scientific work this "little over" part is not accurate enough. To be more precise, we must estimate what fractional part of the book the desk exceeds 5 book-lengths. If we appraise the desk to be $\frac{1}{5}$ of a book longer than the 5 book-lengths, we record its length as $5\frac{1}{5}$ or 5.2 book-lengths. Another person may estimate the fractional part as $\frac{3}{10}$ of a book, and of course he would give the length of the desk as 5.3 books. A more exact measurement could be made by subdividing the book into ten equal parts. Both persons would then measure the desk to be a little more than 5.2 books long. Again they would have to estimate the fractional part of the subdivision by which the desk is longer than 5.2 book-lengths. If one person estimated the fractional part as $\frac{1}{2}$ a subdivision, he would record a length of 5.25 books. Another person might judge the fractional part as $\frac{4}{10}$ of a subdivision, and he would say that the desk is 5.24 books long. The last figure recorded is always the one estimated. These guesses are obviously far more accurate than those for the larger

126

units. The greater the accuracy desired, the smaller the subdivisions must be.

The weight of an object is similarly determined by finding how much heavier it is than some arbitrarily chosen standard weight unit. For example, if a block of wood is 4 times as heavy as a standard pound, its weight is 4 pounds. Also, the smaller the subdivisions we have for the standard weight, the more accurate the weighing can be made.

Measurements are as essential in daily living as they are in scientific work. Here in America, meat is purchased by the pound, dry goods by the yard, gasoline by the gallon, water by the cubic foot, and electricity by the kilowatt-hour. Accuracy is also desired in these measurements.

7-1
Origin of Units

Man originally used the dimensions of parts of his body as units for length measurements. The width of a man's thumb, or from the knuckle to the tip of the forefinger became our *inch*. The *foot* originated as the length of a man's foot. The width of the hand is a unit very familiar to horse lovers for the height of a horse is still measured in *hands*. A hand is about 4 inches. The *span* mentioned in Isaiah was derived from the distance between the end of the thumb and the end of the little finger when the hand was completely distended. It is generally considered as being 9 inches. A convenient unit for measuring cloth was found to be the distance from the tip of a person's nose to the tip of the middle finger of his arm outstretched sideways. This measurement for King Edgar of England has become our *yard*. The *cubit*, also mentioned in the Bible, but no longer used, was the length of the forearm measured from the elbow to the end of the middle finger (approximately 18 inches). According to the Bible, Noah's ark was 300 cubits long, 50 cubits wide, and 30 cubits high. The *fathom*, used in measuring ocean depths, was originated by the Vikings as the distance from the tip of one middle finger to the other when the arms were outstretched in a straight line. From this it is clear that a fathom is equivalent to 2 yards. The ancient people discovered interesting relationships between some of these natural units. They observed that there were 12 thumb widths in 1 foot, and 3 feet in the unit called a yard. The Roman legionnaires stepped off their miles (*milles*) as 1,000 paces, 2 steps to a pace. From this we have obtained a *mile* as 1,760 yards. The parts of the body and the lengths of steps were very convenient measuring devices because they were always available; but since they varied from individual to individual, they could hardly be considered standard units for length measurements.

The Babylonians weighed objects by comparing them with certain stones used for that purpose. A *stone* was until recently used as a unit of weight in

England, and was equal to 14 pounds. The Egyptians used the weight of a wheat grain as a standard which introduced the unit of a *grain* that we use today.

We have already learned that our unit of time came from the apparent motion of the Sun through the sky. The Babylonians took the time from noon to noon as the solar day, and they divided each day into 24 *hours*, each hour into 60 *minutes*, and each minute into 60 *seconds*. We still use the same pattern, except that ours, until recently, was based upon the mean solar day. In 1967 an international General Conference on Weights and Measures took the standard second to be the duration of 9,192,631,770 periods of the natural vibration of the cesium-133 atom because the natural vibration of this atom does not fluctuate with changes in temperature or any other external conditions.

7-2
Need for an International System of Units

In the ancient days there was very little commerce outside of one's own village, and body dimensions as units of measurements were satisfactory for bartering among friends. As commerce developed, so did the measuring problem. By the thirteenth century A.D., the units for measuring length and weight were in a chaotic state. They varied considerably from country to country and even from city to city. This made the trade between cities and countries extremely difficult. The first major step to alleviate this problem was taken by King Edward I of England. He ordered that the distance originally taken from the tip of King Edgar's nose to the tip of the middle finger of his outstretched arm be made the standard yard, and ordered a permanent measuring stick of that distance be made out of iron, the strongest material then known. This master yardstick was called the "iron ulna," *ulna* being the name of one of the bones of the forearm. He also decreed that the foot should be one-third of that standard yard, and one thirty-sixth of the yard should be the inch. For those living in the remote outposts of England, such a permanent yardstick was of very little use because it was not available, and so in 1324 King Edward II decreed that three barleycorns, round and dry, would be one inch. Later the yard was legalized by an act of Parliament, and is now defined as the distance between two marks on a platinum-iridium bar in London. King Edward II also decreed that the pound be the weight of 7,000 grains of barley, and that this pound be divided into 16 ounces.

This standardized the system of units within the British realm, but they still varied throughout Europe. For example the *ell*, an old unit for measuring cloth, had a length of about 45 inches in England, 37 inches in Scotland, 24.7 inches in Denmark, and 27 inches in the Netherlands. The stone as a unit of weight varied from 4 to 26 pounds. Such variability led to great confusion in international trade. The situation became particularly troublesome in central and western Europe, where the countries were small, the languages numerous, and the customs diverse. As early as the eighteenth century, suggestions were made from time to time for eliminating the confusion. A simplified international system of units for lengths and weights was clearly needed.

7-3
The Metric System of Units

The first step in this direction was taken in 1791 after the French Revolution, when the French Academy of Sciences recommended the adoption of international standards for length and weight to replace *all* the national and regional standards then in use. They recommended that the standard unit of length be based upon the size of the Earth so that such a unit could never be lost or damaged, and would not shrink or expand. One ten-millionth of the distance from a pole to the equator, as measured along a great circle, was proposed as the primary unit of length, and was to be called a *meter* (Gr. *metron*, "measure"). It was also recommended that the standard unit of mass, or quantity of matter, be defined instead of a unit for weight, and that this standard be based upon the mass of a definite volume of water as measured by the new unit of length. One millionth of a cubic meter of water at its maximum density was proposed as the primary unit of mass, and was to be called a *gram* (Gr. *gramma*, "small weight"). The mass of any body could then be measured by comparing its weight with that of the standard mass of water. It was realized that these primary units were not of convenient sizes to measure extremely small or very large distances or masses; therefore, a system of fractional and multiple units was proposed. It was a decimal system with the various units related to each other by factors of 10; a measurement in one unit could be converted to another unit merely by moving the decimal point to the right or to the left. The size of each fractional or multiple unit was indicated by the prefix attached to the name of the primary unit. The numerical values of some of these prefixes are given in the Table 7-1. Tables 7-2 and 7-3 give the systems of units for length and mass. The units in italics are the ones in common usage today.

The French National Assembly promptly approved the plan. A standard meter bar and a standard kilogram cylinder were made of platinum and officially adopted.

This system of units attracted the attention of other nations, but many people objected to the change. It was not until 1872 that work was begun which led to the adoption of the metric system as an international system

TABLE 7-1
Values of Units

Prefix	Meaning	Numerical Value	
nano = one-billionth	1/1,000,000,000	0.000000001
micro = one-millionth	1/1,000,000	0.000001
milli = one-thousandth	1/1,000	0.001
centi = one-hundredth	1/100	0.01
deci = one-tenth	1/10	0.1
(UNIT) = ONE	1/1	1
deka = ten	10/1	10
hecto = one hundred	100/1	100
kilo = one thousand	1,000/1	1,000
mega = one million	1,000,000/1	1,000,000
giga = one billion	1,000,000,000/1	1,000,000,000

TABLE 7-2
Lengths

1 *millimeter* (mm) =	0.001 meter (m)
1 *centimeter* (cm) =	0.01 m
1 decimeter (dm) =	0.1 m
METER =	1 m
1 dekameter (dkm) =	10 m
1 hectometer (hm) =	100 m
1 *kilometer* (km) =	1,000 m

TABLE 7-3
Masses

1 *milligram* (mg) =	0.001 gram (gm)
1 centigram (cg) =	0.01 gm
1 decigram (dg) =	0.1 gm
GRAM =	1 gm
1 dekagram (dkg) =	10 gm
1 hectogram (hg) =	100 gm
1 *kilogram* (kg) =	1,000 gm

of units. At that time, a new International Commission on Weights and Measurements assembled in Paris. It consisted of fifty-one delegates from twenty-nine countries, including the United States. The commission set about its business of constructing exact copies or prototypes of the original standard meter and standard kilogram, and distributing them to the participating nations of the commission. These prototypes were made of platinum-iridium alloy.

After the work had been started, new geodesic measurements revealed that the standard meter was not one ten-millionth of the Earth's quadrant, but was slightly smaller (about 0.023% smaller). It was obvious that future refinements in measurements might again change its size; therefore, the *meter* was taken as the length of the original platinum bar at the temperature of melting ice. After a large number of prototypes of the standard kilogram had been distributed, an error in the original kilogram was also discovered. More precise measurements revealed that the original kilogram was the mass of 1,000.027 cubic centimeters of water at its maximum density instead of the mass of 1,000 cubic centimeters, as intended. Instead of destroying all the standards which had been distributed and correcting this error, the commission defined the standard kilogram as the mass of the original platinum cylinder. Although the standard units of length and mass were slightly different from their intended values, the Commission on Weights and Measurements accepted them as the international standards of the metric system. For safekeeping, the prototypes which agreed most closely with the original standards were entrusted to the newly established International Bureau of Weights and Measures, and were palced in a vault in the new International Observatory at Sèvres, near Paris.

In the course of its work, the Commission made accurate copies of both the standard meter and standard kilogram for distribution to all the cooperating countries. The United States received two of each of these standards, and they are carefully preserved in the National Bureau of Standards, in Washington, D.C. One of the standard kilograms is shown in Fig. 7-1.

FIG. 7-1 United States Prototype Kilogram 20, a cylinder 39 mm in diameter, made of an alloy that is 90% platinum and 10% iridium. It is handled very rarely, and only with tongs faced with chamois, to avoid unnecessary wear. Early in 1937 it was taken to Paris for recomparison with the international standard. It had changed only one part in 50 million in approximately 50 years. (National Bureau of Standards.)

In 1960, the International Conference on Weights and Measures in Paris made the original platinum-iridium standard meter rod a useless item when they adopted the wavelength of the orange light emitted by electrically excited krypton-86 gas as a standard unit of length. Krypton-86 is an isotope of krypton with a mass number of 86 (see Chapter 15). They defined the meter as 1,650,763.73 wavelengths, and the inch as 41,929.399 wavelengths of this particular light. Now the standard meters all over the world can be checked periodically without sending them back to Sèvres to be compared with the original standard. This new standard was selected because krypton-86 cannot be lost, stolen, or destroyed since it is present to a small extent in our atmosphere and, according to scientists, the properties of krypton-86 will never change. At any time in the future, this standard unit of length can be accurately reproduced.

7-4
A New Unit of Volume

A unit of volume can be obtained by cubing any unit of length. For example, a volume can be expressed in *cubic centimeters* (cm^3). Since the kilogram did not prove to be the mass of 1,000 cubic centimeters of water, a new unit of volume called the *liter* (Fr. *litron*, an old measure) was introduced. The liter was defined as the volume of a kilogram of water at its maximum density. The milliliter (ml) and not the cubic centimeter (cm^3) is really the volume of 1 gram of water. Consequently, we have two units for volume: the milliliter, derived from the unit of mass, and the cubic centimeter, derived from the unit of length. A milliliter is equal to 1.000027 cubic centimeters. Except for very accurate scientific work, the two units are taken as being numerically equal.

7-5
Measurements in the United States

The adoption of the new international standard did not guarantee that the metric system would immediately supersede all other units in every country. The metric units are now used almost exclusively in scientific work all over the world and are universally used for measurements of everyday dealings except in the United States and a few smaller countries where the English system of units with its feet (ft), pounds (lb), and quarts (qt) are still used in business and industry. England, the nation that developed the imperial system of units has abandoned it in favor of the decimal metric system.

In exercising its power to fix the standards of weights and measures for our country, Congress legalized the metric system for measurements in our everyday affairs, but did not make the use of the metric system obligatory. In effect, the meter was made our only standard of length by an act of Congress in 1866 when it declared the yard to be 3,600/3,937 of the standard meter. Likewise, the kilogram is our only standard of mass, the avoirdupois pound having been fixed in value as 0.4535924277 of a kilogram. We in America have essentially adopted the simpler metric system, but have continued to use the yard, the pound, and the other British units. It is hoped

TABLE 7-4
Metric-English Equivalents

1 meter (m)	= 39.37 inches = 3.28 feet
1 centimeter (cm)	= 0.394 inch
1 kilometer (km)	= 0.62 mile
1 liter (l)	= 1,000.027 cubic centimeters (cm^3)
1 liter	= 1.057 quarts (liquid)
1 gram (gm)	= 0.035 ounce
1 kilogram (kg)	= 2.204 pounds
1 inch (in.)	= 2.54 centimeters
1 foot (ft)	= 30.48 centimeters
1 yard (yd)	= 0.914 meter
1 mile (mi)	= 1.61 kilometers

that someday we will discard this awkward, outmoded system inherited from our mother country, and adopt for daily use the decimal system provided by the International Bureau.

Table 7-4 gives few of the relationships between the metric and English units.

7-6
Scientific Notations

To avoid confusion when dealing with numbers that have a string of zeros after them, or a large number of decimal places before them, the scientist has devised a shorthand way of writing such numbers. In this system we make use of powers of 10. One hundred is 10×10, or 10^2; one thousand is $10 \times 10 \times 10$, or 10^3; and one billion is $10 \times 10 \times 10 \times 10 \times 10 \times 10 \times 10 \times 10 \times 10$, or 10^9. The number 2,080,000,000 may be written as 2.08×10^9. Fractions can be designated by negative exponents; thus the value of 0.01 is $\frac{1}{100}$, or $1/10^2$, or 10^{-2}; and 0.00001 is 1/100,000, or $1/10^5$, or 10^{-5}. Similarly, one one-billionth is 10^{-9}. The fraction 0.000000000480 may be written as 4.80/10,000,000,000, or $4.80/10^{10}$, or 4.80×10^{-10}.

Scientific notation can be understood in terms of shifting the decimal point. A *positive* exponent indicates a shift of the decimal point to the *right*, the number of places equal to the exponent. For example, the velocity of light, 300,000,000 meters per second (m/sec), may be written as 3×10^8 m/sec. A *negative* exponent indicates a shift in the deciaml point to the *left* the number of places equal to the exponent. The quantity 1.6×10^{-12} indicates a value of 0.0000000000016. Five micrograms may be written as 5×10^{-6} gm.

A few approximate dimensions written in scientific notations are given in Table 7-5.

When *mutiplying* numbers expressed in powers of ten, *add* the exponents.

TABLE 7-5
Measurements in Scientific Notations

		Approximately
To distant quasars	=	10^{25} meters
Diameter of Andromeda galaxy	=	10^{21} m
Distance to nearest star	=	10^{16} m
Diameter of Sun	=	10^{9} m
Diameter of Moon	=	10^{6} m
Length of football field	=	10^{2} m
Width of man's hand	=	10^{-1} m
Thickness of a piece of paper	=	10^{-4} m
Diameter of a hydrogen atom	=	10^{-10} m
Diameter of elementary particle	=	10^{-15} m

For example, $10^3 \times 10^2 = 1,000 \times 100 = 100,000$ or 10^5, and $3 \times 10^8 \times 1.2 \times 10^{-3} = 3.6 \times 10^5$. When *dividing* numbers expressed in scientific notation, *subtract* the exponents. For example, $(8 \times 10^5)/(2 \times 10^3) = 4 \times 10^{+2}$; and $(12 \times 10^3)/(4 \times 10^{-2}) = 3 \times 10^5$; and $(6.6 \times 10^{-34})/(1.6 \times 10^{-19}) = 4.1 \times 10^{-15}$.

7-7
Units of Derived Quantities

All quantities in mechanics can be expressed in terms of the three fundamental quantities of length, mass, and time. Although these three are undefined, we nevertheless have an intuitive feeling for their meaning, and have units for measuring them. The mass of a body is a more fundamental property than its weight. The property called mass represents the amount of matter in an object while weight is the gravitational pull on that matter. Other quantities may be derived by combinations of the fundamental quantities. The units of all of these derived quantities depend upon the units of the three basic quantities. When the length is expressed in feet, the weight in pounds, and the time in seconds, we have the *foot-pound-second* or English system of units, which is used in the United States in industry and in daily living. In the metric system, there are two sets of units which only differ in size of units: the *centimeter-gram-second* (cgs) and the *meter-kilogram-second* (mks) systems. The mks system of units is widely adopted because it can be used in electricity as well as in all other phases of the physical sciences, whereas the English system has not been used in electricity because it isn't as convenient. The size of the mks units are more practical than those of the cgs system. From here on, in this book we shall use the metric system exclusively to acquaint the student with the units of the world.

Let us look at a few of the simpler derived quantities to get an idea of how the fundamental units are used. Areas are obtained by multiplying one length by another length; hence, areas are expressed in meters $\times$ meters, or square meters, which is written symbolically as m². The concept of speed, which we have used so frequently in previous chapters, is obtained from our concept of length and time. If we say that a car is traveling at a uniform speed of 80 kilometers per hour, we mean that it goes a distance (length) of 80 kilometers in a time of 1 hour, or a distance of 8 kilometers in $\frac{1}{10}$ of an hour, or any other combination of distance in km and time in hours for which the ratio is 80. Hence, we see that speed is obtained by taking the distance an object travels and dividing it by the elapsed time:

$$\text{Speed} = \frac{\text{Distance}}{\text{Time}}$$

From now on, instead of expressing a speed as so many "kilometers per hour," we shall write it as "km/hr." We may also express it as m/sec, or cm/sec.

Another quantity we have often mentioned is density, and it is defined as the mass per unit volume:

$$\text{Density} = \frac{\text{Mass}}{\text{Volume}}$$

Density may be expressed as kilograms per cubic meter (kg/m³), or in the cgs system as grams per cubic centimeter (gm/cm³).

Whenever we express a physical quantity, its units are as important as its numerical value. In the future we must remember that the newly acquired quantities will also have units which will help us to understand the derived quantities.

7-8
Proportionalities

Most natural phenomena as well as all derived quantities can be represented in mathematical forms, using symbols for the various terms. With these symbols and equations, scientists can express concisely ideas which would otherwise require many words of explanation. Equations show the abstract relationships between quantities without regard to their numerical values. Mathematical reasoning using these relationships is indispensable in the physical sciences, and we shall now discuss some of the most basic of these relationships.

If one quantity A increases or decreases as another quantity increases or decreases—when, for example, one is doubled as the other is doubled—the two quantities are said to be *directly proportional* to each other. This may be written symbolically as follows:

$$A = kB$$

In the above equation k is the *proportionality constant* which has a unit of A/B, and its value may depend upon experimental conditions or may be arbitrarily fixed by the user. The relationship between the circumference and diameter of a circle is an example of the first type of constant mentioned. The larger the diameter of a circle the larger is the distance around its circumference. Thus the circumference C of a circle is directly proportional to its diameter d, or

$$C = kd$$

In this case the k has been determined experimentally to be numerically equal to 3.1416, which we designate by the Greek letter (π). It has no unit since $k = $ meter/meter $= 1$. From this relationship, we see that the circumference of a 10-centimeter-diameter circle is equal to $\pi \times 10$ or 31.416 cm. An example of an arbitrarily fixed constant is in the relationship between the cost and amount of gasoline we buy. The cost C is directly proportional to the number of liters (or gallons) N we purchase, and can be expressed mathematically as

$$C = kN$$

where k is the price per liter and is determined by the company selling the gasoline.

If a quantity A increases as another quantity B increases, but A becomes 4 times as great when B is doubled, and 9 times as much when B is tripled, we say that A is directly proportional to the square of B. An example of this is the distance d an object falls from rest in a certain time t:

$$d = kt^2$$

where k is determined experimentally; for an object falling freely near the Earth's surface, it is equal to 4.9 m/sec². Hence, in 5 seconds an object will fall 4.9 m/sec² $\times$ 5² sec², or 122.5 meters.

A quantity may be directly proportional to any power or root of another quantity. The volume of a sphere depends upon the cube of its diameter: $V = kd^3$. The scattering of light depends upon the fourth power of its frequency f; Scat. $= kf^4$.

If a quantity A increases as B decreases and vice versa, we say that the two are *inversely proportional* to each other. If one is doubled when the other is halved, we write the relationship as follows:

$$A = k\frac{1}{B}$$

For example, doubling the pressure on a confined gas compresses that gas to half its volume. Hence, the volume V of a gas is inversely proportional to the pressure P applied. This statement may be written as

$$V = k\frac{1}{P}$$

where k is an experimental constant the value of which depends on the amount, kind, and temperature of the gas. A quantity can also vary inversely as any power or root of another quantity.

Proportionalities may be combined to form more complete equations. As an illustration, the volume of a gas is directly proportional to the mass of the gas in that volume, directly proportional to the temperature T, and, as previously stated, inversely proportional to the pressure P applied to it. By combining these proportionalities, we obtain the following equation, which is a more complete statement of gas behavior:

$$V = k'\frac{mT}{P}$$

In this equation k' is a different constant from the k used in the previous equation, and is determined experimentally.

7-9
Graphs

A useful way of showing proportionalities is by plotting the data on graph paper. A line or curve drawn through the plotted points gives a picture to a trained mind of the relationship between the variables. If the correct proportionality has been determined from the graph, an equation for that physical phenomenon can be written.

When you make a graph, the dependent variable should be plotted on the vertical, or Y, axis and the independent variable on the horizontal, or X, axis. The scales used for these coordinates should be small enough for the data to fit on the page, but large enough to read with ease. Label each axis with the quantity being measured and with the proper units. After you plot the data, a straight line or a smooth curve drawn through the points helps to determine the type of proportionality involved, and the formula to be used.

For example, we know from experience that a car traveling at a uniform speed of 50 km/hr (31 mi/hr) will travel a distance of 25 km in $\frac{1}{2}$ hr, 50 km in 1 hr,

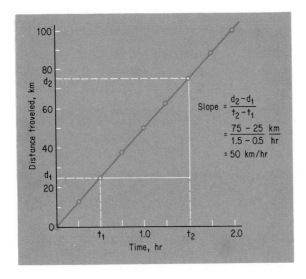

$$\text{Slope} = \frac{d_2 - d_1}{t_2 - t_1}$$

$$= \frac{75 - 25}{1.5 - 0.5} \frac{\text{km}}{\text{hr}}$$

$$= 50 \text{ km/hr}$$

FIG. 7-2 Distance a car travels vs. time of travel. The graph being a straight line represents a direct proportion, doubling the time doubles the distance the car travels. The proportionality constant k for this relationship is the slope of the line, or 50 km/hr.

75 km in $1\frac{1}{2}$ hr, and 100 km in 2 hr. The distance the car travels depends upon the amount of time the car is moving; hence, the distance the car travels in kilometers is put on the Y axis and the independent variable, time, is placed on the X axis. The resulting graph will represent the way these two quantities vary (see Fig. 7-2). Since the graph is a straight line through the origin, we know that the two vraiables are directly proportional to each other, and

$$d = kt$$

The constant k can be obtained from the slope of the graph (the *slope* is the ratio of the number of units of change on the Y axis for a certain number of units of change on the X axis). In this case, k is equal to 50 km/hr, and the complete equation of motion is

$$d = 50t$$

in which d must be expressed in km, and t in hr.

If the ratio of one quantity to another increases, the resulting graph does not yield a straight line, but a curved line as illustrated in Fig. 7-3, in which the distance d that a freely falling object travels is plotted against the time t. To an inexperienced person, however, the shape of this curve may not give a clear picture of the relationship between the distance the object fell and the time. If the distance d is now plotted against the time squared, t^2, as shown in Fig. 7-4, the resulting graph is a straight line through the origin. From this we know that d is directly proportional to t^2 and not t, or

$$d = kt^2$$

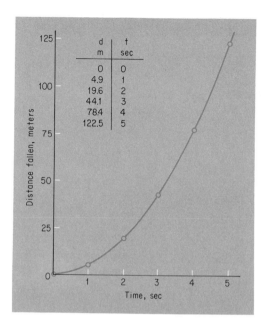

d m	t sec
0	0
4.9	1
19.6	2
44.1	3
78.4	4
122.5	5

FIG. 7-3 Distance an object falls vs. time of fall. The graph shows that the distance a freely falling object travels is not directly proportional to the time of fall; doubling the time more than doubles the distance the object falls.

The number of d units in one t^2 unit is the value of k, and we see from the graph that this is 4.9 m/sec². Therefore,

$$d = 4.9t^2$$

FIG. 7-4 Distance an object falls vs. time squared. The graph being a straight line through the origin represents a direct proportion between the distance the object falls and the time of fall squared.

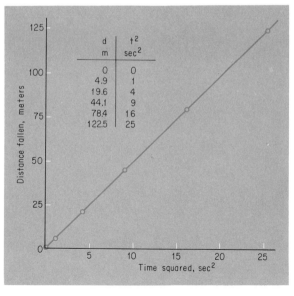

d m	t^2 sec²
0	0
4.9	1
19.6	4
44.1	9
78.4	16
122.5	25

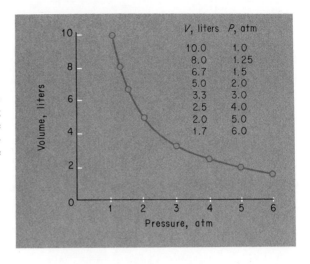

FIG. 7-5 Volume of a gas vs. the pressure applied. The curve being concave upward indicates an inverse proportion between the volume oc- occupied by a gas and the pressure applied to the gas.

If the volume V of a gas is plotted against the applied pressure P (Fig. 7-5), we notice that the curve is concave upward and does not go through the origin. This suggests an inverse function. To check it, we shall plot the volume V against the reciprocal of the pressure $1/P$, as illustrated in Fig. 7-6. From the resulting straight line, we see that the volume is directly pro- portional to the reciprocal of the pressure or that the volume is inversely proportional to the pressure:

$$V = k\frac{1}{P}$$

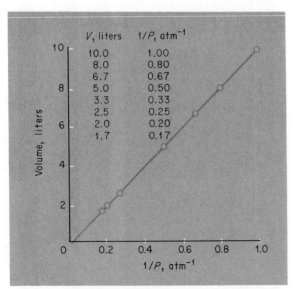

FIG. 7-6 Volume of a gas vs. the reciprocal of the pressure applied. The straight line through the origin indicates that the volume of a gas is directly proportional to the reciprocal of the pressure, or that the volume is inversely proportional to the pressure applied to the gas.

Therefore, if you do not recognize the relationship from the graph where one variable is plotted against the other, select coordinates that will result in a straight line, if at all possible, and you can then determine the true relationship between the variables. Selecting the correct coordinates, such as squares, cubes, roots, or even logarithms, in order to straighten out a curve, is quite a trick in itself, but comes with practice.

Experimental errors cause the points on a graph to be somewhat scattered, and so the actual points obtained in the laboratory do not fall perfectly along a smooth curve or a straight line as shown in the previous graphs. If, however, a smooth curve is drawn through the mean of the points on a graph, the experimental uncertainties are averaged out and the true relationship between the variables can be obtained and expressed in a mathematical form.

The scientist makes great use of the graph. He collects his data and then plots them on a graph to determine the relationship between the variables. If he can choose the proper coordinates to produce a straight line, he can then write the relationship in a mathematical form. If he cannot produce a straight line, he must then see if the data fits some theoretical relationship he or someone else has hypothesized.

QUESTIONS AND PROBLEMS

1. Estimate the length, width, and thickness of this book in centimeters. Measure these dimensions with a meterstick. What is the advantage of subdividing a unit of measurement?

2. Name seven units of length which originated from the dimensions of the various parts of the body.

3. What distance was originally selected as the meter? What mass was originally selected as the gram? What errors were discovered in the original units, and what was done about it?

4. A table is 76.0 cm high. What is its height in millimeters? What is it in meters?

5. What is the price of a piece of silk 1 m long and 25 cm wide at $1.50 per square meter?

6. What is your height in meters and centimeters?

7. What is the diameter, in inches, of a 155-mm (millimeter) shell?

8. Which is longer, the 1,500-m or the 1-mile race? How many meters longer?

9. A ski jumper jumps a distance of 175 meters. How far is that in feet?

10. What is the mass in kilograms of a 16-lb bowling ball?

11. If first-class postal rates are 8 cents per ounce, how much will it cost to mail a 50-gram package by first class?

12. A merchant bought a 12-by-15-ft rug at $7.75/yd² ($7.75 per square yard) and sold it in Mexico at $10.75/m². Did he realize a profit or a loss, and by how much?

13. Why was the liter selected as a unit of volume? Which is larger, a milliliter or a cubic centimeter, and by how much?

14. What is the volume in liters of a rectangular tank 1.5 meters long, 70 cm wide, and 30 cm deep? How many kilograms of water does it hold?

15. Express in scientific notation the number of seconds in 20 days.

16. Express the answer of each of the following in scientific notation:

(a) $300,000 \times 5,000$ (c) $\dfrac{2800}{0.04}$

(b) $5,000 \times 0.002$ (d) $50 \times 60,000 \times 0.003$

17. Solve each and express the answer in scientific notation:

(a) $(3 \times 10^7) \times (5 \times 10^3)$ (d) $(2 \times 10^5) + (4 \times 10^3)$

(b) $(3 \times 10^4) \times (7 \times 10^{-3})$ (e) $(5 \times 10^5) - (25 \times 10^3)$

(c) $\dfrac{(21.2 \times 10^5)}{(2 \times 10^3)}$

18. The mass of the planet Jupiter is 1.94×10^{27} kg, and the mass of the Earth is 6.1×10^{24} kg. What is the ratio of the mass of Jupiter to the mass of the Earth?

19. How long does it take light, traveling at a speed of 3×10^8 m/sec, to travel the distance from the Sun to the Earth?

20. What is the value of the following?

$$\frac{(9.1 \times 10^{-31}) \times (1.6 \times 10^{-19})}{(2 \times 10^{-22})^2}$$

21. If an athlete runs the 100-meter dash in 10 seconds, what is his speed in kilometers per hour (km/hr)?

22. A block of metal 20 cm $\times$ 5 cm $\times$ 4 cm has a mass of 2.4 kilograms. Calculate its density in gm/cm³.

23. What is the difference between fundamental and derived quantities?

24. Give two examples of things in everyday life that are directly proportional to each other, and two examples of things that are inversely proportional to each other.

25. If a force F is applied to a spring and stretches it a distance S, the force and stretch are related as shown in the graph. Interpret the meaning of this graph.

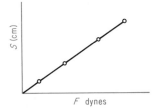

26. If the voltage across a resistance R is kept constant, the number of amperes I of electric current flowing through the resistance depends upon its resistance in ohms as indicated in the graph (below, left). According to the graph, how does I vary with a change in R?

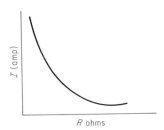
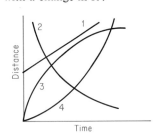

27. The distance a freely falling object moves from rest in a certain length of time is directly proportional to the time squared. Which curve of this graph (above, right) represents that relationship between distance and time? Explain.

28. Plot the following data and then choose coordinates that will produce a straight line:

Y	2	8	18	32	50	72	98
X	1	2	3	4	5	6	7

29. Plot the following data and then choose coordinates that will produce a straight line:

Y	24	12	8	6	4.8	4	3.4	2.4	2
X	1	2	3	4	5	6	7	10	12

30. Plot the following data and then choose coordinates that will produce a straight line:

Y	64	16	7.1	4	2.6	1.8
X	1	2	3	4	5	6

SUGGESTED REFERENCES

DULL, C. E., E. C. METCALFE, and J. E. WILLIAMS, *Modern Physics*, Chap. 2. Holt, Rinehart & Winston, New York, 1963.

Precision: A Measure of Progress. General Motors Corp., Detroit, 1952.

PRIESTLEY, HERBERT, *Introductory Physics*, Chap. 2. Allyn and Bacon, Boston, 1958.

RITCHIE-CALDER, LORD, "Conversion to the Metric System," *Scientific American*, 223, no. 1 (July 1970), 17–25.

8

Force and Motion

8-1
Objects at Rest

Whenever we see an object suddenly begin to move, we assume at once that something has acted or is acting upon it to produce the motion. If that object is a car, we immediately infer that someone is pulling or pushing it, or that it is in gear and the engine is moving it, or that it is on a slight hill with the brakes released. When we look out-of-doors and see the leaves of the trees rustling, we surmise that a wind is blowing and exerting a force upon the leaves. We also observe that to produce any motion requires an outside force. A person cannot lift himself from a sitting position by pushing upward on the roof of his mouth with his tongue, nor can he lift himself by pulling up on his own bootstraps. The only way he can lift his body to a standing position is to push or pull on some object separate from the body. Therefore, experience has taught us that objects at rest remain at rest unless acted upon by some external force.

8-2
Objects in Motion

On the other hand, when we see a hard-hit baseball sail over the wall of a ball park, we do not expect the ball to continue forever. We are inclined to think that it will hit the ground and stop someplace outside of the park. A golf ball, no matter how hard it is hit, will soon come to rest, and we hope that it is on the fairway. An automobile has brakes to stop it quickly, but we are quite confident that it would eventually come to rest without such a mechanism. We are predisposed to say that objects do not tend to continue

144

in motion, and that their natural condition is one of rest. Early philosophers thought that rest was the most perfect position. They believed that for an object to continue its motion, some external force had to propel it, and as soon as that force was removed, the object would naturally stop. Some thought that the planets were pushed around in their orbits by angels, while others felt that the Sun's rays exerted the propelling force.

Certain facts warn us against adopting the idea of rest as the most perfect condition. In the case of the golfball, if the grass of the golfcourse is short and dry, the ball travels much farther than it does under normal conditions. It goes still farther over a stretch of smooth ice. It is apparent that as the retarding forces are reduced, the stopping distance increases. If all the opposing forces were eliminated, would the ball continue to travel indefinitely?

Galileo undertook to solve this problem in a very simple manner about three and a half centuries ago. He allowed a ball to roll down a smooth, inclined plane, and observed how far it rolled up another inclined plane. As shown in Fig. 8-1, he found that it rolled up plane *B* to almost the same height from which it started. When the plane was lowered to position *C*, he

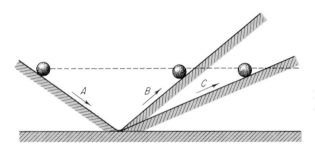

FIG. 8-1 Galileo's experiment on the laws of motion.

found that the ball rolled a greater distance along the plane, and again rose to about its original level. This continued for even smaller angles of the plane. Galileo then wondered what would happen if plane *B* were lowered to a horizontal position. He reasoned that if the ball were unopposed by friction, it would move indefinitely, trying to seek its original height which it could never accomplish. He also analyzed the situation in another manner and came up with the same conclusion. As the ball rolled down the first plane it acquired a certain speed by the time it reached the bottom, and it lost this speed in rolling up the second plane. When the plane was in position *C*, the ball rolled farther; therefore, it lost speed at a slower rate. The smaller the slope, the more slowly it lost speed. If the second plane had no slope, he argued, the ball would not lose any speed and would roll on forever.

Galileo's conclusion can be applied to the golfball. It ultimately stopped, not because rest is its natural position, but because of the opposing forces of the grass and air. In the absence of these retarding forces, it would have traveled on indefinitely.

8-3
Inertia

It may be stated, then, that an object at rest remains at rest and an object in motion will continue moving without changing its speed, unless it is acted upon by an exernal force. This property of matter to resist any change in motion is called *inertia*.

Inertia is evident in our everyday experiences. We pitch forward when the car in which we are riding is stopped abruptly, and we are pushed back against the seats when the car suddenly increases its speed. The effects are more noticeable while riding in a bus in a standing position. When the bus starts moving, our bodies seem to want to stay behind, and we have to brace our feet against the floor or hang onto some support to get moving with the bus. After the bus reaches a constant speed, we no longer have to brace ourselves; our bodies move at that steady speed without any effort on our part. But when the bus slows down, our bodies want to continue traveling at their newly acquired speed, and we must hang onto the supports again to keep from lurching forward. From this it is clear that our bodies tend to maintain their state of motion and resist any change in that condition.

The inertia of objects is utilized in many ways. In driving a nail, the hammer has so great a tendency to continue its motion that it pushes the nail before it. A hatchet is effective by reason of the inertia of the entire tool. To tighten the head of a hammer on its handle, one strikes the handle end against some solid object, and the inertia of the head forces it farther onto the handle (see Fig. 8-2). The tendency of a paperweight to remain at rest is what makes it so useful in keeping the papers on which it is placed from blowing away.

Different objects do not have the same inertia. A sledge hammer is far more effective at driving a post into the ground than is a tack hammer,

FIG. 8-2   Tightening the head of a hammer by using inertia of hammer head.

because it has considerably more inertia. How can we determine the amount of inertia an object possesses? This is done by measuring the quantity of matter in it, as evidenced by its inertia. This quantity is called its *inertial mass*, and as we shall see in the next chapter, it can be obtained by comparing its weight with that of a standard mass. The larger the inertial mass, the greater the tendency an object has to resist any change in its speed.

8-4
Motion along a Curve

It is also a well-known fact that objects in motion tend to move in straight lines. Sparks fly off a high-speed emery wheel in a line tangent to the wheel, and mud flies off a rapidly rotating car wheel in the same manner. Passengers in a car find themselves lurching toward the outside of the curve as the car rounds a turn because their bodies tend to continue traveling along straight lines. They must be pushed toward the center of the curve by the side of the car in order to keep them traveling around the corner with the car. If the curve is too sharp or the speed too great, the car itself may not be able to round the corner, and will leave the road along a tangent to that curve. The car is more likely to fail to make the turn if the pavement is wet or icy because the front wheels are not able to get enough traction to turn the car. In some washing machines, the water is removed from the fabrics by rotating them in a cylindrical metal basket. The adhesive force between the water and the clothes is not sufficient to keep the water on the circular path which the clothes are forced to follow, and the water flies out tangentially through holes in the basket. An athlete whirls a 16-pound hammer to give it a high speed, and when he releases it, the hammer flies off tangentially to its circular path. Instances like these convince us that any moving object tends to travel in a straight line, and will follow a curved path only by the coercion of a force perpendicular to its motion.

8-5
Newton's First Law of Motion

We have learned from experience that the tendency of an object is to resist any change in its speed or direction of motion. This phenomenon was completely described by Isaac Newton, and it is known as his first law of motion. It may be stated as follows: *Every object continues in its state of rest or of uniform motion along a straight line unless compelled by an external, unbalanced force to change that state.* Balanced forces produce no such change in speed or direction of motion. If we pull on a block with a force just equal to the frictional retarding force, there is no unbalanced force on the block and it will not change its state of motion.

When a motorist pushes down on the accelerator pedal, he introduces a large unbalanced driving force by means of the engine, and his car immediately picks up speed. The time rate at which the car increases its speed is called its *acceleration*. This is the "pick-up" or "get-away" about which so many people brag. The pick-up is due to the horsepower of the engine and not the streamline and beauty of the car. If the car increases its speed from 50 km/hr (31 mi/hr) to 70 km/hr in 5 seconds, we know that it picks up speed at an average rate of 4 km/hr every second (see Fig. 8-3). We say that it has an acceleration of 4 km/hr/sec, or 1.1 m/sec/sec (meters per second per second). Hence, we can use an equation to define the quantity:

$$\text{Average acceleration} = \frac{\text{Change in speed}}{\text{Time to change speed}}$$

In the metric system, accelerations are expressed in either m/sec/sec, or cm/sec/sec.

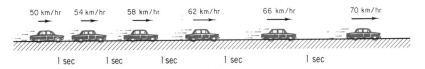

FIG. 8-3   Acceleration of a car.

When the brakes of a car are applied, the car slows down and soon stops. The rate at which its speed decreases is called *deceleration*. If a car traveling 60 km/hr (37 mi/hr) is stopped by the brakes in 3 seconds, it has an average deceleration of 20 km/hr/sec. A car with good brakes and new tires can decelerate on dry pavement at a rate of about 22 km/hr/sec, or 6.1 m/sec/sec. Deceleration is a negative acceleration; the speed decreases instead of increasing a certain amount each second.

In describing any motion, the direction of that motion is as important as its magnitude. For example, if a person were to fly in a private plane to Chicago in a 60-km/hr gale, how would he plot his course? This would be impossible unless he knew the direction of the wind. A headwind would slow him down considerably; a tailwind would speed him on his way; and a crosswind, unless properly accounted for, would blow him off his course. To know the wind speed is not sufficient; we must also know its *velocity*, which is its speed plus its direction. If the person knows that the wind is from the south, he can plot his course without any difficulty; therefore, a wind velocity of 60 km/hr from the south is more complete than a wind speed of 60 km/hr. To give the proper direction to acceleration, we must define it as the rate of change of velocity. It can be written symbolically as follows:

$$a = \frac{v - v_0}{t} \tag{1}$$

where v is the velocity at the end of the time t, and v_0 is the velocity at the beginning of that time. To account for the directions, the quantities v_0, v, and a are generally made *positive* if they are in the direction of the motion, and *negative* if opposite that motion. Let us use this equation to determine the deceleration of the car in the above problem:

$$a = \frac{0 - 60}{3} = -20 \ km/hr/sec$$

The minus sign means that the car is being decelerated.

It is a well-know fact that freely falling objects pick up speed as they fall. We also find that at a particluar location on Earth all objects, regardless of their inertial masses, fall in a vacuum with the same acceleration. The value of this acceleration due to gravity varies with altitude and latitude, but only slightly. The accepted value used for general work is 980 cm/sec/sec, or 9.8 m/sec/sec. This means that if an object is dropped from a rest position, it will be traveling toward the Earth at a speed of 9.8 m/sec at the end of the first second, 19.6 m/sec at the end of the second second, 29.4 m/sec at the end of the third second, 39.2 m/sec at the end of the fourth second, and so forth until the air resistance is large enough to deviate it from this pattern. An acceleration indicates how a body changes its velocity, but it does not tell us how far that body moves in a given time.

8-7
Distance Traveled

Most motorists determine mentally how far they can travel in a certain time, provided they know roughly their average speed. They do it by multiplying their average speed by the time:

Distance = Average speed × Time

For example, if a person is averaging 80 km/hr, he knows that in 4 hours he can go 320 kilometers. He can also determine how long it will take him to travel the next 560 kilometers; this time is equal to the distance to travel divided by his average speed:

$$t = \frac{560 \ km}{80 \ km/hr}$$

or 7 hours.

We see that it is rather simple to compute the distance we travel if we are moving at a uniform or constant speed, but how can we determine the distance traveled during a uniformly accelerated motion? All we have to do is average the initial and final speeds, which we will designate as v_0 and v, and substitute this average speed, $(v_0 + v)/2$, into the distance equation. Doing this we have

$$d = \frac{v_0 + v}{2}t \qquad (2)$$

If the final speed v is not known, it can be eliminated by substituting the value of v obtained from equation (1) into equation (2). The resulting equation is

$$d = v_0 t + \tfrac{1}{2}at^2 \qquad (3)$$

Let us determine the distance the car mentioned in section 8-6 traveled in stopping. Since the time was given in seconds, the speed must have the same unit of time; therefore, the 60 km/hr must be converted to km/sec or m/sec, the latter being more desirable. In this case v_0 is 16.7 m/sec, v is 0, and t is 3 seconds. From equation (2) we can compute the stopping distance for the car to be $\tfrac{1}{2}(16.7 + 0) \times 3$, or 25 meters. Let us see if we get the same answer by using equation (3). The deceleration of the car is $(0 - 16.7)/3$ or -5.57 m/sec/sec, and the stopping distance is $(16.7 \times 3) + \tfrac{1}{2}(-5.57) \times 3^2$, or 25 meters. If this car had been traveling at a speed of 120 km/hr (33.3 m/sec), and decelerated at the same rate, it would have taken 6 seconds to stop it, and its stopping distance would have been $\tfrac{1}{2}(33.3 + 0) \times 6$, or 100 meters. Therefore, when we double the speed of our car, we must remember that it takes 4 times the distance to stop it. If we triple our speed, the braking distance will be 9 times as great. Hence, we see that the stopping distance of a car is directly proportional to the square of its velocity.

Freely falling objects pick up speed at the rate of 9.8 m/sec each second, but how far will they fall in a certain time? From equation (3), we see that an object dropped ($v_0 = 0$) will fall $\tfrac{1}{2} \times 9.8 \times 1^2$ or 4.9 meters in the first second, $\tfrac{1}{2} \times 9.8 \times 2^2$ or 19.6 meters in 2 seconds, and $\tfrac{1}{2} \times 9.8 \times 3^2$ or 44 meters in 3 seconds. In Chapter 1, it was mentioned that to measure the height of a bridge over a deep canyon, a stone was dropped from the bridge and observed to strike the canyon floor in 4.75 seconds. By using equation (3), the height of the bridge above the canyon floor could be computed to be $\tfrac{1}{2} \times 9.8 \times (4.75)^2$, or 110 meters, or 360 feet, which is sligthly higher than the actual height because air resistance was not taken into consideration in the calculation.

8-8
Newton's Second Law of Motion

The acceleration of an object depends partly on the applied external force, and partly on the inertial mass of that object. The exact way in which each of these factors affects the motion of an object may be understood from a simple illustration. Let us imagine a loaded cart drawn along a level road by a horizontal force. If the force applied is just sufficient to overcome friction and air resistance, the external forces are balanced and the speed of the cart will remain unchanged. If, however, the pull exceeds the opposing forces, the cart will accelerate. If the excess force is doubled, we find that the acceleration is doubled, and if the force is tripled, the acceleration is tripled. Therefore, *the acceleration given an object is directly proportional to the unbalanced force producing it.* If the load on the cart is increased, we find that the cart becomes more difficult to start or stop. If the total mass of the cart and load is doubled, we find that for a given external force, the acceleration the cart receives is only half as much as before. If the mass of the load and cart is tripled, the acceleration is one-third as much. Thus, *the acceleration is inversely proportional to the mass being accelerated.*

These two relationships can be combined into one statement of motion: *The acceleration given an object varies directly as the magnitude of the applied net force producing the acceleration and inversely as the mass of the object being accelerated.* This is essentially Newton's second law of motion, and can be written symbolically as $a = F/m$, or simply as

$$F = ma \qquad (4)$$

Although it is not necessary to have a force to keep a body moving at a uniform speed, an *unbalanced force* is required to speed it up, slow it down, or deflect it from a straight-line course.

For this law to be useful, we must find some way of expressing the force. The mass of an object can be determined by comparing it with the standard kilogram mass, and the acceleration can be ascertained from the rate at which the object's velocity is changing. Knowing these two quantities, m and a, we can use Newton's second law, $F = ma$, and define a unit of force, which is the unbalanced force necessary to give a 1-kilogram mass an acceleration of 1 m/sec/sec. It is equal to 1 kg × 1 m/sec², or 1 kg × m/sec². This is a unit of force, but what shall we call it? The unit of kg × m/sec² has been given a name, which honors the man who discovered the law. It is called a *newton* (nt), Thus the newton is a derived unit since it is defined in terms of length, mass, and time.

In the cgs system of units, the unbalanced force necessary to give a 1-gram mass an acceleration of 1 cm/sec/sec is called a *dyne*. This is an extremely small force, but it is very useful in some scientific work, as we shall see in later chapters. *One newton is equal to 100,000 dynes.*

As an illustration of Newton's second law, let us suppose that a 1,500-kilogram automobile is traveling along a level road at a speed of 15 m/sec (54 km/hr), and is stopped by the brakes in 5 seconds. The unbalanced force necessary to stop the auto can be determined as follows:

$$\text{Deceleration} = \frac{0 - 15}{5} = -3 \text{ m/sec}^2$$

$$\text{Mass} \quad = 1,500 \text{ kg}$$

$$\text{Force} = ma = 1,500 \text{ kg} \times (-3 \text{ m/sec}^2)$$

$$= -4,500 \text{ newtons}$$

The minus sign means that the unbalanced force is opposite the direction of motion; this is quite logical if the auto is to be stopped.

One may say that this value of an unbalanced force may not mean much because he does not know what 4,500 newtons really is. Let us see if we can obtain a better understanding of the unit called a newton. If a 1-kilogram mass is allowed to fall freely, we know that, neglecting air resistance, it will be accelerated at a rate of 9.8 m/sec^2; hence, the force pulling the kilogram mass toward the Earth, which is its weight, is 1 kg $\times$ 9.8 m/sec^2, or 9.8 newtons. The same gravitational pull will be acting upon it whether it is falling or held stationary. Therefore, by lifting a kilogram mass one can experience a force of 9.8 newtons, or 9.8×10^5 dynes. For those acquainted with the English system, a newton is equivalent to a force of 0.225 pounds (approximately $\frac{1}{4}$ pound).

Aristotle believed that heavy objects fall faster than lighter ones because things tend to seek their natural places. Almost 2,000 years later Galileo refused to accept such a conclusion as the truth. He dropped balls of various weights from a given height and, as the story goes, he dropped them from the top of the Leaning Tower of Pisa. He found that they fell to the Earth in approximately the same time. He overlooked the slight difference in time, and concluded that all objects fall with the same acceleration. Shortly after Galileo's experiments, the vacuum pump was invented, enabling scientists to drop objects in a vacuum. A feather and a coin were dropped inside a long, evacuated glass tube, and were found to fall together the entire length of the tube (see Fig. 8-4). Hence, Galileo's conclusion was verified experimentally.

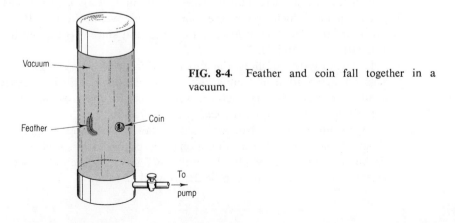

FIG. 8-4. Feather and coin fall together in a vacuum.

Galileo determined how objects fall, but he did not know why; this was left for Newton to explain.

Let us see how Newton's second law explains why all objects fall with the same acceleration (neglecting air resistance). If two balls of 2 and 4 kilograms are allowed to fall, the more massive ball has twice the force acting upon it because the weight becomes the unbalanced force in free fall. This, you might say, ought to produce twice the acceleration, but you must remember that it is twice as massive, requiring twice the unbalanced force to accelerate it. Both the 2-kg ball and the 4-kg ball have the same unbalanced force per unit mass acting upon them, thus producing the same acceleration. We may also consider the problem in a mathematical manner as follows: The 2-kg ball has a gravitational force or weight of 2×9.8, or 19.6 newtons acting upon it. Therefore, its free-fall acceleration is equal to F/m, where F is the weight of the ball, and its acceleration is $(19.6 \text{ nt})/(2 \text{ kg})$, or 9.8 m/sec^2. The 4-kg ball has a gravitational force of 39.2 newtons acting upon it. Hence, its acceleration is equal to $(39.2 \text{ nt})/(4 \text{ kg})$, or 9.8 m/sec^2. Since the ratio of the gravitational force and the mass of all objects is the same, their free-fall acceleration must be the same. Consequently, Weight/Mass $= g$, the acceleration due to gravity; hence, $W = mg$.

An object traveling at a constant speed around a *circular path* is continually changing its direction of motion. Therefore, its velocity is changing although the speed is constant, and the object experiences an acceleration. Since the direction of the velocity is constantly changing toward the center of the circular path, the object must be accelerated in that direction also. Hence, a force toward the center must be applied to the object to keep it on a circular path. This centrally directed force is called a *centripetal force* (Latin *centrum*, "center," plus *petere*, "to seek"). For uniform circular motion, the acceleration toward the center is equal to v^2/R, where v is the magnitude of the velocity of the object and R is its radius of curvature. Hence, the centripetal force required to keep an object traveling in a circular path can be obtained from Newton's second law as follows:

$$F_c = \frac{mv^2}{R}$$

As an illustration, let us determine the centripetal force necessary to whirl a 200-gram object in a horizontal plane at the end of a 1-meter string with a speed of 500 cm/sec. In the mks system,

$$m = 200 \text{ gm} = 0.2 \text{ kg}$$

$$v = 5 \text{ m/sec}$$

$$R = 1 \text{ meter}$$

$$F_c = \frac{0.2 \text{ kg} \times (5 \text{ m/sec})^2}{1 \text{ m}} = \frac{5 \text{ kg-m}}{\text{sec}^2} = 5 \text{ newtons}$$

To apply a force on one object, we must be able to push against some other object. To walk, the foot pushes back against the floor, which exerts a forward force on the foot and, through the foot, to the body to propel it forward. To start a car moving, the rear tires push backward on the road, as evidenced by the direction in which the tires throw dirt, and the road reacts with a forward force upon the wheels, as indicated by the motion of the car. While a person is sitting in a chair, he pushes down on the chair with a force equal to his weight, and the chair pushes upward on the person with an equal force. If he pushes on his forehead with a finger, he can feel both forces; the one on the forehead produced by the finger, and the other on the finger produced by the forehead. The harder the push, the greater these forces become, but they are always equal and opposite. Newton observed that forces always came in pairs, and he stated his third law as: *For every force of action there is an equal and opposite force of reaction.* This means that whenever one object exerts force upon another object, the second object exerts an equal and opposite force on the first object. It must be emphasized that these two forces do not act upon the same object. In the case of the car, one force is on the ground and the other is on the car. For the person sitting in the chair, one force is on the person and the other is on the chair.

If this law is correct, then a cart pulls back on a horse with the same force that the horse pulls forward on the cart. This looks like a balanced tug-of-war between the horse and cart. How does a horse ever get the cart moving? The answer lies in the fact that these are not the only forces in operation. The horse pushes backward on the ground, and it, in turn, pushes forward on the horse with an equal amount. By pushing backward on the ground the horse is able to exert a forward force on the cart, and if this force is larger than the retarding frictional force of the ground upon the cart there will be an unbalanced force, and the horse will be able to move the cart. During the motion, the force with which the cart pulls back on the horse is still equal to the force with which the horse pulls forward on the cart.

Does Newton's law of paired and equal forces apply to an accelerated motion, where unbalanced forces are essential? For any action there is always an equal and opposite reaction, which seems to be general and must apply to accelerated objects as well as those at rest. There is no contradiction between the two laws, for the paired forces never act on the same object, while the unbalanced forces must act on the object being accelerated. For example, if a person pulls on an 8-kg box with a force of 40 newtons and the retarding frictional sliding force between the box and the floor is 16 newtons, there will be an unbalanced force of 24 newtons acting upon the box. According to Newton's second law of motion, the box will experience an acceleration of (24 nt)/(8 kg), or 3 m/sec². Newton's third law merely states that for the person to apply the force of 40 newtons, he must push in the opposite direction on some other object, like the floor, with an equal force of 40 newtons. During the accelerated motion, the box pulls back on the person with a force of 40 newtons and pushes forward on the floor with a frictional force of 16 newtons. Notice again that the paired forces are *not* on the same object. The forward force of 40 newtons is on the box while the backward force of 40 newtons is on the person. The backward frictional force of 16 newtons is on the box while the forward frictional force of 16 newtons is on the floor. However, the force on the box itself is unbalanced, 40 nt — 16 nt, producing the accelerated motion. If the applied force is increased to 50 newtons, the unbalanced force on the box increases to 34 newtons, and the box receives a different acceleration of (34 nt)/(8 kg), or 4.25 m/sec². During this acceleration, the box pulls back on the person with a force of 50 newtons and pushes forward on the floor with a force of 16 newtons.

When a bullet is fired from a gun, the forces on the bullet due to the explosion and the friction along the barrel are unbalanced, and the bullet accelerates along the gun barrel. The forces on the gun are also unbalanced, giving the gun a backward motion as observed by its kick. At any time while the bullet is within the gun barrel, the backward force on the gun is equal to the forward force on the bullet. Again, note that the action and reaction are not on the same object. When a big truck runs head-on into a small compact car, each vehicle experiences a large unbalanced force. While in contact, the force on the truck is exactly equal and opposite to that on the car, but the effect of this unbalanced force on the smaller car is far greater.

In the case of a car turning a corner, the road must exert a frictional force on the car toward the center of the curved path while the car, due to its tendency to travel in a straight line, exerts an outward force on the road. These two forces are equal and opposite. The inward force on the car is the centripetal force, whereas the outward force on the road is called the *centrifugal force*. Note that the centripetal force is the only force acting upon the moving object. If a stone is whirled at the end of a string, the string pulls inward on the moving stone to keep it on a circular path, and the stone, due to its tendency to fly off tangentially, exerts an outward force on the string, which is felt by the hand whirling the stone. These two forces do not act upon the same object; the centripetal force is on the stone while the centrifugal force is on the hand. From these two examples we see that the *centripetal force is always on the moving object*, while the *centrifugal force is on the object producing the circular motion* (see Fig. 8-5). According to Newton's third law, these forces are exactly equal in magnitude but opposite in direction.

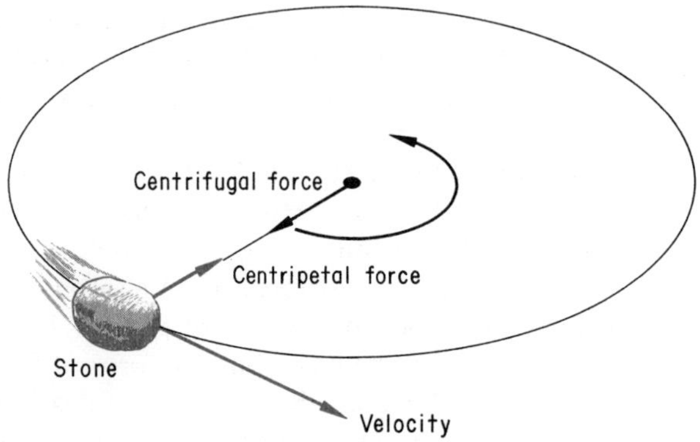

FIG. 8-5 Centripetal and centrifugal forces.

8-10
Momentum

If an object A collides with another object B, each object experiences an unbalanced force at impact. While the two objects are in contact, the force on A is exactly equal and opposite to that on B:

$$F_A = -F_B$$

Applying Newton's second law, we may write:

$$m_A a_A = -m_B a_B$$

or

$$\frac{m_A(v_A - v_{0A})}{t} = \frac{-m_B(v_B - v_{0B})}{t}$$

Since the time that object A acts on B is the same as the time B acts on A, the t's cancel in the above equation, and

$$m_A(v_A - v_{0A}) = -m_B(v_B - v_{0B})$$

Transposing and changing signs, we obtain

$$m_A v_{0A} + m_B v_{0B} = m_A v_A + m_B v_B$$

The product of the mass of an object and its velocity is defined as the *momentum* of that object. Therefore, we see from the above equation that the sum of the *momenta before impact is equal to the sum of the momenta after impact* (see Fig. 8-6). This principle can be used to determine the velocities of objects after collision. For example, if a 20-gm dart traveling 10 m/sec strikes a 500-gm block of soft wood which is suspended by strings from the ceiling, what is the combined velocity after impact, providing the dart sticks in the wood?

$$0.02 \text{ kg} \times 10 \text{ m/sec} + 0.5 \text{ kg} \times 0 \text{ m/sec} = (0.02 + 0.5)\text{kg} \times v$$

$$v = \frac{0.2 \text{ kg-m/sec}}{0.52 \text{ kg}}$$

$$v = 0.384 \text{ m/sec}$$

This basic principle of mechanics may be stated in a slightly different way as follows: *The total momentum of a system of objects remains unchanged unless acted upon by some force outside the system.* This is an extremely important law in science, and is known as *conservation of momentum.* This is merely another way of saying that forces of interaction always occur in equal and opposite pairs.

If a 3.0-kg rifle shoots a 2-gm bullet with a muzzle velocity of 300 m/sec, what is the recoil velocity of the gun? Before the trigger was pulled, the momentum of this system relative to the ground was zero. Hence, the sum of the momenta after firing must also be zero:

$$0 = 0.002 \text{ kg} \times 300 \text{ m/sec} + 3.0 \text{ kg} \times v$$

$$v = \frac{-0.6}{3.0} = -0.2 \text{ m/sec}$$

The minus sign means that the velocity of the gun is opposite that of the bullet causing the recoil action.

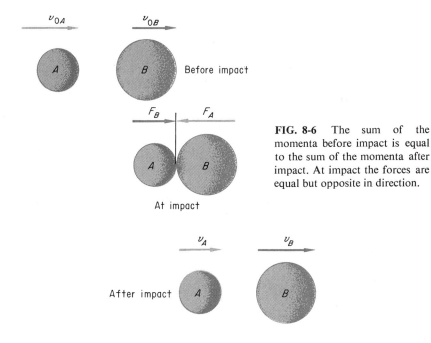

FIG. 8-6 The sum of the momenta before impact is equal to the sum of the momenta after impact. At impact the forces are equal but opposite in direction.

Newton's *first law of motion* tells us that a force is not necessary to keep a body moving. This means that as soon as we get a spaceship away from the domineering influence of the Earth, the Sun, or a star, the engines can be turned off and the ship will continue traveling through space at a uniform speed. The *second law* informs us that when an unbalanced force is applied to an object, it will be accelerated. If, while a ship is gliding through space, a short burst is fired from one of its rockets, we know that the force will either speed up the ship, slow it down, rotate it, or, if properly applied, push it off its course. The *third law* assures us that to apply a force on any object, we must have another object to push against. When a rocket engine fires we observe the burning gases rushing out of the engine nozzles. For the gases to have received this accelerated motion, they must have pushed on something while inside the engine and, of course, that was the engine. The reaction on the rocket is equal and opposite to the force on the exhaust gases. The momentum given the rocket is equal to the momenta given the gases. By aiming the nozzles downward, the rocket can be pushed into the sky. Some people believe that rocket engines need the air to push against, but this is completely false. The pushing is all done inside the engine, forcing the gas in one direction and the rocket in another. Air only introduces a frictional drag which decreases the resultant motion. Fortunately for space travelers, a rocket engine is more efficient in a vacuum than it is in air.

QUESTIONS AND PROBLEMS

1. According to Newton, what happens to an object that experiences no external unbalanced force?

2. What is inertia? How would you show that a brick has inertia?

3. Name three instruments not mentioned in this chapter for whose operation inertia is essential.

4. A car rounding a sharp corner of a gravel road at high speeds pushes outward on the road as indicated by the direction that the gravel is pushed, but if that car hits a smooth, icy spot in the road, it does not move outward but travels across the ice tangent to the curve. Explain.

5. What is meant by *acceleration*? Distinguish between a speed of 20 meters/sec and an acceleration of 20 meters/sec/sec.

6. In the unit for acceleration, "per second" is repeated. Is this necessary?

7. On what factors does the acceleration of an object depend, and how does it depend upon each?

8. The velocity of a car is plotted as a function of time as shown in the accompanying graph. Explain the motion of the car between *A* and *G*.

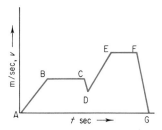

9. If a sprinter runs the 100-meter dash in 10 seconds, how fast is he traveling in m/sec, cm/sec, and km/hr?

10. Two balls are dropped simultaneously from two windows in a tall building. One ball is dropped from a point 5 meters above the other ball. Do the balls remain 5 meters apart as they fall? Explain.

11. A stone is dropped from the top of a 30-meter-tall building. How long will it take the stone to reach the ground?

12. What acceleration will a 20-kilogram mass receive when acted upon by a net force of 10 newtons? 100 nt?

13. If an unbalanced force of 2×10^{-20} dyne acts upon an electron, which has a mass of 9.1×10^{-28} gram, what acceleration is given the electron? Starting from rest, what will be the velocity of the electron after 3 seconds?

14. An automobile traveling 100 km/hr is decelerated at a rate of 6 meters/sec/sec. How long will it take to stop the auto?

15. A soft rubber ball and a hard rubber ball of the same mass are traveling at the same speed when they strike a person. Which will hurt the most? Explain.

16. What unbalanced force is required to give a 15-kilogram mass an acceleration of 4 meters/sec/sec?

17. What is the acceleration of the Moon toward the Earth as it revolves around the Earth?

18. A 2-gram bullet reaches the end of a 1-meter barrel of a gun with a muzzle velocity of 340 m/sec. What is the average force of explosion acting upon the bullet? How long was the bullet in the barrel of the gun?

19. Why is it difficult to drive a nail into a loose board?

20. A $\frac{1}{2}$-kilogram hammer, moving at a speed of 300 cm/sec, strikes a nail and drives the nail 1 cm into a block of wood. What average force did the hammer exert upon the nail?

21. Why doesn't a 10-kg mass fall freely with twice the acceleration of a 5-kg mass?

22. Why can a hammer exert a force many times its own weight?

23. An object moving with a constant speed around a circular path is accelerated. Why?

24. Can the velocity of an object be zero, and the object still have an acceleration? If your answer is yes, give an example.

25. Why does the nozzle of a garden hose push forcibly backwards when throwing a swift stream of water?

26. A large electric fan operated on batteries is mounted at the stern of a sailboat to blow air into the sails when there is no wind. Explain what happens when the fan is turned on.

27. Since action and reaction forces are always equal and opposite, why don't they always balance each other and never produce motion?

28. A proton of mass 1.7×10^{-27} kilogram is moving with a speed of 2×10^6 m/sec. What is the momentum of the proton? If the proton is acted upon by a retarding force of 5×10^{-8} dyne, what is its acceleration?

29. Would a "centrifugal" clothes dryer be as effective on the Moon as on the Earth? On Mars? On Jupiter? Explain.

30. How would a boy standing on a frictionless surface ever be able to get off that surface without help from someone that is not on the frictionless surface?

31. When a satellite travels in an orbit around the Earth, is the *centrifugal force* (a) outward on the satellite, (b) outward on the Earth, or (c) earthward on the satellite? Explain.

32. What is the momentum of a 3-kg stone after it has fallen freely for 4 seconds?

33. If a 7-kg object traveling at a speed of 200 cm/sec hits a 3-kg block of wood and sticks to it, what will be their combined velocity after impact?

34. A head-on collision takes place between a 10,000-kg truck traveling 80 km/hr and a 1,400-kg automobile traveling 110 km/hr in the opposite direction. If they stick together after impact, in what direction and with what speed does the wreckage travel after the collision?

SUGGESTED REFERENCES

BEISER, ARTHUR, *The Mainstream of Physics*, Chap. 2. Addison-Wesley Publishing Co., Reading, Mass., 1962.

FORD, KENNETH W., *Basic Physics*, Chap. 9. Ginn & Blaisdell Publishing Co., Waltham, Mass., 1968.

LAGEMAN, ROBERT T., *Physical Science: Origins and Principles*, 2nd ed., Chap. 14. Little, Brown and Co., Boston, 1969.

WHITE, HARVEY E., *Modern College Physics*, 5th ed., Chaps. 5, 7, and 12. D. Van Nostrand Co., Princeton, 1966.

9

Gravity, Tides, and Satellites

One of the natural phenomena we learn early in life is that objects are drawn toward the Earth. An infant begins to learn this when his toys slip from his hands. After losing a few, he knows where to look for them—on the floor. He later gleefully throws them from his high chair to see them fall and hear them hit the floor. Before he is a year old, he learns to use the muscles of his arms to pull himself up into a standing position and, after a few spills, he is no longer surprised when he tumbles back to the floor. After he is able to walk, he uses his arm muscles to pick up his toys. He notices that some are harder to lift than others, and he cannot always tell which are the most difficult to lift by looking at them. When he starts to talk, he learns that the attraction of the Earth on an object is called its *weight*. Later, in school, he discovers that this gravitational force causes an object to fall with a uniform acceleration, and is the force that holds our solar system together. As he gets older, he may wonder what there is about the Earth that causes it to attract objects, and whether there is some place in the universe where gravity produces a repelling force instead of one of attraction.

9-1
Law of Gravitation

The earliest recorded speculator about gravity was Aristotle in 350 B.C. He explained that certain objects fell because of their property of "heaviness," and that smoke, fire, and air rose because of their property of "lightness." This enabled him to divide all objects into two well-defined classifications. In the next twenty centuries a few scientists puzzled over this problem, but not much was accomplished until Galileo performed his famous experiments on falling bodies. Then, in the seventeenth century, Isaac Newton formulated

162

the law of universal gravitation. Newton had a creative imagination and an uncanny ability to combine ideas into a whole. His gravitational law knit together seemingly unrelated ideas of falling objects and planetary motions that were previously merely speculative. His law may be stated as: *Every particle in the universe attracts every other particle with a force which is directly proportional to the product of the masses of the particles and inversely proportional to the square of the distances between them.* This statement implies that matter is somehow capable of producing a force that can act across millions of miles of seemingly empty space on some other matter.

Newton's law may be stated symbolically as:

$$F = \frac{Gm_1m_2}{d^2}$$

In this equation, F is the force of attraction between any two particles with gravitational masses of m_1 and m_2, d is the distance between then, and G, the proportionality factor, is a universal constant. Newton did not presume to explain the origin or nature of this force, but merely to show how two gravitational masses attract each other.

The attraction of the Earth upon an object was known to be almost as great at the top of a mountain as it is at sea level. Since it decreased so little at great height, Newton wondered whether this force might extend out to the Moon to keep it moving around the Earth. Using d in the gravitational equation as the distance between the centers of the Moon and the Earth, plus his laws of motion, he computed the period of the orbital motion of the Moon around the Earth, and found that it agreed very well with the observed facts. He then wondered if the Sun might be exerting similar gravitational forces on the planets to keep them in their orbital paths. As a check, he computed the motions of the planets, and the calculated movements agreed with all three of Kepler's empirical laws. This not only established his gravitational law, but gave an explanation for Kepler's laws.

Although it may be slightly technical, let us nevertheless see how Kepler's third law can be obtained from Newton's laws of gravity and motion. The force that the Sun, mass M, exerts upon a planet of mass m can be written as:

$$F = \frac{GMm}{d^2}$$

where d is equal to the radius of the planet's orbit. Assuming that the planet travels in a circle, this gravitational force is the central, or centripetal, force keeping the planet on its curved path. Hence,

$$\frac{GMm}{d^2} = \frac{mv^2}{d}$$

The speed of the planet relative to the sun can be obtained by dividing the circumference of its circular orbit ($2\pi d$) by the time for 1 revolution, which is its period of revolution P. Therefore, the speed of the planet is equal to $2\pi d/P$. Substituting this quantity into the preceding equation, we obtain:

$$\frac{GMm}{d^2} = \frac{m(2\pi d/P)^2}{d}$$

or

$$\frac{P^2}{d^3} = \frac{4\pi^2}{GM}$$

Since G, M, and $4\pi^2$ are constants, P^2/d^3 must be the same for all planets. Hence,

$$\frac{P_1^2}{d_1^3} = \frac{P_2^2}{d_2^3}$$

This is Kepler's third law (see Chapter 1).

About 125 years after Newton's announcement of the law of gravitation, Henry Cavendish, an English scientist, succeeded in measuring the attraction between two large metal spheres of known masses at a known distance apart, and determining the value of G. From his experiment it was learned that two 1-gram masses 1 centimeter apart would attract each other with a very minute force of 0.0000000667 dyne. This value may be more conveniently written in scientific notation as 6.67×10^{-8} dyne. Substituting the above values into the gravitational equation, and solving for G, yields a value of 6.67×10^{-8} dyne $\times$ cm^2/gm^2 for the *gravitational constant*. This universal constant in the mks system of units is 6.67×10^{-11} newton $\times$ m^2/kg^2. Knowing this constant, the gravitational forces between objects can be computed.

As an example, a girl of 50 kilograms and a boy of 65 kilograms, sitting on a park bench 50 centimeters apart, have a gravitational attraction for each other. This attractive force can be computed approximately as:

$$\text{Attraction} = 6.67 \times 10^{-11}\frac{50 \times 65}{(0.5)^2}$$

$$= 8.67 \times 10^{-7} \text{ newton}$$

$$= 8.67 \times 10^{-2} \text{ dyne}$$

$$= 3 \text{ micro-ounces}$$

However, gravity is seldom the main attraction between a girl and a boy while sitting on a park bench.

9-2
Weight and Mass

Although gravitational forces between objects of ordinary size are insignificant, they assume great importance for ponderous bodies such as the stars, the Sun, the planets, and the Moon. The gravitational attraction of the Earth on an object is called the *true weight* of that object. A 10-kilogram body is pulled toward the Earth with a force of 98 newtons. The body is said to weigh 98 newtons. There is also a mutual interaction because the body pulls on the Earth with a force of 98 newtons.

On top of a moutain, an object is farther from the center of the Earth and the gravitational force on it is slightly smaller than at sea level. The greater the elevation, the less an object weighs. On top of Mount Everest, a man of ordinary size weighs about 1.7 newtons, or 6 ounces, less than at sea level. Weight also varies with latitude. At the equator, the Earth's surface is actually 22 kilometers farther from its center than it is at either pole. Thus an object at the equator has a smaller gravitational force acting upon it. A man weighs approximately 3.3 newtons, or 12 ounces, less at the equator than at the poles. Therefore, we may say that the weight of an object does not remain constant, but varies with elevation and latitude. On the surface of the Moon, the gravitational force on a body is only $\frac{1}{6}$ of what it is here on Earth. Consequently, on the Moon a person would weigh only $\frac{1}{6}$ as much as he does on Earth. Out in space between the stars, or interstellar space, we would experience no significant unbalanced gravitational force, and would be essentially weightless.

The *weight* of an object, as we have seen, varies from place to place, but its *mass*, either gravitational or inertial, is a property of the matter of which that body is composed and under ordinary conditions remains constant throughout the universe. If a man were to kick a brick in outer space, he would find that the act would hurt his toe as much as it does here on Earth, because the mass of the brick would be the same in both places. Since the weight of an object varies with location while its mass remains constant, there must be one place where a 1-kilogram mass weighs 9.8 newtons, and this is at sea level and 45° N latitude. Very seldom do we measure masses by weighing them at sea level and 45° N latitude. We usually compare them with a standard mass. Since the weight of an object at any location is directly proportional to its gravitational mass, a mass can be determined by comparing its weight with that of a standard mass, and this can be done at any location. When we say that we are weighing something in grams or kilograms, we are really determining its mass as compared to a standard mass.

It is not always necessary, or even practical, to measure the mass of an object in terms of its weight. It would be rather difficult to determine the mass of an atomic particle, such as an electron, in this manner. Any mass, however, can be determined by applying a known, unbalanced force to the object and measuring its acceleration. According to Newton's second law of motion, the mass is equal to the ratio of the applied force to the acceleration: $m = F/a$. The greater the force needed to produce a certain acceleration, the greater is the mass of the object accelerated. This, of course, is a measure of the object's inertial mass, or its tendency to resist any change in motion along a straight line. The question then arises of how this inertial mass compares with the gravitational mass. According to Einstein's equivalence principle, the effect produced by gravity can in no way be distinguished from the effect produced by an acceleration. Hence, the gravitational and inertial effects of mass are simply two aspects of the same property of matter. We shall refer to this property as *mass* with no differentiation between the gravitational and inertial effects. Therefore, a mass can be determined either by comparing its weight to that of a standard mass, or by the ratio of an applied force to the acceleration produced.

It is possible from the results of Cavendish's experiment to determine the mass of the Earth. The attractive force between the Earth and a 1-kilogram mass at sea level and 45° N latitude is 9.8 newtons. The radius of the Earth at that location is about 4,000 miles, or 6.43×10^6 meters. Substituting these values into Newton's gravitational equation and solving for the mass of the Earth, we obtain a mass of 6.1×10^{24} kilograms, or 6.1×10^{21} long tons. The average density of the earth can be computed by dividing its mass by its volume. The density turns out to be 5.5 gm/cm^3, or 5.5 times as heavy as water. Loam, clay, coal, and the like have densities of only 1.3 gm/cm^3. Marble and granite are among the densest rocks, and their densities are in the neighborhood of 3 gm/cm^3. Hence, the interior of the Earth must be composed of material much more dense than these. The geologists tell us that the Earth has a relatively thin crust of granitoid rock resting on an 1,800-mile-thick mantle of ultrabasic silicate rock. Below this is a metallic core. The outer part of the core is molten iron and nickel. The inner core, with a radius of about 800 miles, is solid iron and nickel. Under high pressure this core has a very high density, making the total density of the Earth much greater than that of the surface material.

9-3
Tides

The periodic rise and fall of the ocean along coast lines has been observed since ancient times. In the open ocean, as viewed on small islands, the level varies only a few feet, but on the shores of continents, it is often much more. It varies somewhat according to the shape of the shoreline. In the Bay of Fundy, the tide rises to a height of 27.4 meters. Ancient people also noted a correspondence between the tides and the motions of the Moon. They noticed that the tides were exceptionally high when the Moon was new or full, and lower in height when there was a first- or third-quarter moon. Man was unable to explain these tidal actions until Newton introduced his gravita-

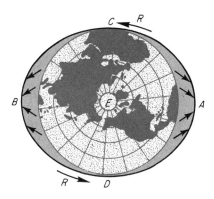

FIG. 9-1 The tides.

tional theory. He showed that the gravitational attractions of the Moon and Sun upon the ocean water produced the observed effects, and that because of its nearness the Moon had a much greater effect than the Sun.

Although a complete explanation of the tides is rather complex, we can get a fair understanding of them by considering only the influence of the Moon. As shown in Fig. 9-1, the Moon M attracts the surface at A with a larger force than it attracts the center of the Earth E because A is nearer to the Moon. This produces a bulge of water outward toward the Moon. The center of the Earth E is also attracted with a larger force than the surface at B pulling the Earth away from the water at B, and producing a mound of water on the opposite side of the Earth, away from the Moon. Hence, there are two tidal bulges, which are always on opposite sides of the Earth. These tides, in turn, produce a lowering of the waterlevels at C and D. As the Earth E rotates from west to east, these highs and lows travel westward with the Moon. They successively pass an observer on an ocean shore approximately 6 hours apart. When the high tide reaches the shore it piles the water up onto the land, and when low tide comes the water recedes from the shoreline. If the Moon were stationary, the time between a high tide and a low tide would be exactly 6 hours, but since the Moon moves in the direction the Earth is turning, the high and low tides are about 6 hours and 12 minutes apart. Remember that this discussion is only approximate because the Sun has some effect upon the tides, and, in addition, the spinning Earth tries to drag them with it.

The fact that the Moon has a greater tide-producing effect than the Sun is a little surprising and may need further explanation. It is true that the Sun attracts the Earth with a force 175 times as great as that of the Moon, but this force in itself does not produce tides. It is the difference between the gravitational forces of the Sun on a kilogram of the surface water of the ocean and on a kilogram at the center of the Earth that tends to pull the water away from the Earth and produce the tides. The greater the difference between these two forces, the higher the tide. The center of the Sun is 1.497×10^8 kilometers from the center of the Earth and 1.49636×10^8 kilometers from its surface. Since these distances differ by only 1 part in 23,300, the difference in the gravitational forces on a kilogram of matter is relatively small, thus producing a very small tide. The center of the Moon, on the other hand, is about 384,400 kilometers from the center of the Earth and 378,000 kilometers from its surface. This represents a difference in distance of about 1 part in 60. The resulting difference in gravitational forces is larger than that of the Sun, although the force of attraction is not as large. Knowing the radius of the Earth and the masses of, and distances to, the Moon and Sun, the tide-producing force of the Moon and Sun can be computed. In this manner it has been found that the Moon is more than twice as effective as the Sun. During full and new moons, the Sun and Moon act together, producing extrahigh tides called *spring tides*. The open ocean water rises about 1.2 meters above normal during spring tides; a 85-cm rise is produced by the Moon, and a 35-cm rise by the Sun. During the first- and third-quarter moons, the Sun and Moon counteract each other, but since the Moon is more effective than the Sun, a small high tide is produced. This is called a *neap tide*.

As the Earth spins faster than the tides move, it tries to drag the tides with it, thus introducing a frictional force in the water. This tidal friction causes the Earth to slow down, increasing the length of a day by about 1/1,000 second in a century!

9-4
Dawn of Space Age

For ages man has dreamed about traveling in space. As early as A.D. 160 Lucian of Samosata wrote a traveler's tale about a trip to the Moon with the aid of the wings of two large birds, one a vulture's wing and the other an eagle's wing. In 1609, Kepler added to the imaginative literature when he wrote about a voyage to the Moon. He sent it as a letter to Galileo, and disguised it as a dream so that it would not be censored by the church. He imagined a person traveling to the Moon in the shadow of the Earth during a lunar eclipse so that the traveler would not be harmed by the Sun's penetrative rays. To remain in the Earth's shadow for the entire trip, the person had to travel to the Moon in less than $4\frac{1}{2}$ hours, which is the longest duration of a lunar eclipse. This meant that he had to travel at an average speed of 84,000 km/hr or 23,300 m/sec. Kepler did not mention how that was to be accomplished. About a half-century later, Sir Isaac Newton suggested the idea of artificial satellites when he discussed the trajectory path of a cannon-

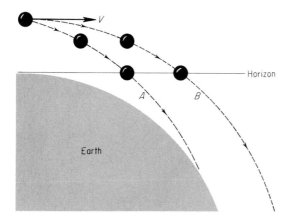

FIG. 9-2 Projectile paths of cannon balls suggested by Newton. Curvature of path *B* is the same as that of the Earth.

ball fired horizontally from the top of a high mountain (see Fig. 9-2). He explained how the cannonball, as it was moving forward, fell toward the ground and would strike the surface a certain distance away. He pointed out that the faster it was fired the farther it would go before hitting the ground, thus decreasing the curvature of its path. He then concluded that if the horizontal velocity of the cannonball were great enough, the curvature of the falling ball would be the same as the curvature of the Earth and the cannonball would go all the way around the Earth. Newton presented this line of reasoning to explain the motion of the Moon around the Earth, but he also certainly gave us a tip as to how to put man-made satellites into orbit.

Not much more appeared on the subject until the latter part of the nineteenth century, when several science fiction novels introduced the ideas of a velocity to escape from the Earth's gravitational pull, rocket engines to propel spaceships, and the filling of the ships with growing plants to supply the passengers with oxygen. In 1898, Ziolkovsky, a Russian schoolteacher, wrote a paper on space travel in which his spaceship, called "*Sputnik*" (Russian, "traveling companion"), was propelled into space from the Moon by large rockets using liquid fuel burned by liquid oxygen. His paper did not arouse very much interest, although it did suggest observation stations orbiting around the Earth. By the early part of the twentieth century patents were being issued for liquid-fuel and solid-fuel rockets. Uses of rockets in space received serious consideration after the extensive research work carried on separately by Goddard of the United States and Oberth of Germany. During World War II the Germans developed rockets and their guidance systems, as Great Britain well knows. On October 4, 1957, the Space Age was born when the Soviet Union put the first artificial satellite, *Sputnik I*, into orbit.

On April 12, 1961, space travel became a reality when the Russians placed a manned ship into orbit around the Earth at an altitude of about 160 kilometers (100 miles). Since then the United States and the Soviet Union have sent exploring probes to the Moon and planets, and have put satellites around the Sun. These man-made satellites follow Kepler's laws, just as any natural satellite or planet does. In 1969 American astronauts landed on the Moon, and as Neil Armstrong stepped onto the surface of the Moon, he said, "That's one small step for a man, one giant leap for mankind." Since then man has explored several regions of the Moon's surface.

9-5
Launching a Satellite

In order for a satellite to be put into a circular orbit, it must be shot horizontally at a high altitude with a speed great enough so that the falling satellite has a curved trajectory about the same as the curvature of the earth, as described by Newton for his cannonballs. Since we have no mountains high enough, we must rely upon rockets to lift the satellite to the desired elevation, aim it in the proper direction, and accelerate it to the critical orbital speed. This requires a system of two to five rockets. Let us consider a three-stage launching. The space capsule, or "payload," is placed in the nose of a multistage rocket that is mounted vertically on a firing pad (see Fig. 9-3). The bottom rocket is by far the largest, because it has to overcome the greatest gravitational force and push the rocket system through the most dense portion of our atmosphere. At the end of a countdown the first stage is fired

FIG. 9-3 The Atlas launch vehicle stands ready for launch at Complex 14, Cape Kennedy, Florida. (National Aeronautics and Space Administration.)

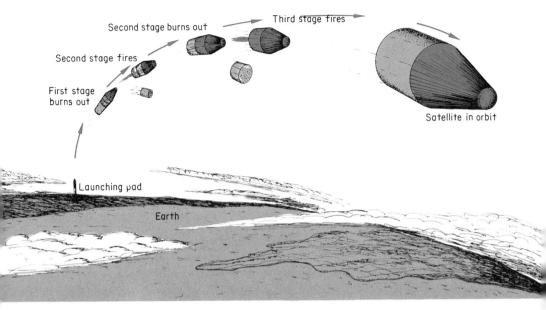

FIG. 9-4 Launching of a satellite.

and the whole system is accelerated to a speed of about 1,780 m/sec at a height of 64 kilometers or more. Then the second stage fires, releasing the first stage with its engine and empty tanks (see Fig. 9-4). This decreases the mass to be accelerated by the following stages. The second stage places the rocket system on a predetermined course and lifts it to almost the desired orbital path. Due to its upward motion, the rocket rises higher, but after its fuel is spent, it gradually levels off for its descent back to Earth. When it reaches a nearly horizontal position, the second stage is jettisoned, the third stage is fired, and its speed is increased to its critical orbiting value. The satellite is now in orbit, falling freely as it revolves around the Earth. Some systems have a fourth stage, to remove the satellite from the third stage's spent motor, which also stays in orbit. Any error in the firing angle of the third stage or the final velocity received will result in either an elliptical orbit or a plunge to destruction in the Earth's atmosphere.

9-6
Orbital Speed

To stay in a circular orbit, the gravitational attraction of the Earth on the satellite must be equal to the centripetal force needed to keep the satellite on a circular orbit. The magnitude of this orbital speed can be determined as:

$$\frac{GMm}{d^2} = \frac{mv^2}{d}$$

or

$$v = \sqrt{\frac{GM}{d}}$$

where M is the mass of the Earth and d is the distance between the centers of the Earth and satellite. From this equation, we notice that the higher the satellite is to be orbited, the smaller the circular speed needed. In Table 9-1, the speeds and periods of revolution for a few circular orbital paths are given as calculated from the foregoing equation.

TABLE 9-1
Orbital Speed versus Altitude

Altitude (kilometers)	Orbital Speed (km/hr)	(m/sec)	Period of Revolution
160	28,400	7,890	86.5 min
500	27,700	7,690	93.4 min
2,000	25,100	6,970	126.0 min
36,200	11,100	3,080	24.0 hr
380,000	3,700	1,030	27.3 days

The last satellite in Table 9-1 is our Moon, and we see that the calculated values agree quite favorably with the measured ones. If a satellite is put into orbit with a little larger velocity than that in Table 9-1, it will follow an elliptical orbit (see Fig. 9-5). The first satellite the United States launched in January 1958, *Explorer I,* had an elliptical orbit with a perigee of 360 km and an apogee of 2,550 km above the Earth's surface, whereas *Midas III* followed almost a circular path with a 9,420-km radius (altitude of 2,980 km).

Most satellites are launched in an easterly direction, to take advantage of the motion of the Earth. We launch many of ours from Cape Kennedy

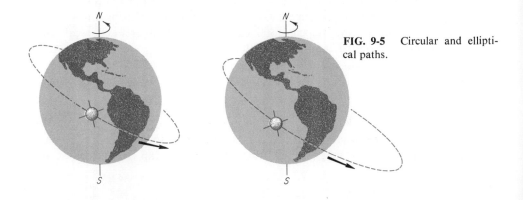

FIG. 9-5 Circular and elliptical paths.

in a southeast direction at an angle of about 35° so that their initial paths, where the first couple of stages fall, is over the Atlantic Ocean instead of over populated countries. Others are launched from the Vandenberg Base in California. They are fired southward over the Pacific Ocean and follow polar orbits. The Russians launch theirs from Baikonur, near the Aral Sea, out over Siberia at an angle of 65° northeast.

Satellites follow circular or more commonly elliptical paths with the center of the Earth at the centers of the circles or one of the foci of the ellipses, and the planes of their orbits remain almost fixed in space while the Earth spins under them. If a satellite requires 2 hours to make one revolution, the Earth in that time will turn eastward 30°. Thus, with each revolution, a satellite passes over the Earth 2 time zones farther west. The orbital plane of a satellite, however, does precess slowly.

9-7
Life of a Satellite

If there were no air resistance, a satellite would continue to travel around the Earth indefinitely. Although 99% of our atmosphere lies below an altitude of 32 kilometers, there is still enough drag due to air and charged particles at the higher altitudes to cause a satellite to fall slightly each trip around. The smaller the satellite and the higher it is, the longer it will stay aloft. *Vanguard I*, a 1.4-kg satellite at a height varying from 640 to 3,860 kilometers, is expected to remain aloft for 200 years, while *Sputnik III*, a 1,300-kg spaceship with a perigee of only 240 kilometers, had a lifetime of about 5 months. Manned capsules have retrorockets to slow them down below orbital speeds; hence, they can come down at any time. When the astronaut is ready to descend, he turns his capsule around by means of side jets until the retrorockets are on the forward side, and fires the rockets in the direction he is moving. This pushes back on the capsule and slows him down enough so that he plunges earthward. When he enters the thick part of our atmosphere, parachutes on the capsule open and it glides back to Earth, either on water or on land. When he reenters the atmosphere the capsule acts like a "shooting star" and would burn up except for a special material on the leading side of the capsule that melts and scours off without excessively heating the ship.

9-8
Uses of Satellites

Artificial satellites provide us with means of securing data which are virtually unobtainable by any other method. They can measure the Earth's magnetic

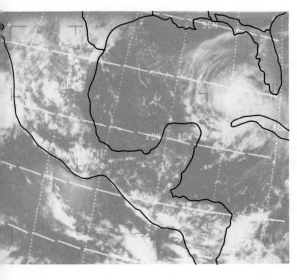

FIG. 9-6 Photograph of hurricane Inez taken by satellite *ESSA 3* on October 5, 1966. It shows Inez entering the Gulf of Mexico. (National Oceanic and Atmospheric Administration.)

and gravitational fields, the density of the air, the number of charged particles in our outer atmosphere, the amount of solar radiation received from the Sun, and the intensity of X rays and primary cosmic particles that are entering the Earth's atmosphere. Satellites can also be used to take pictures of world cloud patterns, to aid in weather forecasting, to locate hurricanes and typhoons (see Fig 9-6), to act as spies in the sky to take pictures of military movements, to receive and rebroadcast television programs, and to aid in transoceanic communications. Space probes will also be used to study the planets before sending out exploring parties to those celestial bodies.

9-9
Space Travel

For interplanetary and interstellar travel, we cannot use the conventional chemical combustion rockets because the fuel and liquid oxygen would add too much mass to the various stages. Instead, we can use either nuclear rockets or ion rockets, the latter being preferred for deep space travel. Both are powered by nuclear energy, which requires no oxygen and a relatively small mass of fuel. In the nuclear rockets, hydrogen gas is pumped through a small nuclear reactor core where it is heated to an extremely high temperature and then escapes through exhaust nozzles. The reaction of the gas rushing out of the nozzles pushes the ship forward. In the ion-rocket engine, a nuclear reactor drives a turbine to generate electrical power. This electricity ionizes cesium, and the resulting charged particles are repelled out of the engine, giving the ship a small forward thrust (see Fig. 9-7). By varying the directions of the nozzles or stream of charged particles, the spaceship's

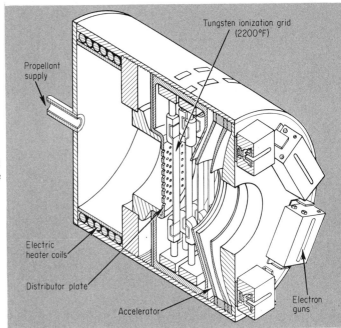

FIG. 9-7 Model of an ion rocket cell. (National Aeronautics and Space Administration.)

direction of travel can be controlled. A nuclear reactor develops a considerable amount of heat which must be radiated into space or the ship will get too hot; therefore, large, black radiators must be attached to the reactor. Since these radiators are rather bulky and difficult to streamline, such spaceships cannot enter the atmosphere of any of the planets without tearing off these radiators. Therefore, ionic spaceships will have to take on passengers at some space depot that is in orbit well above a planet's atmosphere (see Fig. 9-8). A regular combustion rocket will be needed to take us from the

FIG. 9-8 An artist's concept of a spacecraft approaching a space stations's docking area. (National Aeronautics and Space Administration.)

Earth up to such a space depot where we will transfer to the ionic spaceship, and then head for any destination in outer space. If the planet we are to visit does not have a space station, the ionic spaceship will have to be put into orbit above the atmosphere, and the passengers will be lowered in rockets to the surface below. Here on Earth, we might place our space depot above the equator at an elevation of 36,200 kilometers. As we have seen in Table 9-1, a satellite at this elevation makes one revolution around the center of the earth in 24 hours, which is the time required for the Earth to make one rotation. Hence, at this elevation, the space depot would remain fairly fixed above a certain location on the Earth's equator. Such a station could be assembled at that altitude, and remain there for future use.

After leaving the space depot, the ion rockets would drive the spaceship faster and faster until it approaches its limiting speed, which is the speed of light, 3×10^8 m/sec. Since some cosmic particles enter our atmosphere at speeds of 99% of that of light, why can't we travel at such speeds? According to Einstein's theory of relativity, everything at such speeds would to us here on Earth appear more massive, shorter in length, and the clocks would run more slowly. The equations governing these variations were found by Einstein to be as follows:

Relativistic mass m at velocity v:

$$m = \frac{m_0}{\sqrt{1 - v^2/c^2}}$$

where m_0 is its rest mass.

Lorentz contraction:

$$L = L_0\sqrt{1 - v^2/c^2}$$

where L_0 is the rest length in one corrdinate system and L is the length observed from another system in which the two are traveling with the velocity v relative to each other.

The time dilation:

$$t = \frac{t_0}{\sqrt{1 - v^2/c^2}}$$

where t_0 is the time observed in one system of coordinates and t is the same time observed in another system.

. For example, if a spaceship were traveling at 99.5% the speed of light, the quantity $\sqrt{1 - v^2/c^2}$ would be equal to 0.0999. Hence, everything abroad the ship would be $m_0/0.0999$ or 10 times as massive. This might reduce the rate at which chemical reactions take place in the body. A person's metabolism might be slowed down, and it has been speculated that he would grow older more slowly. For a 1-hour interval of time observed by a person in the spaceship, a person on Earth would observe that same interval of time with his clock to be:

$$t = \frac{1}{0.0999} = 10 \text{ hours}$$

Hence, the person on Earth would say that the clock on the spaceship is running way too slow, $\frac{1}{10}$ of what it ought to. The greater the v, the greater is the time dilation. Since the traveler's clock runs slower, he would not notice a change in aging if it did occur. If this traveler went to the nearest star, Proxima, and back again at this speed, everyone on Earth would say that he was gone a little over 8.6 years, but according to his clock he would have been gone for only 26 months. Would he be 8.6 years or 1.08 years older? Moreover, if our space traveler measured the length of his spacecraft in the direction he is moving as 300 feet, we on Earth would see it as 300×0.0999 or 30 feet long.

You may very well ask how we know that such a time dilation and length contraction occurs, and to answer this we have to refer you to the observed behavior of unstable particles, or muons, which are created by cosmic particles in our upper atmosphere, at altitudes of 5,900 meters or higher. Although these muons travel at a speed of about 99.5% of the speed of light, or 2.985×10^8 m/sec, they decay in 2×10^{-6} second, and can only travel a distance of $2.985 \times 10^8 \times 2 \times 10^{-6}$ or 597 meters in a lifetime. Hence we ought not observe any at the surface of the Earth—but we do. Let us examine this problem by observing the muon from the Earth's coordinate system. The distance to the Earth is of course 5,900 meters, but the lifetime of the muon would appear to us to decay in

$$t = \frac{2 \times 10^{-6}}{\sqrt{1 - (0.995c/c)^2}}$$
$$= 2 \times 10^{-5} \text{ sec}$$

The distance the muon can travel in this time is $2.985 \times 10^8 \times 2 \times 10^{-5} = 5,970$ meters. Hence it can reach the ground.

Let us now look at it from the muon's point of view. His lifetime would be 2×10^{-6} sec, but the 5,900 meters would appear traveling at his speed to be:

$$L = 5,900\sqrt{1 - (0.995c/c)^2}$$
$$= 590 \text{ meters.}$$

Hence the muon would say that it can reach the ground.

A traveler in space will have to take along food, air, water, waste disposal unit, and some means of absorbing the carbon dioxide he exhales. His spaceship must be pressurized and its temperature controlled by heating and air-conditioning units. The food, oxygen, and carbon dioxide problems might be solved by growing algae in a container of water on the trip. The algae would absorb the carbon dioxide from the air, take in water, and with the aid of sunlight or starlight would grow, releasing oxygen in the process. Besides being a carbon dioxide absorber and an oxygen generator, the algae would supply the traveler with food; maybe not the most appetizing food, but it would be nourishing. A gas such as nitrogen could be added to produce an air pressure of about 1 atmosphere in the cabin. The most annoying feature will be weightlessness. We know that man can live under such conditions, but the objects in the ship will be floating all around the place unless fastened down. If algae were growing, how would the water be kept from spreading throughout the cabin? This weightlessness might be overcome by rotating the cabin of the ship around the rocket assembly. If the cabin were rotated at the right speed, everything inside the cabin would push out against the side of the cabin, which would be its floor, with a force equal to its weight here on Earth. The greatest danger to the traveler would be from the radiations in space. This might be controlled by lining the cabin with some material that would absorb as much of the radiations as our atmosphere does.

Now that we can travel in space, where are we going? Mars is the only planet worthy of visiting, but the existence of life there is questionable. There might be planets like the Earth farther out in our galaxy. Some scientists believe that many of the single stars have a planetary system like ours. Therefore, out of the trillions and trillions of stars there might be thousands of planets identical to our Earth. Hence, for those seeking to better understand the universe there might be other worlds like ours to explore.

QUESTIONS AND PROBLEMS

1. State Newton's law of gravitation. Why wasn't the gravitational constant known to Isaac Newton, the man who formulated the gravitational law?

2. The centers of a 10-kg ball and a 40-kg ball are 50 centimeters apart. What force does one ball exert upon the other?

3. A 115-kg man stands so that his center of gravity is 60 cm from the center of gravity of a 51-kg woman. What is the gravitational attraction of one of these persons on the other?

4. Distinguish between inertia, mass, and weight. Which is the most fundamental quantity?

5. Does the Earth have weight? Can an object have mass without having weight? Explain.

6. Is one interested in mass or in weight when buying meat? A hammer? An anchor? A plumb bob?

7. A man owns a grocery store which is located near the top of a high

mountain, and he weighs the products he sells on a spring balance that was calibrated at sea level. Is this to his benefit?

8. What would a 10-kg mass weigh at the Earth's surface? What would it weigh 30,000 kilometers above the surface of the Earth?

9. The mass of the Moon is $\frac{1}{80}$ that of the Earth. How far above the surface of the Earth, on a line between the Moon and the Earth, is the Moon's gravitational force on an object equal to that exerted by the Earth?

10. If a space traveler who weighs 700 newtons on Earth finds a planet that has a mass 20 times the mass of the Earth and a radius 4 times that of the Earth, how much will he weigh on that planet? What is his mass, in kilograms, on Earth? What is his mass on the planet? What is the value of "g" on the planet?

11. If a space explorer has only a spring balance with him, how can he determine the mass of any object he finds on that planet?

12. How are tides produced? What are spring tides? Neap tides?

13. Why are the ocean high tides sometimes more than 12 hours apart?

14. Calculate the speed necessary to put a satellite in a circular orbit at an altitude of 6,500 kilometers. How long will it take this satellite to make one trip around the Earth?

15. What is the approximate acceleration of a satellite toward the center of the Earth when the satellite is in a circular orbit at an altitude of 3,620 kilometers?

16. A 70-kg astronaut aboard a rocket, which is rising under full power, experiences an apparent weight 5 times as great as his normal weight. What is the acceleration of the rocket?

17. What produces the driving push for an ion-rocket engine?

SUGGESTED REFERENCES

ABELL, GEORGE, *Exploration of the Universe*, 2nd ed., Chap. 5. Holt, Rinehart, & Winston, New York, 1969 (celestial mechanics).

GAMOW, GEORGE, and JOHN M. CLEVELAND, *Physics: Foundations and Frontiers*, 2nd ed., Chap. 6. Prentice-Hall, Englewood Cliffs, N.J., 1969.

GLASSTONE, S., *Sourcebook on the Space Science*, Chap. 2. D. Van Nostrand Co., Princeton, N. J., 1965.

LEY, W., *Rockets, Missles, and Space Travel*. Viking Press, New York, 1957.

Physical Science Study Committee, *Physics*, 2nd ed., Chap. 19. D.C. Heath, Boston, 1965 (inertial and gravitational masses).

"Space Travel," *The World Book Encyclopedia*, XV, 7610a–h. Field Enterprises Education Corporation, Chicago, 1957.

10

Mechanical Energy

A quantity very basic to the understanding of physical phenomena is *energy*. This quantity is rather difficult to define precisely, but most of us have a concept of what it is. We are well aware that our existence here on Earth depends on the energy recieved from the Sun. It is stored in the foods we eat to stay alive, in the coal and gas we burn to keep us warm, and in the gasoline our engines consume to help us commute from one place to another. We depend on electrical energy to furnish us with light at night and to operate all the appliances we have in our modern homes. What is this thing called "energy" that is so varied, but yet so very essential to each of us? What do we mean when we say that a person is very "energetic"? At first glance there seems to be nothing in common among all these energies, but upon further study we see that any form of energy is capable of doing something useful. Therefore, we define *energy* as *ability* to *do work*. Fig. 10-1 shows a giant at work. Not all forms of energy are easily converted to work, but all forms through suitable transformations can do work. The word *energy* was derived from the Greek *en*, meaning "in," and *ergon*, meaning "work."

10-1
Work

In everyday usage, the word *work* is used when referring to almost any kind of useful activity which makes us tired. In mechanics, however, it is understood in a more restricted sense: there it means *the effect that is accomplished when a force is exerted upon some object and moves it a certain distance*. If there is no motion, there is no work. A boy who sits down quietly with a book to study does no mechanical work. A less studious boy who goes outdoors and plays a game of tennis does work. The first boy may have

FIG. 10-1 A giant at work, stripping the overburden from coal. The shovel is electrically operated. The length of the boom is 215 ft; the length of its handle is 133 ft, and the capacity of the dipper is 180 cu yd. The machine weighs 27,850,000 lbs. Notice the two men standing at base of machine. (Marion Power Shovel Company, Inc.)

accomplished a much more useful result; he may have conceived a new idea that will bring him fame and fortune as well as help all of mankind. But he has exerted no mechanical force, nor moved an object; therefore, he has has done no work. The other boy has probably accomplished something useful too in terms of health, but that in itself does not constitute work. The essential difference is that he has exerted forces and moved objects. He has exerted forces upon the racket, the ball, and upon his own body, and made them move. He has done work.

The amount of work done in any instance depends in part upon the magnitude of the force applied, and in part on the distance the object moves in the direction of the external force. If a 50-kg block of wood is raised a vertical distance of 5 meters, the force to lift the block is 50 × 9.8 or 490 newtons, and the amount of work done on the block is 490 nt × 5 m or 2,450 newton-meters. This is a derived unit, and is called a *joule* (commonly pronounced "jool"). The joule is the amount of work done when a force of 1 newton moves an object through a distance of 1 meter. It is also the work done when $\frac{1}{2}$ newton moves the object 2 meters, or when a 2-nt force acts through a distance of $\frac{1}{2}$ meter. If the object is lifted, the work is done against gravity. If a force of 10 newtons slides a block at a constant speed a distance of 20 meters across the floor, 200 joules of work is done against friction. If 15 newtons is then applied to the block, and the block is again moved 20 meters, the work done is now 300 joules. Since 200 joules was done to overcome friction, against what was the extra 100 joules of work done? The unbalanced force of 15 nt — 10 nt or 5 newtons accelerated the block, and so the 5 × 20 or 100 joules was used to overcome the inertia of the block. Hence, we see that the amount of work done, regardless of the type of motion, can be determined by multiplying the force exerted by the distance the object moves in the direction of that force:

Work = Force × Distance moved in direction of force

In the cgs system, the unit for work is the dyne-centimeter, which is called an *erg*. This is an extremely small unit of energy. It is approximately the amount of work that an ordinary ant does when it crawls 2 millimeters up a vertical wall. The erg is only one ten-millionth as large as the joule:

$$1 \text{ joule} = 1 \times 10^7 \text{ ergs}$$

In the United States, mechanical energy is expressed in pounds × feet, or foot-pounds (ft-lb). The foot-pound is equivalent to 1.356 joules.

10-2
Power

A certain amount of work might be done in a second, in a week, or in a month. How fast the work is done is very important. This is particularly true for machines in this age of automation. They are used to run factories, to drive dynamos for generating our electricity, to power our automobiles, trains, airplanes, and for many other purposes. The value of a machine depends on how much work it can do per hour or per second. A diesel engine must be able to exert a large force on a long train to accelerate it and move it at a high speed. A large force acting over a great distance each minute means that many joules of work per minute are being done. A locomotive capable of doing work so rapidly is shown in Fig. 10-2.

The rate at which work is done is called power:

$$\text{Power} = \frac{\text{Work}}{\text{Time}}$$

What is meant by the saying "More power to you?" According to our definition of power, it literally means that the same amount of work must be done in less time, or more work in the same time, neither of which is very complimentary. Power can be expressed in joules per second, or ergs per second. The joule/second is called a *watt*. Incandescent lamps used in the home range in power from 7 watts for night lamps to 300 watts or more for floor lamps. Electrical energy plants, whether driven by water, steam, or nuclear energy, generate electricity at the rate of hundreds of megawatts. Electrical appliances are not the only things rated in kilowatts; European automobile engines are also rated in these units. Some small cars have 30-kilowatt engines which are regular 4-cycle engines. In the United States machines are rated in horse-

FIG. 10-2 Two diesel-electric locomotives pulling a freight train across the country. Each locomotive is driven by electric motors that are supplied with power from a dynamo run by a 3000-hp diesel engine. (Alco Products, Inc.)

power, and we have accepted 550 ft-lb/sec as 1 horsepower, which is equivalent to 0.746 kilowatt.

10-3
Potential Energy

Raising an object off the ground requires work, and the amount of work done is equal to the weight of the object multiplied by the vertical distance it is raised. As a result, the object can do work when it falls back to the ground. While held stationary at a certain height, no mechanical work is being done, but the object definitely possesses the ability of doing something. This ability to do work because of elevated position is called *gravitational potential energy*, because gravity is trying to restore it to its original position. A brick resting on the top of a building has stored up energy equal to the work done to carry it up there. The brick may remain on the roof for years, and during that time it will continue to possess the same amount of potential energy. If, for example, a 3-kilogram brick is carried to the top of a 20-meter building, the force to lift the brick is 3 × 9.8 or 29.4 newtons, and the work to carry the brick to the top of the building is 29.4 nt × 20 m or 588 joules. Hence, the brick while on the top of the building possesses 588 joules of potential energy with respect to the ground. It will continue to possess 588 joules of energy as long as it remains on top of the building. Whenever the brick is allowed to fall to the ground, it will do 588 joules of work in falling. Thus,

Gravitational potential energy = Weight × Height = *Wh*

If the hammer of a piledriver were raised by a machine to a certain height, it would be given a definite amount of potential energy. If allowed to fall freely and strike a pile, all of this energy would go into the work of driving the pile into the ground:

$$\text{Weight of hammer} \times \text{Height}$$
$$= \text{Average force on pile} \times \text{Distance pile moves}$$

where the height is the height of the hammer above the stopping point. For example, a 250-kilogram piledriver hammer is raised 6 meters above a pile, and dropped onto the pile, driving it 8 centimeters into the ground. What is the average force exerted on the pile by the hammer while driving the pile 0.08 meter into the ground? Since the hammer drops 6.08 meters before stopping, its potential energy with respect to its stopping position is (250×9.8) nt $\times$ 6.08 m or 14,900 joules. This energy goes into the work of driving the pile into the ground: $F \times 0.08$. Hence,

$$14,900 \text{ joules} = F \text{ nt} \times 0.08 \text{ m}$$

or $$F = 186,000 \text{ newtons}$$

This is the average force on the pile while it is being driven into the ground. According to Newton's third law, it is also the force the pile exerts upon the hammer to stop its motion.

Dammed-up water also has the ability to do work. It may flow down a flume and strike a waterwheel or a turbine, causing it to rotate. The water-wheel or turbine could drive other machinery, or a generator, to produce electrical energy. The higher the level of the water behind the dam, the more energy it possesses per unit mass.

Instead of an elevated object, we may have a bent spring or a stretched rubber band. Each of these exerts a force of reaction in opposition to the bending or stretching force. If released, both the spring and the rubber will return to their original states. Each has the capacity for doing work; therefore, each possesses potential energy when bent or stretched. In both cases this energy can be utilized. The spring, for example, may be that of a watch, which keeps the balance wheel and hands in motion until the spring is un-wound and the watch is run down. The stretched rubber may be that of a slingshot used to shoot small stones into the air. Mechanical potential energy of any object is the energy it possesses because of its elevated position, or its elastic deformation. There are many forms of potential energy other than mechanical. The ability of any stationary object to do work is considered potential energy.

10-4
Kinetic Energy

An object in motion also possesses the ability to do work on whatever it strikes. We swing a hammer to drive a nail into a board. The heavier the hammer or the faster it moves, the farther it drives the nail into the wood. We also know that the faster a car is traveling, the harder it is to stop. The energy a moving object possesses is called *kinetic energy*. It does not depend on the elevation or deformation of the object, but depends on its mass and the square of its velocity:

$$\text{Kinetic energy} = \tfrac{1}{2} \times \text{Mass} \times \text{Velocity}^2$$

or $$\text{K.E.} = \tfrac{1}{2}mv^2$$

The energy of motion increases very rapidly as the speed increases. If the speed of a car is doubled, it will have 4 times as much energy and require 4 times the work to stop it. If, in the above equation, the mass is in kilograms and the velocity is in meters/sec, the kinetic energy is kg $\times$ (m/sec)^2, or kg $\times$ (m/sec^2) $\times$ m, or newton $\times$ meters, or joules. For example, a 4-kg sledge hammer moving at a velocity of 5 m/sec possesses $\tfrac{1}{2} \times 4 \times 5^2$ or 50 joules of energy.

If the mass is expressed in grams and the velocity in cm/sec, the kinetic energy is gm $\times$ (cm/sec)^2, or gm $\times$ (cm/sec^2) $\times$ cm, or dynes $\times$ cm, which is ergs.

Kinetic energy represents the amount of work a *moving* object can perform upon another body. In driving a nail into a block of wood, the kinetic energy of the moving hammer goes into the work of driving the nail into the wood. The hammer exerts a force on the nail and moves it a certain distance:

Kinetic energy of hammer = Average force on nail $\times$ Distance nail moves

The smaller the distance the nail is driven into the wood, the larger the resulting force, because the product of these two quantities must be equal to the kinetic energy of the hammer. Therefore, extremely large momentary forces can be produced by moving objects. Such forces are necessary to overcome the large resistance that the wood offers to the penetration of the nail, or that the ground presents to the penetration of the pile. As an example, let us find the force that a 400-gm hammer traveling at a speed of 6.0 m/sec exerts upon a nail which is driven 1 cm into a wooden block:

$$\tfrac{1}{2} \times 0.4 \text{ kg} \times (6 \text{ m/sec})^2 = F \times 0.01 \text{ m}$$

Solving for the force, we obtain

$$F = 720 \text{ newtons}$$

The weight of the hammer is only 0.4 $\times$ 9.8 or 3.92 newtons. Hence, the hammer in this particular case exerts a force 184 times as large as its own weight. Most of us who have hit the wrong nail know this to be true.

10-5
Other Forms of Energy

We have discussed in detail two kinds of mechanical energy, that of position or deformation, and that of motion, but there are many other kinds of energy that are capable of doing useful work. The most common of these is *heat energy*. Steam, diesel, and gasoline engines prove that heat is capable of doing work. The kind stored in coal and other fossil fuels is *chemical energy*. From this stored energy, we can accomplish many useful things. In a beam of sunlight there is another form of energy; we call it *radiant* or *electromagnetic energy*. An electric current flowing in a wire possesses *electrical energy*, for it has the ability to run motors and do useful work. A nuclear reactor gets its energy from the loss in mass during the nuclear reactions; hence, we can consider *mass* a form of energy. Most of these energies we shall study in detail in later chapters.

10-6
Transformation of Energy

Energies are like Dr. Jekyll and Mr. Hyde—they change from one form to another, but in the case of energies no one form is bad. Because of this continual changing in form, we have never obtained a clear and concise concept of energy itself except to express it in terms of what it can do. We usually think of different *kinds of energies* rather than different *forms of energy*.

In the case of the piledriver, the potential energy of the elevated hammer is transformed to kinetic energy as the hammer descends. At the midpoint position, half of the potential energy has been transformed into kinetic energy, and at the instant before the hammer strikes the pile, all of the potential energy with respect to the top of the pile has been converted into motion energy. As the hammer drives the pile into the ground, all of this kinetic energy plus the potential energy the hammer still has relative to its final resting position are converted into work (force $\times$ distance), driving the pile. If the hammer is raised by a diesel engine, a series of energy transformations takes place. Through the combustion of the fuel, chemical energy is converted into heat energy. This moves the pistons of the engine and the energy is converted to mechanical energy. The engine, through some kind of mechanical mechanism, raises the hammer, thus converting the energy of the pistons into the potential energy of the elevated hammer. When the hammer is released, this potential changes to kinetic, and finally into work, driving the pile into the ground.

10-7
Loss of Energy

Not all of the energy released by the combustion of the fuel goes through this series of transformations. Some of the heat energy is discharged through the exhaust. A certain amount heats the engine and its parts, and is transferred to the surrounding air. Some of the mechanical energy derived from the heat energy is dissipated in overcoming friction. This energy is converted back into heat in the machinery and is lost to the surroundings. As the hammer falls, some of the potential energy is converted into heat, instead of kinetic energy, because of the air resistance. Energy is dissipated all along the way. Only a small part of the original chemical energy is utilized in driving the pile into the ground.

Anytime friction is involved useful energy is lost. *Sliding friction* is the resistance encountered when one surface slides over another. The opposition is due to interlocking of irregularities in the two surfaces. The energy wasted in overcoming this opposition is always converted to heat. This loss can be reduced by carefully lubricating the surfaces or by the substitution of rollers or ball bearings.

It must not be assumed that friction is always bad just because it reduces the available energy. In many instances it is highly desirable. Walking is difficult enough on icy pavement, but it would be wholly impossible if there were no friction between the shoe and the pavement. In the case of a car, the wheels would spin without moving the vehicle. If you managed to get the car moving, how would you stop it without friction? Belts are often used in conveying power from one part of a machine to another part or to another machine. In the absence of friction this could not be done. The driving wheel would not move the belt; neither would the belt run the pulleys or wheels to be driven. Nails would not hold in wood without friction and would be useless. Therefore, we often sacrifice the energy lost for the advantages derived from the friction.

10-8
Efficiency of Machines

The energy delivered by a machine in the form of useful work is always less than that supplied. In the case of a steam engine, this loss is about 90%. In the case of our automobile engines, the loss is less, but it is still 70 to 75%. In the car engine, about 25% of the heat energy is dissipated through the radiator to keep the engine from overheating. Another 25% is unavoidably lost by way of the exhaust. This loss is in the form of unburned fuel and heat produced by combustion. Still further lossess occur within the engine in overcoming friction. Only 25 to 30% of the available energy is used to move the car.

The machines that utilize the greatest fraction of the energy supplied them are usually electrical. A well-designed electric motor, when running at its rated load, will deliver as useful work 80 to 85% of the energy supplied it.

An alternating-current transformer, which has no moving parts, and consequently no frictional losses in the usual sense, is still more efficient. Such devices frequently utilize 98% or more of the energy with which they are supplied.

The term *efficiency* is used to indicate the fractional part of the energy received by a machine that is finally delivered from it in the form of useful work. It is defined as the ratio of the work output to the work input. The car engine transforms into useful work about 30% of the supplied energy, and so we say that it has an efficiency of 0.30, or 30%.

10-9
Conservation of Energy

In any energy transformation, there is some loss, but no energy is destroyed. The part lost is simply dissipated, and thus made unavailable for useful work. If all of the energies wasted were added to the usable energy, the total would be found to be equal to that supplied. The form may be altered, but the amount remains unchanged. The fact that energy can be changed from one form to another, but can be neither created nor destroyed, constitutes the most important law in science, the *law of conservation of energy*. No one form of energy can be conserved, but the *total* is conserved. A machine may be designed to lift a much larger load than the force applied but it can never produce more work than was supplied it. In other words, a machine cannot have an efficiency greater than 1. Since man cannot create or destroy energy, he must use the energy that is available to him.

It was a great step forward for mankind when machines were devised for doing the heavy back-breaking labor that had formerly been done by muscular effort. The advantage was twofold. It relieved man of much of the drudgery he formerly had to endure, thus allowing him time to develop his intellectual life more fully; and it facilitated more abundant production of desirable goods. But to run machines requires energy of some sort, such as a waterfall, coal, gas, or mass energy. If this requirement could be eliminated, goods could be made cheaper and more abundant. Many ingenious devices have been designed for doing work without the need of supplying the outside power. These are called *perpetual-motion machines*. The inventors of such devices are usually men of great mechanical ingenuity, but with inadequate understanding of the behavior of nature. We cannot say, however, that a perpetual-motion machine is impossible because it violates the conservation of energy or any other physical law. The machine knows nothing about these laws; it just does what comes naturally. Physical laws are merely man's way of describing physical phenomena, and the description may not be exactly correct. All we can say about perpetual-motion machines is that they have

FIG. 10-3   Atmos, the perpetual motion clock. For hundreds of years, men tried to harness the bellows movement of an aneroid barometer as the driving force for a clock. LeCoultre has solved the problem with the Atmos clock. It runs silently, accurately, indefinitely, powered alone by the unfailing daily changes in the temperature and pressure of the air. Atmos requires no electricity, no hand-winding, no attention—even no oil. (Courtesy of LcCoultre Watches, Inc., a division of Longines-Whittnauer Watch Co.)

never been successful. The device coming the closest to perpetual motion is the Atmos clock (see Fig. 10-3), which winds itself when it experiences only slight fluctuations in atmospheric pressure and temperature.

Although we believe that perpetual-motion machines are impossible, we do expect improvement in the efficiency and usefulness of our machines. It is the primary aim of the physical sciences to discover previously unknown facts and relationships in nature. It is the aim of engineering and technology to develop new and better ways of applying this knowledge, both new and old, to the improvement of human welfare, but without excess pollution of our environment.

QUESTIONS AND PROBLEMS

1. Is it adequate to say that work is force times distance? Explain.
2. Is it possible for a force to act upon a body and yet do no work?
3. Does centripetal force do any work on a whirling object? Explain.
4. A person holds a 10-kilogram mass at arm's length and 1.5 meters above the floor for 10 minutes. How much work does he do in the 10 minutes?
5. A man is paddling a canoe upstream, but he remains in the same position with respect to the shore. Is he doing work? Explain.
6. Distinguish between work and power.

7. Does a machine increase one's power? Does it increase the amount of work he can do?

8. Show how the following are related and how they are different: (a) force and energy, (b) work and energy, (c) energy and power.

9. Neglecting friction, is work done while a body is being accelerated? Explain.

10. If a 1-kilogram mass has the same kinetic energy as a 4-kilogram mass, which has the most momentum?

11. A 73-kilogram man runs upstairs, a vertical distance of 9 meters, in 22 seconds. How many joules/sec did he develop? What horsepower was this?

12. How much work, in joules, is done to lift a 2-kilogram object 100 meters above the Earth? What is the potential energy of the object when at that 100-meter elevation? If the object falls back to Earth with no air resistance, what is its kinetic energy just before it strikes the ground? With what momentum does it strike the ground?

13. If the object in question 12 is allowed to fall, what is its potential energy, kinetic energy, and momentum after it has fallen for 4 seconds? Assume the initial velocity to be zero.

14. In moving around the Sun, which has more kinetic energy: the Earth or Mars?

15. A 200-kilogram piledriver hammer is dropped from a height of 6 meters above the top of a pile, and drives the pile 4 cm into the ground. What average force does the hammer exert upon the post?

16. A 2-gram bullet acquires a speed of 300 meters/sec when it reaches the muzzle of a gun. If the barrel is 90 cm long, what is the average force, in newtons, acting upon the bullet while it is in the barrel of the gun? For how long is the bullet in the barrel?

17. A 2-gram bullet, traveling at a speed of 300 m/sec, penetrates a 2.5-cm wooden plank and emerges with a speed of 250 m/sec. How many such planks would be required to stop an identical bullet with the same speed? (*Hint:* The bullet loses the same amount of energy in each plank.)

18. What is meant by conservation of energy? Can both energy and momentum be conserved at the same time?

19. What is the efficiency of an electric motor that receives 100 kilowatts of electrical power and delivers 70,000 joules/sec?

20. What is the source of energy in a piece of coal? In the tides? In a windstorm? In your muscles? In a waterfall?

21. ·Is the motion of the Earth around the Sun an example of perpetual motion?

22. Does the continued motion of the planets in their orbits around the Sun contradict the law of conservation of energy? Explain.

SUGGESTED REFERENCES

MILLER, FRANKLIN, JR., *College Physics*, 2nd ed., Chap. 6. Harcourt, Brace & World, New York, 1967.

SEMAT, H., *Fundamentals of Physics*, 4th ed., Chap. 5. Holt, Rinehart & Winston, New York, 1966.

WHITE, HARVEY E., *Modern College Physics*, 5th ed., Chaps. 10 and 11. D. Van Nostrand Co., Princeton, N.J., 1966.

11
Heat Phenomena

Heat is a very common physical quantity which we all use extensively in our daily lives, but do we really know what it is? For ages man used heat to cook his food and warm his home without making any attempt to learn its true nature. Primitive people respected fire with reverence. The Greeks considered it one of the primordial elements of the universe. The alchemists resorted to fire in their attempts to change the baser metals into gold. Heat is closely associated with life and living things; our very existence here on Earth depends on the amount we receive from the Sun. Heat can be produced by burning substances, by rubbing surfaces over each other, by striking one object against another, and by passing electric currents through conducting materials. We also know that it can be transferred from one body to another. What is this quantity called heat? Is it a physical property of a substance, or is it something extraneous to matter? Before we can intelligently answer this question, we must understand certain facts and principles of heat. Therefore, in this chapter we consider thermal phenomena, leaving the discussion of its nature for the next chapter.

11-1
Temperature

Early in history man became aware of the sensations of things being hot and cold. For centuries, he relied upon his sense of touch to measure the degree of "hotness" and "coldness." He evidently used his finger to tell whether or not his stew was too hot to eat. The early doctor had to gauge the extent of a patient's fever by placing his hand on the patient's forehead. Soon man realized that this method of measuring temperatures was not very reliable. We can check its unreliability by placing one hand on a piece of wood and the other on a piece of metal, both of which have been exposed to cold air for the same length of time. The metal will seem much colder than the wood, although they are at the same temperature. The sense of touch is only accurate enough to tell whether a substance is hot, tepid, or cold. Accurate temperature measurements had to wait until man had developed the appropriate instruments.

11-2
Galileo's Thermometer

The first instrument for comparing temperatures was made by Galileo in 1593. This device, called a *thermoscope*, consisted of a glass bulb about the size of a hen's egg with a long straw-like tube for a stem. To prepare the thermoscope for use, the bulb was heated slightly and the end of the stem immersed in water in a small bottle. When the bulb cooled, the water rose part way up the stem (see Fig 11-1). Galileo's thermoscope indicated higher temperatures by a decrease in the height of the water in the tube, and lower ones by a rise in the water level. It had the serious disadvantage of responding to changes in atmospheric pressure as well as to changes in temperature. In spite of this defect it was very useful especially to physicians. By putting the bulb in his armpit and then in that of his patient, the physician could determine whether the patient had a fever and roughly how much. No temperature scales had been devised at that time.

The first improvement in this device was made by a French physician, Jean Rey. In 1631, he inverted Galileo's thermoscope and filled the bulb

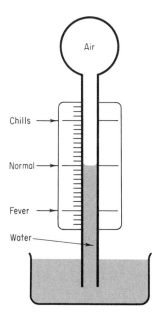

FIG. 11-1   Galileo's fever thermoscope.

and part of the stem with water. Temperature variations were indicated by the rise and fall of the water level in the stem. Since the volume of water changes much less than that of air as it is heated or cooled, Rey's thermometer was far less sensitive than Galileo's. It had reduced the effect of atmospheric pressure, but it introduced another error, that of evaporation of water from the stem. This defect was corrected about 10 years later by evacuating and sealing the upper end of the stem. A further improvement was made by using colored alcohol or mercury instead of water as the thermometer liquid.

11-3
Thermometric Scales

Up to this date there was no accepted thermometric scale. Each investigator set his own standard. Gabriel Daniel Fahrenheit, a German scientist, was the first to introduce a reliable scale based upon two fixed temperatures. To avoid negative readings, he chose for his zero a temperature colder than the coldest day in his home town of Danzig: he sent a thermometer to a friend in Iceland, who recorded the lowest observed temperature on the thermometer, and Fahrenheit took that as his zero. For the other fixed point, he took the oral temperature of a healthy person as 96°. Later Fahrenheit found that he could approximately reproduce the zero temperature by mixing sea salt and ice. In 1724, he revised his scale by taking the lowest temperature obtainable with a mixture of sea salt and ice as zero, and the boiling point of water at normal atmospheric pressure as 212°. On this scale, the melting point of ice is 32°, and the normal temperature of the human body is 98.6°. The adoption of this scale gave us our present-day *Fahrenheit thermometer.*

In 1742 Anders Celsius, a Swedish mathematician, used a scale on which the boiling point of water was marked 0° and the melting point of ice as 100°. After a few years, the scale was inverted, giving us the present *Celsius scale*, commonly called the *centigrade scale*. In 1948 the name "Celsius" was adopted by international agreement as the correct name for the degrees on this scale, which is used throughout the world for scientic work, and in many countries for all purposes.

In America, where both the Fahrenheit and the Celsius (or centigrade) scales are used, it is often necessary to find what reading on one scale corresponds to a given reading on the other. The method will be easily understood from Fig. 11-2. There are 180 Fahrenheit divisions between the freezing and boiling points of water, and only 100 Celsius (centigrade) divisions in the same range. Hence, 180 Fahrenheit divisions are equal to 100 Celsius divisions, or 9 Fahrenheit divisions equal 5 Celsius divisions. One F division = $\frac{5}{9}$ C division. Conversely, 1 C division = $\frac{9}{5}$ F divisions. To find what reading on the Celsius scale is equivalent to a given reading on the Fahrenheit scale, the number of Fahrenheit degrees between the given temperature and the

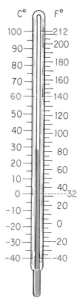

FIG. 11-2   Celsius and Fahrenheit scales.

freezing point is multiplied by $\frac{5}{9}$. To find the Fahrenheit temperature that corresponds to a given Celsius temperature, the latter with its algebraic sign retained is multiplied by $\frac{9}{5}$, and the product is added algebraically to 32°. These processes may be expressed symbolically as follows:

$$°C = \tfrac{5}{9}(°F - 32)$$

or
$$°F = \tfrac{9}{5}°C + 32$$

In Fig. 11-2, we observe that 40° below zero Celsius is also 40° below zero Fahrenheit. This is the only temperature at which the two scale readings are numerically the same. Another conversion method can be based upon this fact, and those who have difficulty in solving equations may find this method more to their liking. If a temperature is 20° C, the mercury level will be 60 Celsius (centigrade) degrees above this common temperature point. Since a Fahrenheit division is $\frac{5}{9}$ as large as a Celsius division, there will be $\frac{9}{5}$ as many in a certain temperature range. Hence, the mercury level is $\frac{9}{5} \times 60$ or 108 Fahrenheit divisions above the common point. The temperature being measured is 108 — 40 or 68° above the Fahrenheit zero, and is designated as 68°F. This conversion process is reversible. 68° Fahrenheit is 68 + 40 or 108 Fahrenheit degrees above the common temperature point. This represents $\frac{5}{9} \times 108$ or 60 Celsius degrees above that point. The mercury is therefore 60 — 40 or 20 degrees above the Celsius zero, and so the temperature reading is 20° C. To convert from one scale to another, simply take the following steps:

1. Add 40 to the temperature reading.
2. Take $\frac{9}{5}$ or $\frac{5}{9}$ of that sum.
3. Subtract 40 (or add —40).

Proper algebraic signs must be retained throughout the operation.

The zero temperature adopted by Fahrenheit was not the lowest temperature then thought obtainable. In about 1702 Amontons devised an air thermometer by means of which temperatures were measured by the pressure—the force exerted per unit area—of a fixed volume of air. The pressure rose or fell approximately in proportion to the change in temperature, and it was the same at all points on the scale. Amontons inferred that the temperature might be reduced to such an extent that the air in his thermometer would exert no pressure. This would represent the limit of coldness or an *absolute zero*. Later observations of a similar kind have shown that this absolute zero is about 273 Celsius degrees below the freezing point of water. A temperature scale using Celsius divisions and the absolute zero as its zero is called the *absolute Celsius* or *Kelvin scale*. Any absolute temperature can be found by adding algebraically 273 to the Celsius reading:

$$°K = °C + 273$$

There is another absolute scale; this one uses Fahernheit divisions and is called the *absolute Fahrenheit* or *Rankine scale*. Any absolute temperature on this scale can be found by adding 460 to the Fahrenheit reading:

$$°R = °F + 460$$

There is no such limitation at the other extreme as far as we know. We think of boiling water as hot (100° C), but molten lead is hotter (232° C), and molten iron is hotter still (1,530° C). These are relatively cool compared to our Sun and the stars. As we have previously learned, the surface temperature of the Sun is about 10,300° F, and the temperature at its center is about 25,000,000° F. Some stars, we think, have temeratures at their centers of hundreds of millions of degrees.

Now we know how to measure temperatures, but do we know what it is we are measuring? This we will learn in the next chapter.

11-5
Expansion of Substances

Most of our thermometers depend on the fact that substances expand when their temperatures rise, and contract when their temperatures drop. There are many evidences of this phenomenon. We have seen the bottom fall out of a fruit jar when boiling water was poured into it. The bottom expanded more than the rest of the jar and the glass could not withstand the internal forces introduced. We are all aware of the separators between the slabs of concrete on a highway. On a hot summer day the slabs expand, pushing the separator out from between them, and we hear the periodic thumps as the wheels of the car pass over them. From the "clickety-clack" sound we hear on a train, we know that small spaces must be left between the rails of the track. On cold winter nights, the telephone wires become taut and "sing" in the wind. In the summer, the wires expand, become less taut, and no longer "sing" in the breeze. One end of every long steel bridge is placed on rollers to allow for expansion. The Golden Gate Bridge in San Francisco varies about 1.5 meters in length from winter to summer. We make use of the expansion of solids in thermostats to control the temperatures in our homes, refrigerators, ovens, and many other things. The expansion of gases in the cylinders of the automobile engine drives the car.

The expansion of various materials when heated differs widely. Steel expands about 50% more than ordinary glass, aluminum about twice as much as steel, and ebonite almost 4 times as much as aluminum. The amount a unit length of a solid expands or contracts when its temperature rises or falls 1 degree is called the *coefficient of linear expansion* of the substance. If 1 centimeter of steel at 0° C is heated to 1° C, its length increases to 1.000012 centimeters. Thus the coefficient of linear expansion of steel is 0.000012 per degree Celsius. Knowing this coefficient, which is determined experimentally, we can compute the expansion or contraction for any temperature change:

Expansion = Coefficient × Length × Change in temperature

Practically all solids, liquids, and gases, if not restricted, expand the same in all directions as the temperature rises, thus changing the volume of the substance. In general, gases expand more than liquids, and liquids expand more than solids. The amount a volume expands or contracts per unit volume for a 1-degree change in temperature is called the *coefficient of volume expansion*. One cubic centimeter of mercury at 0° C increases to 1.00018 cubic centimeters when its temperature rises to 1° C. Therefore, its coefficient of volume expansion is 0.00018 per degree Celsius. Different substances have different coefficients. All gases at constant pressure have approximately the same coefficient of volume expansion, which is 0.00366 per degree Celsius.

Mercury expands uniformly over a relatively wide range of temperatures, which makes it very valuable as a temperature indicator. Water does not vary uniformly, especially near 4° C. At 4° C, water expands when heated, and also expands when cooled. It has its maximum density at that temperature. The volume of 1 gram of water at temperatures between 0° and 12° C is represented by the graph in Fig. 11-3. This exceptional behavior of water has important effects in nature. In the winter, as the water in our lakes and rivers cools to near its freezing point, it rises to the surface where it freezes. Immediately below the ice the temperature is 0° C, but from a few feet below the ice to the

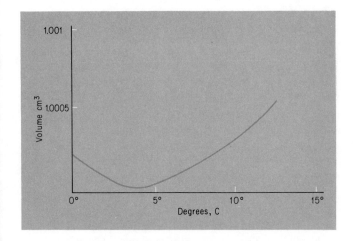

FIG. 11-3 The volume of 1 gm of water at different temperatures.

bottom, the temperature remains at 4° C during the coldest days of the winter. This is very important for the survival of the aquatic life in the lakes and rivers.

Now we know how substances expand, but *why* should they expand when their temperatures rise?

11-6
Measurement of Heat

If a small pan of water and a tubful are heated over identical burners, we know from experience that the water in the pan will begin to boil long before the tubful. The temperature rise from room temperature to the boiling point is the same for the two, but the amount of heat added to achieve this temperature rise for the water in the tub is much greater. Hence, a quantity of heat cannot be the same as a degree of hotness; heat and temperature are not synonymous terms. Since the addition of heat usually warms a substance, the development of the thermometer has made it possible for us to determine the amounts of heat added or removed from any substance. Water is used as a standard because it is readily available. The unit of heat is defined in terms of the amount of heat required to raise the temperature of a unit mass of water 1 degree. The most commonly employed units are the following:

A *calorie* (*cal*) is the amount of heat needed to raise the temperature of 1 gram of water 1 degree Celsius.

A *kilocalorie* (*Cal*) is the amount of heat required to raise the temperature of 1 kilogram of water 1 degree Celsius. This is the food calorie about which we are so concerned in our diets.

$$1 \text{ Calorie} = 1,000 \text{ calories}$$

A *British thermal unit* (Btu) is the amount of heat needed to raise the temperature of 1 pound mass of water 1 Fahrenheit degree. It is the unit employed in engineering and commercial work in the United States.

1 Btu = 252 calories

The number of calories or Btu developed by fuels, chemical reactions, electricity, and others can be determined by observing the rise in temperature produced by that amount of heat in a known quantity of water.

11-7
Specific Heat

By heating a small block of aluminum and an equal mass of water over two identical burners, we observe that after a few minutes the block is too hot to touch, while a finger may be placed in the water without discomfort. The water requires more heat to raise its temperature 1 degree than does an equal mass of aluminum. Hence, we see that it takes different amounts of heat to raise the temperature of different substances 1 degree. It requires only about one-tenth of a calorie for 1 gram of iron, and about one-thirtieth of a calorie for a gram of lead. The amount of heat required to raise the temperature of the entire object 1 degree is called its *thermal capacity*, while heat needed to raise the temperature of a unit mass of that object 1 degree is called its *specific heat capacity*, which we will shorten to *specific heat*. From the definitions of the heat units, we see that the specific heat of water is 1 calorie per gram per degree Celsius, written as 1 cal/gm × C°. (One Celsius degree temperature *interval* is written as *1 C°* while 1 degree Celsius *reading* is written as *1° C*.) Specific heat is a characterstic of the material of which an object is composed, and very few substances have higher specific heats than water. Table 11-1 gives some specific heats.

TABLE 11-1
Specific Heats

Substance	Specific heat, cal/gm × C°
Aluminum	0.22
Copper	0.093
Glass	0.16
Ice	0.50
Iron	0.11
Lead	0.03
Silver	0.056
Water	1.00

Oceans and large lakes have marked moderating effects upon the climate of the regions adjacent to them because of their large thermal capacities. By absorbing and storing up heat during the hot weather and returning it to the air during cold periods, the oceans and lakes tend to prevent the extreme and sudden changes in temperature so often observed in regions far removed from any such stabilizing agencies.

11-8
Calorimetry

The quantity of heat Q required to raise the temperature of a substance depends on the amount of mass m to be heated, its specific heat c, and the amount its temperature is to be changed $(T_2 - T_1)$. These quantities are related as follows:

$$Q = mc(T_2 - T_1)$$

To illustrate this relationship, let us determine the amount of heat required to raise the temperature of 1,000 grams of silver from 20° C to 80° C:

$$Q = 1,000 \text{ gm} \times 0.056 \frac{\text{cal}}{\text{gm} \times \text{C}°}(80° \text{ C} - 20° \text{ C})$$

$$= 3,360 \text{ calories}$$

Heat measurements are usually made by using a *calorimeter* (see Fig. 11-4) and a procedure known as the *method of mixtures*. If two or more substances, initially at different temperatures, are placed in good thermal contact with each other, and allowed to come to a common temperature without losing any heat to the surroundings, the hot objects lose heat and the cold ones gain heat. By setting the heat lost equal to the amount of heat gained, any of the thermal quantities can be determined.

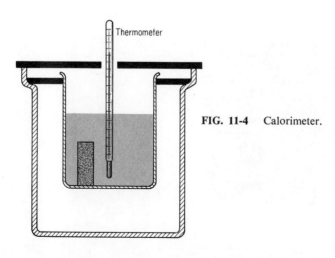

Thermometer

FIG. 11-4   Calorimeter.

For example, a 200-gram block of an unknown metal is heated to 100° C in boiling water. It is removed from the boiling water and dropped into 50 grams of water at 25° C. The hot metal, in cooling, raises the temperature of the water to 30° C, which is also the final temperature of the metal. What is the specific heat of this unknown metal?

$$Q \text{ lost} = Q \text{ gained}$$

$$200 \text{ gm} \times (c)(100° \text{ C} - 30° \text{ C}) = 50 \text{ gm} \times 1(\text{cal/gm-C°})(30° \text{ C} - 25° \text{ C})$$

$$14,000 \text{ gm-C°}(c) = 250 \text{ calories}$$

$$c = 0.018 \text{ calorie/gm/C°}$$

11-9
Heat Required to Melt a Solid

When the weather turns warm after a long period of cold and heavy snow, many days of sunshine may have to pass before all the deep drifts disappear. Even after the snow has been warmed to the melting point, a great deal of heat must be supplied to convert it into water: about 80 calories for each gram. All this is added without causing any change in the temperature of the snow. When ice melts from streams and lakes, the same amount of heat is also required to change each gram of ice, already at the melting point, into water at the same temperature. The amount of heat required to change one unit mass of a substance from the solid into the liquid condition is called the *latent heat of fusion* of the substance. Thus the latent heat of fusion of ice is 80 calories per gram.

Just as water is formed from ice by the addition of heat without a change in temperature, so ice is formed from water by the withdrawal of heat, also without a change in temperature. At normal pressure, both processes take place at 0° C. Which process will occur is determined entirely by the surroundings. A well-stirred mixture of ice and water is always at 0° C. If the mixture is in a region where the temperature is above 0° C, heat is absorbed by the mixture and there is melting. In a region where the temperature is below 0 °C, heat of the mixture is lost to the surroundings and there is freezing.

As compared with that of ice, the latent heats of fusion of most solids are quite low. That of tin, for example, is 14 calories per gram. Those of lead and gray cast iron are about 5.8 and 5.5 calories per gram, respectively; that of mercury is less than 3. In solidifying, each of these metals liberates the same amount of heat it absorbs in melting.

The high heat of fusion of ice is another important reason why in the neighborhood of large bodies of water autumn weather does not change suddenly into winter, nor winter into spring.

11-10
Heat Required to Vaporize a Liquid

Just as heat is required to change a substance from a solid into a liquid, so heat is also required to change it from a liquid into a gas or vapor. The amount of heat needed to bring about the latter change is, in some instances, surprisingly great. Here again, water is a notable example. A pan of water over a large burner may be brought to the boiling point quickly. A much longer time is required to boil the water away. When the water has reached the boiling point, an additional 540 calories must be supplied to each gram to convert it into steam, without causing any further rise in the temperature. It requires about 204 calories to vaporize 1 gram of alcohol at the boiling point, and only about 65 calories for 1 gram of mercury.

The amount of heat required to vaporize a unit mass of a liquid without changing its temperature is called its *latent heat of vaporization*. Thus the latent heat of vaporization of water at its normal boiling point is 540 calories per gram. That of mercury is 65 cal/gm.

Bathers may feel distinctly cool when coming out of the water. This coolness is due to rapid evaporation of water from the skin—the heat to evaporate the water is supplied largely by the body. Evaporation of perspiration during vigorous exercise enables the body to maintain its normal temperature. Air conditioners in some dry sections of the country keep the house cool by the evaporation of the water in the air-conditioning unit.

When a vapor condenses, it gives off the same amount of heat as the liquid absorbed when it vaporized. The effect is sometimes observed in summer when a shower is followed by a rise in temperature. The heat of vaporization is released in the condensation of the moisture, and it warms the air. The same effect is often noticed during or following a gentle snowstorm. In this case, the vapor is converted directly to a solid in which process both the latent heat of vaporization and fusion are released.

11-11
Heat Transfer

To be useful, heat must be transferred from the device in which it is generated to the place where it is to be used. Our planet would be a cold, barren place if the heat from the Sun could not reach the Earth. There are only three ways by which heat is transferred from a warm to a cold region: conduction, convection, and radiation.

Conduction A spoon placed in a cup of hot coffee soon becomes warm throughout. Heat has been transferred by the metal from the parts that touch the liquid to the parts that do not. The heat was transmitted from the hot part of the spoon through the metal to the cool handle, raising its temperature. The outside of the firebox of a furnace becomes hot because of the fire inside. The heat is passed through the metal, from the hot inside to the colder outside. This method of heat transfer through the substance is called *conduction*. Silver and copper are the best of all heat conductors. Aluminum is much better than iron. For this reason, a burner heats the bottom of an aluminum pan more uniformly than that of an iron pan, and so there are no hot spots to burn the food.

Convection   The heating of a room by a radiator, or an entire house by a warm-air or hot-water furnace, involves a second method of heat transfer: *convection*. In heating the room, the air in contact with the radiator becomes warm, expands, and rises because it is less dense than the air around it. The cooler, heavier air moves in to take its place. The circulation set up in this way carries heat to every part of the room. In the case of a hot-air furnace, the air is heated by the furnace, expands and rises into the rooms through the pipes carrying the heat with it. The cold, heavier air in the rooms drops through the cold-air ducts to the furnace, thus setting up a circulation. A forced warm-air heating system as shown in Fig. 11-5 has a blower to increase that circulation. In convection, the medium itself moves and carries the heat from the warm to the cool region.

Radiation   The third method of heat transfer is *radiation*. It is by this method that the heat of a bonfire reaches the people standing nearby, and

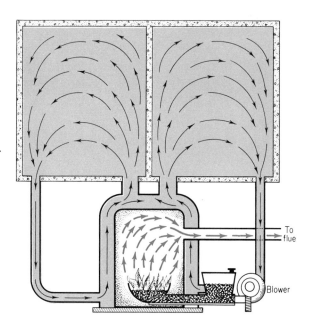

FIG. 11-5   A warm-air heating plant.

that the Earth receives its heat from the Sun. Radiant heat is transmitted with the speed of light, 3×10^8 m/sec. The energy is carried by electromagnetic waves. These waves are emitted by a warm substance, pass through space, are absorbed by an object upon which they fall, and raise the temperature of that object. These waves are like light waves but are much longer; therefore, since the optic nerve is sensitive only to a narrow range of wavelengths, heat waves do not stimulate the nerves of the eye and are invisible.

Regardless of the method of transfer, heat always "flows" spontaneously from a warm object to a colder one.

11-12
Limiting the Transfer of Heat

A ready flow of heat is not always desirable. In handling a heated object, such as a hot flatiron or baking dish, precautions are taken to limit the amount of heat reaching the hand. The flatiron is provided with a wooden or plastic handle, and the baking dish is held by a cloth or pad over the hands. Wood and cloth are poor conductors of heat. There are many others, including asbestos, cork, cotton, wool, leather, rubber, silk, many liquids, and all gases.

For year-round comfort we insulate our homes and use storm windows. This prevents unnecessary loss of heat through the walls and windows in the winter, and entrance of the heat through the same channels in the summer. The body is heated by its internal "fires." One of its functions is to conserve this heat. Complete heat insulation is neither possible nor desirable. Enough heat should be able to escape to allow the body to maintain easily its normal temperature. During vigorous exercise, the amount of heat dissipated must be greater than during inactivity. Because of the large amount of air they contain, furs and loosely woven garments are warmer than firm and more solid ones. In general, wool is warmer than cotton, and cotton warmer than linen.

QUESTIONS AND PROBLEMS

1. In what two respects do the Fahrenheit and Celsius (centigrade) scales differ?

2. Convert the following Celsius readings to Fahrenheit: (a) 120°C, (b) 75°C, (c) 5°C, (d) −10°C, (e) −20°C, (f) −40°C.

3. Convert the following Fahrenheit readings to Celsius: (a) 410°F, (b) 95°F, (c) 23°F, (d) 14°F, (e) −22°F, (f) −169°F.

4. Normal body temperature is 98.6°F. What is it in degrees Celsius, and in degrees Kelvin?

5. What Fahrenheit temperature is twice its equivalent Celsius temperature?

6. A hole is drilled through a steel plate and the plate is then heated. Will the hole get larger or smaller, or will it remain the same size? Explain.

7. A steel tape for measuring distances is accurate at 20°C. The tape is used to lay out a 400-meter track when the temperature is −10°C. (a) Is the track longer or shorter than 400 meters? (b) If the coefficient of linear expansion is 11×10^{-6} per degree Celsius, what is the true length of the track?

8. What is the most important physical property a liquid should have if it is to be used in a thermometer? Why?

9. A glass bottle is filled with mercury at 20°C. At that temperature the volume of the bottle is 100 cm³. How much mercury will spill out of the bottle when its temperature is raised to 125°C? (The coefficient of volume expansion of mercury is 18×10^{-5} per C°, and the coefficient of volume expansion of glass is 72×10^{-6} per C°.)

10. Which has the greater thermal capacity: 1 kilogram of copper or 100 cm³ of water?

11. What is the difference between thermal capacity and specific heat?

12. Two hundred grams of a given metal at 90°C is placed in 100 grams of water at 30°C, and the final temperature of the water and metal is found to be 40°C. What is the specific heat of the metal?

13. Four hundred grams of acetone at a temperature of 60°C is mixed in a calorimeter with 600 grams of chloroform at a temperature of 20°C. The final temperature of the mixture is 30°C. How does the specific heat of the acetone compare with that of the chloroform?

14. If 30 grams of iron shot at 100°C is poured into 180 gm of water at 20°C, what is the final temperature after the shot and water have come to thermal equilibrium?

15. If 200 grams of aluminum shot at 100°C is poured into 150 gm of water at 10°C in a 50-gm copper calorimeter cup, what is the final temperature of the contents when thermal equilibrium is reached?

16. A stone and a brick of the same mass are placed in some water, and both transfer the same amount of heat to the water. If the stone has a lower specific heat than the brick, what else can one be sure of?

17. Can a tumbler of water be cooled faster by holding an ice cube near the bottom of the water, or by letting it float at the top of the water?

18. How might a tub of water in a fruit cellar keep the fruit from freezing during a cold winter night?

19. Name a quantity of heat which does not use water as a standard.

20. A 50-gram mass of ice at 0°C is placed in 200 grams of water at 75°C. What is the final temperature of the water?

21. An athlete lost 450 milliliters of water by evaporation during a contest. How many calories of heat were lost in the process?

22. What is unique about the expansion of water? Why do water pipes sometimes burst during cold weather?

23. How much ice at 0°C can be melted by 50 grams of steam at 100°C?

24. State the three ways by which heat can be transferred from one place to another. Give an example of each.

SUGGESTED REFERENCES

GAMOW, GEORGE, and JOHN M. CLEVELAND, *Physics: Foundations and Frontiers*, 2nd ed., Chap. 10. Prentice-Hall, Englewood Cliffs, N.J., 1969.

KRAUSKOPF, KONRAD, and ARTHUR BEISER, *Fundamentals of Physical Science*, 5th ed., Chap. 6. McGraw-Hill Book Co., New York, 1966.

PRIESTLEY, HERBERT, *Introductory Physics*, Chaps. 11, 12, and 13. Allyn and Bacon, Boston, 1958.

ROLLER, D., *Early Development of the Concepts of Temperature*. Harvard University Press, Cambridge, 1950.

RUSK, ROGERS D., *Introduction to College Physics*, Chap. 15. Appleton-Century-Crofts, New York, 1960.

12
Kinetic Theory
of Heat

12-1
Caloric Theory of Heat

The true nature of heat was not known until near the end of the eighteenth century. Before that time, many scientists thought of it as a fluid that could pass from one object to another. This imaginary fluid was called *caloric*. All objects were assumed to possess a certain amount of it. When more was added, the temperature rose. When some was lost, the temperature fell. If two objects at different temperatures were placed in contact with each other, the fluid flowed from the hot object to the cold one. The hot object lost caloric and the cold one gained it until both were at the same temperature. Different substances had the ability to absorb different amounts of caloric when the temperature was raised 1 degree, thus accounting for the different specific heats. Expansion was due to the mutual repulsion of caloric; therefore, as more caloric was added to a substance, not only did its temperature rise but it got larger. The development of heat by friction was attributed to the fact that friction causes an object to lose some of its ability for caloric, thus liberating some of the caloric it possessed, and raising the temperature of the object.

One difficulty with this theory was that although considered as a fluid, caloric could not have any weight because an object was no heavier when hot than when cold. Another difficulty was the fact that the supply of caloric that could be derived from an object by rubbing it seemed almost unlimited. Either the object in its normal condition must possess an unbelievably large store of the fluid, or it was created while the rubbing was going on.

Count Rumford of Bavaria (formerly Benjamin Thompson of Massachusetts) found during the boring of cannons that the amount of heat developed depended markedly on the condition of the drill. If it was very dull, the amount of heat developed seemed to be extremely large and depended only on the amount of work done in the boring. The advocates of the caloric theory accounted for the generated heat by saying that the caloric was squeezed out of the shavings in the boring process to appear as heat. Therefore, the shavings were less able to contain caloric (had a smaller specific heat) than the original block. The specific heat of the borings, however, was determined experimentally and found to be exactly equal to that of the metal from which they came. No caloric should have been liberated.

Humphrey Davy, an English scientist, succeeded in melting ice to which no heat was allowed to flow merely by rubbing two pieces of ice together. The amount of ice melted seemed to depend only on the amount of work done in the rubbing. In this case, the evidence against the caloric theory was even more convincing. Since the specific heat of water is twice that of ice, caloric should have been absorbed instead of released to melt the ice. In theory, this was a perfectly logical experiment, but there is some question as to whether Davy was able to insulate his apparatus sufficiently to prevent heat transfer from the surroundings.

12-2
Heat is Energy

Rumford and Davy were agreed that heat is not a fluid, not anything material, but rather an energy capable of doing work. The results of later investigators have entirely confirmed their views. By 1850, James Prescott Joule, an Englishman, had performed his well-known experiment of agitating a liquid with paddlewheels. From the work done by the paddles and the heat developed in the liquid, he succeeded in showing not only that heat was generated whenever work was done in overcoming frictional resistance, but also in finding just how much energy was converted into heat to yield 1 calorie. According to Joule,

$$1 \text{ calorie} = 4.186 \text{ joules}$$

Rowland, an American, arrived at the same result. Therefore, we conclude that *heat is not a fluid, but a form of energy.*

Since heat energy seems to be associated somehow with matter, we must first look at the properties of matter to determine any possible connection. We know that matter exists in the three forms of solids, liquids, and gases, and that it can be subdivided into smaller and smaller amounts, always retaining the characteristics of the original substance. We known from experience that this cannot be continued indefinitely, and the limiting subdivision that retains all of the original properties is called a *molecule*. If a cube of sugar were subdivided in the extreme, there would finally be obtained the tiniest particle that could exist and retain the sweetness of sugar. This is the sugar molecule, and if subdivided any more into atoms, the sugar properties would disappear. These limiting particles are very minute in size. They cannot be seen singly even with the aid of a high-powered microscope. In 1 gram of water there are 3.3×10^{21} (thousand billion billion) molecules. If 300,000 of these water molecules were laid side by side, the length of the resulting chain would be equal to the thickness of this page.

Not only is matter made up of these extremely small molecules, but we know that the molecules are in continuous, random motion. In 1827, Robert Brown, a Scottish botanist, while looking through his microscope at some pollen grains suspended in water, observed that these microscopic particles did not remain stationary as he would have liked, nor did they move constantly in one direction. Each particle moved independently, and in an irregular zigzag manner somewhat as represented in Fig. 12-1. Brown was unable to account for this haphazard motion, but it was explained later by William Ramsay as the result of the bombardment of the pollen grains by the invisible water molecules in which they were suspended. At the instant a pollen grain is at *O* in the figure, if it is struck more vigorously on the left side than on the right by a number of molecules, it will be driven suddenly to some point *P*. There it will receive impacts that are predominantly from another direction and be driven to the next sharp bend in the line. This process continues, giving the pollen grain its zigzag path, which is known as the *Brownian movement*. Because of this haphazard motion of the molecules of matter, there is no visual outward evidence of these internal activities. Since there are as many molecules moving in one direction as another, the object itself does not move.

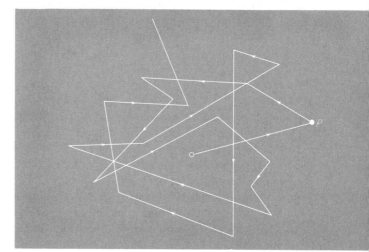

FIG. 12-1 Brownian movement.

In gases, the molecules are dashing around madly like a great swarm of gnats. This idea of flying molecules colliding and rebounding in all directions off other moving molecules accounts for the fact that a confined gas completely fills a container, regardless of its shape or size. In liquids, the molecules are packed quite closely together as the imcompressibility of liquids indicates, but they are still mobile. They roll and flow around each other, permitting the liquid to take the shape of the lower part of the container. Molecules this close together exert large attractive forces on each other, and are pulled toward the interior of the liquid, producing a meniscus over the upper surface. This meniscus acts like a stretched membrane. In solids, the molecules do not migrate around, but vibrate back and forth slightly about fixed positions within the material. Consequently, solids retain their original shapes. The molecules of any gaseous, liquid, or solid substance are moving about in some translatory, or oscillatory manner, and possess a certain amount of kinetic energy. Since all the molecules exhibit attractive forces for each other and are removed some distance from their neighbors, they also possess potential energy. In addition to these random kinetic and potential energies, the molecules themselves may be rotating and vibrating; thus, they have some rotational and vibrational energies. The total of all the random molecular energies is called the *internal energy* of the entire substance. If the internal energy increases without any work done on the substance, we say that *heat is added* by an amount equal to the increase in internal energy. If the internal energy decreases without the substance doing work on something, we say that *heat is removed* from the substance. Hence, *heat* is the amount of energy transferred to or from a substance by molecular activities. When we speak of *heat* we mean energy flow due to a difference of temperature. When the transfer is over, the word *heat* no longer has any meaning. The quantity of heat is the amount of energy shifted from one body to another. Sometimes we say *heat* when we really mean *internal energy*. Whenever we use it as such, we shall write it within quotation marks as: "heat."

12-3
Temperature

By observing the Browinan movement of tiny particles suspended in a liquid, we can gain some information about the activity of the invisible liquid molecules. We notice that the molecular activity increases as the temperature is raised and decreases as the temperature is lowered. Therefore, temperature must be an indication of this molecular motion. Since the molecules zigzag about within a wide range of speeds (see Fig. 12-2), the temperature indicates the average linear kinetic energy of the molecules. When the molecules of a substance have no translatory motion in the X, Y, and Z directions, we

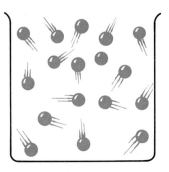

FIG. 12-2   Random motion of molecules.

consider the temperature of that substance to be zero. This is the absolute zero mentioned in Chapter 11, and is the coldest value obtainable. The molecules may still possess some rotational and vibrational energy. This we call the "zero-point energy." *Temperature, measured on the absolute scale, is directly proportional to the average linear kinetic energy of the individual molecule.* We can now differentiate between heat and temperature. *Heat* is the energy transferred due to a temperature difference, resulting in a change in the internal energy of a substance if no work is done on the substance; whereas *temperature* is only a measure of the average linear kinetic energy of the molecules. When we say that a substance is heated, we mean that the total energy of all its molecules has increased. When we say that the temperature of a substance is raised, we mean that the average kinetic energy of the molecules has increased. To determine a temperature directly from the molecular activity would be next to impossible; but as the molecules become more active, they strike against each other with greater force and are pushed farther apart. The faster they move around, the more room they require. Therefore, a temperature can be determined from the amount that a gas, a liquid, or a solid expands. The distances the molecules are pushed apart for a given increase in kinetic energy vary from substance to substance. Ordinary thermometers are calibrated in terms of the expansion of certain liquids, such as mercury and colored alcohol. Since these liquids expand rather uniformly, equal increments of temperature produce equal changes in the height of the liquid column.

Let us visualize what happens when a hot solid is dropped into some cold water. The vigorously vibrating molecules of the solid strike the slower water molecules and impart to them some of their kinetic energy; the molecules of the solid slow down, and the water molecules speed up. This process continues until the molecules of the two substances have the same average kinetic energy. Then no energy will be transferred from one to the other, and the solid and the water will be at the same temperature. We say that the heat "flowed" from the hot to the cold substance because energy was transferred from the rapidly oscillating molecules of the solid to the slow-moving water molecules. It must be emphasized that heat is not the total internal energy, but in this case is the amount the internal energy changes. The hot solid lost internal energy by the same amount that the water gained energy.

In a solid, the molecules or charged particles are arranged in an orderly pattern and are so located that the attractive forces exerted upon them by their neighbors are as large as possible. As the temperature rises, these molecules oscillate more rapidly back and forth with respect to fixed positions. The higher the temperature, the faster they move, and eventually the kinetic energy of some of the molecules is large enough to overcome the binding energy. They fly away from the solid, and bounce around in a haphazard manner among the other liquid molecules (see Fig. 12-3). As heat is added, more and more break loose from their orderly arrangement and the solid gradually changes to a liquid; we say that it is *melting*. At a definite kinetic energy, the molecules are able to break away from their neighbors in the solid. No molecules can have kinetic energies larger than this and remain in the solid state. Hence, the temperature of most solids rises to the melting point and then remains constant, until all of the solid has changed to a liquid. Since the liquid produced is in contact with the solid, the average kinetic energy of the liquid and solid molecules remains the same. When ice melts, the water formed stays at $0°$ C, if thoroughly mixed with the ice, until all of the ice has melted. The molecules of the liquid have more potential energy than do the molecules of the solid; therefore, the total internal energy of the liquid is larger than that of the solid. The amount of heat added per unit mass is called the *latent heat of fusion*. For ice this is 80 calories/gram.

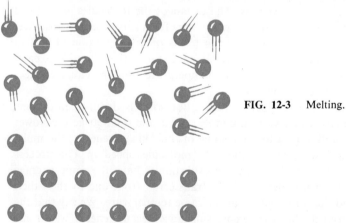

FIG. 12-3   Melting.

The process of freezing is the reverse of melting. As a liquid cools, the zig-zag motion of the molecules decreases. When some of the slower ones collide, the force of attraction may be sufficient to hold the molecules together. They release their potential energy and start vibrating about a common point. As more heat is removed, more molecules will unite in an orderly manner. Thus the solid gradually increases in size. All of the heat absorbed in melting is released upon solidification.

12-5
Evaporation

Some of the more energetic molecules near the surface of a liquid may have an upward speed great enough to break through the surface film and fly into the space above the liquid as vapor molecules (see Fig. 12-4). This process is called *evaporation*. Only the faster molecules are able to escape the attractive forces of their mobile neighbors. This leaves the slower ones behind,

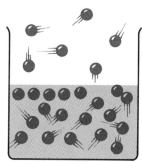

FIG. 12-4   Evaporation.

thereby decreasing the temperature of the remaining liquid. Hence, evaporation produces a cooling effect. In some liquids, however, the attractive force between the molecules is much weaker than in others and, consequently, a greater number of molecules are able to escape in a unit length of time. This increases the evaporation rate and produces a greater cooling effect. For example, if some denatured or rubbing alcohol is placed on the back of one hand, and water, at the same temperature, is put on the back of the other hand, the skin under the alcohol will feel much cooler because of the more rapid evaporation.

The escaping molecules mingle and collide with the air and other vapor molecules above the liquid surface. These fast-moving molecules give up a little of their kinetic energy to the air and vapor molecules, and after a few collisions, slow down until their temperature is the same as that of the surroundings. Some of the molecules also ricochet back into the liquid. Other vapor molecules strike the side of the container and exert a small force on a unit area of the container. This is called *vapor pressure*, and at room temperature it is considerably less than the force per unit area or pressure produced by the air molecules. Since alcohol evaporates faster than water, more alcohol molecules will be liberated; hence, it produces a greater vapor pressure than water.

12-6
Boiling

As the temperature of the liquid is raised, the activity of the molecules within the liquid increases, and more molecules escape. Evaporation takes place at a faster rate. The increase in the number of vapor molecules, plus their higher speeds, enables them to exert a larger vapor pressure. At some temperature the molecules in the liquid will have enough kinetic energy to overcome the cohesive forces of their neighbors and produce a vapor bubble inside the liquid (see Fig. 12-5). This will happen as soon as the vapor pressure is equal to the atmospheric pressure. The bubble formed rises to the surface and releases its vapor molecules into the air. If more heat is applied, more bubbles will be formed, leaving only the slower molecules in the liquid state.

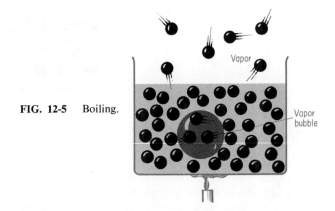

FIG. 12-5 Boiling.

When they, in turn, gain the proper kinetic energy, they too will depart from their neighbors and form more vapor bubbles. When the bubbles are continually forming and rising in the liquid, we say that it is *boiling*. This boiling process continues at a constant temperature until all the molecules have been changed to the vapor state. If an external pressure is applied to the liquid, the escaping molecules will have to obtain a larger kinetic energy to break away from their neighbors and push against this opposing pressure. Hence, an increase in pressure raises the boiling point, and a decrease in pressure lowers it. A pressure cooker raises the boiling point of the enclosed water, and the foods cook much faster at the higher temperature.

The vapor molecules have more potential energy than those in the liquid state; thus vapor has more energy than liquid. Although steam and boiling water are at the same temperature, steam produces a more severe burn than boiling water because of its excess potential energy. The heat needed to vaporize a unit mass of a liquid is the *latent heat of vaporization* of that liquid. For water it is 540 cal/gm.

Condensation is the reverse of vaporization. As the vapor cools, its molecules slow down, and soon the slower ones reach a low enough kinetic energy so that when they collide, they can be held together by their attractive forces. The excess potential energy of the vapor's molecules is released as heat to its surroundings.

If, on the other hand, the temperature of the vapor is raised high enough, the molecules as they collide will not be able to hold onto each other regardless of the amount of pressure applied. The minimum temperature at which this happens is called the *critical temperature.* Above this temperature, a substance is called a gas, and cannot be condensed into a liquid.

12-7
Transfer of Heat Energy

In Chapter 11, we learned that molecular activities can be transferred from one place to another by conduction, convection, and radiation. Let us examine the molecular processes involved in these three types of transfer.

Conduction   If one side of a solid is at a higher temperature than another side, the molecular activity on the warmer surface is greater than on the cooler. By collision, the fast molecules impart some of their energy to their slower neighbors, and make them vibrate faster. These neighbors, in turn, strike the ones next to them. This bumping continues through the substance. The kinetic energy is passed from molecule to molecule from the region of higher temperature to that of lower temperature. This process continues until the average kinetic energies of the molecules on the two sides are equal. Substances vary greatly in their ability to conduct heat. In general, metals are very good conductors; copper is a much better conductor than wood. Heat can be transferred from molecule to molecule in liquids and gases as well as in solids. Gases are usually very poor conductors; it takes a fairly long time to pass the kinetic energy from one molecule to its distant neighbor. For this reason, loosely woven sweaters, which contain more air, are much warmer than those tightly woven.

When a thermometer is placed in a liquid, for example, the liquid molecules strike the glass molecules in the glass bulb, and transfer some of their energy to the glass. The glass molecules on the outer surface pass their newly acquired kinetic energy from molecule to molecule to the inner surface.

There the molecules of the glass impart some of their energy to the mercury molecules which move about faster, causing the mercury to expand and rise up the fine bore in the thermometer. After a short time, the mercury molecules will reach the same kinetic energy as those of the liquid being measured, and the height of the mercury column is a true indication of the linear kinetic energy of the liquid.

In the case of a furnace, the energy released by the burning fuel sets the metal atoms on the inside surface of the firebox into rapid vibration. The kinetic energy is passed from atom to atom through the firebox to the outer surface. This outer surface will soon reach the inside temperature unless some heat is removed.

When we say that cold comes into the house through the doors and windows in the winter, we speak incorrectly. Cold is not a substance or a form of energy. It is the absence of "heat." (Some say, however, that cold travels slower than heat, because anybody can catch a cold!) The "heat" inside the house is conducted outward through the doors, windows, and walls, leaving the inside surfaces colder and, unless some heat is supplied, the inside temperature will soon reach that of the colder outside temperature. Cold air, however, may come in through cracks or other openings in or around the doors and windows.

Convection   In liquids and gases, where the molecules are mobile, another form of heat transfer is possible. The molecules in the warm region receive some energy, get farther apart, and this less dense substance rises. Cooler material is forced into the region vacated by the warmer substance, and is heated. The more active molecules move to another region, collide with the slower molecules there, and impart to them some of their energy. After considerable mixing, some of the molecules of the fluid get closer together, and this part of the fluid becomes more dense and falls. Hence, a circulation, or *convection current*, is set up. The heat is transferred by the molecules moving from a warmer to a cooler region. Winds are convection currents on a large scale. The molecules in a southern breeze received their energies in the warmer south, brought them north, and imparted them to us.

When the air molecules surrounding the furnace firebox touch the hot metal, they receive some kinetic energy from the metal atoms and fly about much faster, causing the air to expand. This less dense air is pushed upward by the cooler, heavier air, and rises through the hot-air ducts to all parts of the house. When these fast-moving air molecules collide with the molecules of colder objects, such as the furniture and walls, they give some of their kinetic energy to the slower molecules and raise the temperature of those objects. The air molecules, in turn, lose some kinetic energy, slow down, and get closer together. This more dense air flows back through the cold-air returns to the furnace to receive more kinetic energy. The molecules of the air carried the energy directly from the furnace to the cold objects, with no middleman involved.

Radiation Radiation is a completely different type of heat transfer. It does not rely upon molecules to pass or carry the energy from one place to another, but sends the energy by means of an electromagnetic wave. Every vibrating molecule acts like a little broadcasting station and sends out waves which are similar to radio waves but much shorter. Such waves can pass through a vacuum, but when they strike an object, their energy is absorbed by the molecules of that object. This increases the kinetic energy of the molecules and raises the temperature of the object. In this type of heat transfer, some of the molecular kinetic energy is converted into radiant energy; when the waves are absorbed by another substance, the radiant energy is converted back to kinetic energy of the molecules. The first substance becomes cooler and the second warmer. The carrier wave possesses the energy, but it has no temperature, because temperature is an indication of molecular activity. If an object absorbs more radiant energy than it emits, its temperature rises. If it radiates more energy than it absorbs, the object cools off. In the daytime the Earth absorbs more energy from the Sun than it emits into space, and it becomes warmer; at night, it radiates more energy into space than it absorbs from the Moon and stars, and it cools off.

Radiant energy has the same characteristics as those of light. It is absorbed by black, rough surfaces, and is reflected by white, shiny ones. Dark garments worn in the summer absorb these radiations and become warmer than do similar white garments. Snow melts quite rapidly under a piece of black soot. Insulation bats used in house construction usually have one side covered with aluminum foil to keep the radiant energy from passing through the walls of a house. In the winter we wish to keep the radiant energy inside, and in the summer we hope to keep it outside. The fluffy rock wool decreases the rate at which heat is conducted through the walls of the house.

12-8
Rise in Temperature due to Friction and Concussion

A poorly lubricated bearing becomes hot, even smoking hot, by friction. When one surface rubs over another, the irregularities in the surfaces interlock, slide over each other, and interlock again. Since the molecules of one surface are continually striking against the molecules of the other surface, they are set into more rapid vibration. The more the surfaces are rubbed together, the faster the molecules vibrate, and the warmer the substances become.

A piece of metal resting on a solid support will become warmer if struck a few blows with a hammer, because the hammer imparts some energy to the atoms in the metal, increasing their random vibrational motion. Therefore, the temperature of the metal rises. A person notices that his hands are much warmer after prolonged applause; sometimes they actually "burn." The impact of the hands increases the speed of the molecules in the skin, giving the sensation of warmth.

12-9
Warming a Gas by Compression

A tire pump is warmed with use. Some of the heat is generated in overcoming the friction between the piston and the barrel. A great amount, however, results from the repeated compression of the air. This appears chiefly near the bottom of the pump, as indicated in Fig. 12-6.

In the cylinder of a diesel engine, air drawn in from the outside is quickly compressed by the piston to about $\frac{1}{16}$ its original volume. The pressure inside the cylinder increases to about 48 times that of normal atmospheric pressure, or 48 atmospheres, and the temperature rises to almost $600°$ C. A fine spray of oil is then injected into this hot air. The oil burns and produces the power stroke. No other provision is made for the ignition of the oil.

As a gas is compressed, work is done on it, and its temperature rises because some of its molecules are struck by the fast-moving compressor piston and receive additional kinetic energy. This added energy is then distributed among the rest of the enclosed molecules, raising the temperature of the entire gas. If a gas is rapidly compressed, the molecules hit by the piston are given tremendous speeds, and the gas becomes extremely hot. All of the work required to compress the gas is converted into random molecular energies, and the internal energy of the gas has increased the same as if it had been heated.

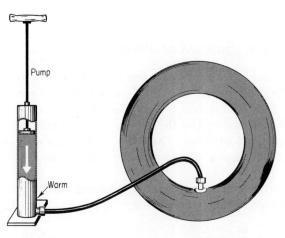

Pump

Warm

FIG. 12-6 Rise in temperature produced by the compression of a gas.

12-10
Cooling of a Gas by Expansion

The temperature of a gas generally falls when it is allowed to expand. The process is the converse of that taking place in the tire pump. The gas in expanding does work upon its surroundings. The energy used is supplied by the gas at the expense of its internal energy. Hence, the kinetic energy of its molecules decreases, and its temperature drops.

This action occurs on an extensive scale in nature when a mass of air rises, as on the windward side of a moutain. As the air goes up the mountain slope, the diminishing pressure at increasing altitudes permits an expansion and progressive cooling of the air; and often it is cooled below the saturation point of the water vapor, thus producing a cloud and maybe rain.

Cooling by evaporation and expansion is utilized in ice-manufacturing machines, air conditioners, and mechanical refrigerators. Let us examine the operation of a home electric refrigerator. A compressor in the base of the appliance compresses the vaporized refrigerant, which is usually Freon, and forces it into a set of condensing coils. Air circulating around these coils cools and condenses the vapor. The resulting liquid then passes into the freezing unit of the food compartment. When this liquid evaporates, the freezing unit is cooled. The kinetic energy of the molecules is converted to potential energy. As the resulting vapor expands, more cooling is produced. The vapor is compressed again and the cycle is repeated until the inside of the freezing unit is cooled to a certain temperature selected by the operator, and then a thermostat turns off the electric motor which runs the compressor and the fan. The refrigerant removes energy from the cold refrigerator and transfers it to the warmer room. This can be accomplished only by doing work upon the refrigerant, and the compressor does this work.

12-11
Pressure in Gases Due to Molecular Motion

A gas exerts a pressure upon any surface with which it is in contact. Since the molecules of the gas are in continuous motion at high speeds, each molecule that strikes the wall of the container imparts a tiny impulse to the wall. With huge numbers of such impacts upon each square centimeter every second, the total force per square centimeter, or total pressure, can be considerable.

When a gas is compressed, the number of molecules in each cubic centimeter is increased. If the temperature remains the same, the number of molecular impacts per second is increased, thus increasing the pressure produced by the gas. At a constant temperature, the pressure of an ideal gas varies inversely as the volume occupied by that gas. This inverse relationship is known as *Boyle's law*, and can be written as:

$$P_1 V_1 = P_2 V_2$$

An ideal gas is one in which the molecules exert no forces upon each other, and have no volume of their own.

If two or more gases which do not react chemically are crowded into the same container, the molecules of each gas can go into the spaces between the molecules of the other gases and both will occupy the entire volume of the container. The molecules of each gas strike the container walls and exert a pressure which is independent of the pressure produced by the pounding of the other gas molecules. The pressure each gas exerts is called its *partial pressure* and is the same pressure it would exert if the other gases were removed. *The total pressure of a mixture of gases is the sum of the partial pressures.* This is known a *Dalton's law of partial pressures.*

Imagine that we have two steel tanks of identical size. Into one tank oxygen is forced until its pressure is twice the normal atmospheric pressure or 2 atmospheres, and into the other nitrogen is forced under a pressure of 6 atmospheres. Now assume that the tanks are connected. The gases diffuse, and in a short time both tanks will be filled with oxygen and nitrogen, with each gas going into the spaces between the molecules of the other gas. Since the volume of each gas has been doubled, the partial pressure of each will be half of its orginal value; for the oxygen it will be 1 atmosphere, and for the nitrogen 3 atmospheres. Therefore, the total pressure after the two gases have mixed will be 4 atmospheres, the sum of the partial pressures.

12-12
Gas Laws

We have previously learned that compressing a gas raises its temperature and expanding a gas lowers its temperature. Is the converse true? If so, how does a change in temperature affect the pressure and the volume of a gas? When energy is added, the gas molecules receive more kinetic energy, fly about faster, and exert larger forces upon whatever they strike. Hence, a temperature rise causes the pressure to increase. If, for example, heat is added until the average speed of the molecules is doubled, their kinetic energy ($\frac{1}{2}mv^2$) will be quadrupled. The absolute temperature, which is proportional to the average kinetic energy, will become 4 times as great. The speeding molecules will strike the walls of the container twice as often, provided the walls remain stationary; and at each impact, according to Newton's second law, they will exert twice the force. Since both factors are doubled, the average pressure produced by the gas will be 4 times as large. Thus, *the pressure of an ideal gas is directly proportional to its absolute temperature, provided the volume remains constant.*

This is known as *Gay-Lussac's law*, and can be expressed mathematically as:

$$\frac{P_1}{T_1} = \frac{P_2}{T_2}$$

where P_1 and T_1 are the initial pressure and absolute temperature, and P_2 and T_2 are the final pressure and absolute temperature of the gas.

If the hot gas in the above example were allowed to expand, both the pressure and the temperature would decrease. But if more heat were added to keep the temperature constant, the pressure would decrease according to Boyle's law: $P_1 V_1 = P_2 V_2$. To reduce the pressure to its original amount, the volume of the gas would have to be quadrupled. Therefore, we can conclude that if the pressure had remained constant, the volume would have become 4 times as large when the absolute temperature was quadrupled. Hence, *at constant pressure, the volume of an ideal gas is directly proportional to its absolute temperature.* This is known as *Charles's law,* and is written as:

$$\frac{V_1}{T_1} = \frac{V_2}{T_2}$$

The three gas laws, Boyle's, Gay-Lussac's, and Charles's, can be combined into a single law called the *general gas law for* ideal gases:

$$\frac{P_1 V_1}{T_1} = \frac{P_2 V_2}{T_2}$$

In this equation, the pressure, volume, and temperature may all vary.

Let us apply the general gas law to a specific problem. If a certain sample of gas occupies a volume of 400 milliliters at a pressure of 3 atmospheres and a temperature of 100° C, what volume will it occupy under standard conditions (1 atmosphere and 0° C)? *Solution:*

$$\frac{3 \times 400}{373} = \frac{1 \times V_2}{273}$$

$$V_2 = 878 \text{ milliliters}$$

12-13
Energy Conversions

When a car traveling along the road is stopped by the brakes, the macroscopic motion of the car is converted to microscopic random motion of the molecules in the brakes, tires, and part of the road. The molecules of the car were all moving forward in unison with a certain kinetic energy, and after the car stopped, the organized motion was converted to random motion of the molecules. The mechanical energy disappeared and an equal amount of thermal energy appeared. This thermal energy, however, cannot be converted back into kinetic energy of the car, and it is rendered unavailable.

When oil is burned in the combustion chamber of a boiler to supply the steam necessary to run a turbine for generating electricity, only a small amount of the chemical energy released by the combustion of the oil is converted into electrical energy. In each step of the process, some energy is converted into random thermal energy. The available electrical energy plus the sum of the heat energies developed is equal to the original energy released by the burning oil, but only a very small amount of the total energy is actually utilized. Much of the energy is lost and cannot be recovered.

An electric motor converts electrical energy to mechanical work, but again not all of the electrical energy goes into mechanical energy. Some is lost through heat. Energy is conserved, but not all of the energy is utilized.

As we have seen in these examples, the total amount of energy remains the same, but energy tends to transform itself into less useful forms. This "running down" of energy is called *degradation of energy*. The natural tendency of anything is to go by itself from a state of order to one of disorder, organization to chaos. A measure of the extent of the disorder is called *entropy*, and in every natural process the entropy or disorder of a system increases. If one were to push a deck of cards off a table, they would not land on the floor in suits, but land in a disorderly arrangement. The entropy has increased. If they are thrown back onto the table, they wouldn't arrive there as a neat deck of cards, but in a bigger mess than they were on the floor. Things by themselves go from order to disorder. If some hot water is poured into some cold water, the fast-moving molecules of the hot water collide with the slower-moving molecules of the cold water. Heat flows from the hot water to the cold water and soon all of the molecules of the cold water will have the same average kinetic energy as those of the hot water, and the flow of energy will cease. In the process energy was conserved but entropy was created. As the hot water lost its high degree of randomness or disorder, its entropy would decrease. The cold water would gain some more randomness and its entropy would increase. We find that the increase turns out to be larger than the decrease and the entropy of the system increases. Heat will always flow in such a way as to increase the entropy of the system, and this is from hot to cold.

Stars release vast amounts of energy into space around them in the form of electromagnetic waves, light being one of them. This energy is absorbed by the surrounding celestial objects raising their temperatures. Although the total energy of the universe will always remain the same, the available energy for doing work decreases, or the entropy of the universe increases. Eventually all objects of the universe will reach the same temperature, and then there will be no transfer of energy. All energy will then be unavailable. The entropy of the universe will be at its maximum value, and the universe will have run down. This has been labeled the "heat death" of the universe. Do not become too alarmed about this for it will take billions of years before the universe reaches this thermal equilibrium.

QUESTIONS AND PROBLEMS

1. What was the caloric theory of heat? Why is it no longer accepted? Was it a good or a bad theory? Explain.

2. How do you think that conduction of heat was explained by the caloric theory? How do you think convection was explained?

3. What is the nature of heat? What do you mean when you say that heat is added to something?

4. Differentiate between *heat* and *temperature*. How are they related?

5. Does a thermometer measure the amount of heat in an object? How does a thermometer measure average linear kinetic energy of the molecules?

6. How much work, in joules, must be done by a refrigerator that is 70% efficient to freeze a 300-gram tray of water into ice cubes?

7. A 2-gram bullet traveling 300 meters/sec strikes a target. If half of the heat developed remains in the bullet, what is the rise in temperature of the bullet?

8. What is meant by *absolute zero*? By *zero-point energy*?

9. What is the likelihood of ever attaining a temperature below absolute zero?

10. What happens to the absolute temperature of a gas when the average velocity of the gas molecules is increased from 0.4 m/sec to 1.2 m/sec? Show your reasoning.

11. Oxygen molecules are 16 times as massive as those of hydrogen. At the same temperature, how do the velocities of the molecules of the two gases compare?

12. How would the velocities of the hydrogen and oxygen molecules compare if the oxygen is at 400°K and the hydrogen is at 200°K?

13. Does an electric fan cool the air in a room? Explain.

14. Why does the temperature of water rise as it is heated until it reaches the boiling point, and then remain constant as long as there is any water in the container?

15. Does adding heat always raise the temperature of a substance?

16. Does food cook more rapidly in water that is boiling vigorously than in water that is boiling slowly?

17. Why does the metal part of a car feel hotter than the glass windows or windshield if the whole car has been standing in the Sun the same length of time and all parts are at the same temperature?

18. Mrs. Piemaker decides that her kitchen is too hot on a warm August day, and so she leaves the refrigerator door open to cool off the kitchen. Will this cool off the kitchen? Explain.

19. In the conduction of heat, what is really being conducted?

20. Which produces a more servere burn, steam or boiling water, assuming the same amounts of steam and boiling water?

21. A sample of a gas has a volume of 300 ml under a pressure of 70 cm of mercury. What will be its volume under 1 atmosphere of pressure (1 atm is 76 cm of mercury)? Assume no change in temperature.

22. If a 4-liter tank of oxygen at a pressure of 3 atmospheres is connected to a 2-liter tank of hydrogen at 5 atmospheres, what is the final pressure in the tanks?

23. If the temperature of a certain volume of gas is 20°C, to what Celsius temperature must the gas be raised in order to double the pressure?

24. A gas in a tank is found to have a total pressure of 2 atmospheres. If the kinetic energy of the molecules is increased until the molecules have twice their original velocity, what is the new pressure of the gas?

25. A cylinder has air at 20°C and 1 atmosphere of pressure sealed in it. If the cylinder can withstand pressures up to 5 atm, at what temperature will the cylinder burst?

26. A certain gas has a volume of 400 ml at a temperature of 27°C. What will the volume become at a temperature of −23°C, providing there is no change in the pressure of the gas?

27. Fifty liters of air at 20°C are cooled at a constant pressure of 5 atm until the volume is 30 liters. What is the final temperature of the gas?

28. A perfect gas at 1 atmosphere is compressed from 10 liters to 2 liters and simultaneously cooled from 200°C to 0°C. What is the final pressure of the gas?

29. A given gas occupies a volume of 50 liters at a pressure of 1 atm and a temperature of 50°C. What volume will it occupy at a pressure of 0.6 atm and a temperature of 90°C?

SUGGESTED REFERENCES

Booth, Verne H., *Physical Science*, Chaps. 13 and 14. The Macmillan Co., New York, 1962.

Ford, Kenneth W., *Basic Physics*, Chap. 13. Blaisdell Publishing Co., Waltham, Mass., 1968.

Priestley, Herbert, *Introductory Physics*, Chaps. 10 and 12. Allyn and Bacon, Boston, 1958.

Zemansky, Mark, "The Use and Misuse of the Word *Heat* in Physics Teaching," *The Physics Teacher*, 8, no. 6 (1970), 295–300.

13
Electrical Energy

13-1
Early Concepts of Electricity

As early as 500 B.C., Thales, one of the seven wise men of Greece, discovered that after an amber rod was rubbed with wool, the amber attracted small pieces of paper or straw. He felt that this attraction was due to some property within the amber which was aroused into action by the friction caused by the rubbing. This amber phenomenon was truly interesting, but for some reason or other it did not seem to arouse the curiosity of man. Very little was done with this phenomenon until A.D. 1600 when Dr. William Gilbert, the physician to Queen Elizabeth I and King James I, became interested in the mysteries of the amber rod. Gilbert's fame came as the result of his activities as a physicist rather than from practicing his profession as a physician. To study the amber effect, he constructed a device which he called a *versorium*. It consisted of a very light metal needle which was balanced on a sharp point. When a rubbed amber rod was brought near the versorium, it attracted the end of the needle nearest the rod. With such a device he studied the effect of rubbing upon various materials. Those that acted like amber he called "electrics" after the Greek word *electros*, for amber. He made a rather complete list of electrics, which we now call poor conductors. Those which he could not electrify by rubbing he called "nonelectrics," and they are known today as metals. We now know that metals can be given an electric charge if properly insulated. In describing his device he used the term "electric attraction," but it was expressed in very vague terms. Forty years later, Sir Thomas Browne coined the word *electricity* for this amber phenomenon.

Otto von Guericke, mayor of Magdeburg, found that normal rubbing could produce only a limited amount of the electricity, and so he developed the first electrostatic machine. His machine consisted of a large sulfur ball which was rotated in a wooden frame. When a wool cloth was held against the spinning sulfur sphere, the sulfur became highly charged through intimate contact in the rubbing. The electrified sphere could then be used to charge other objects. Guericke observed that the sulfur could send its electricity through a linen thread to other objects. In 1732 Stephen Gray, an English scientist, reported that certain substances could conduct this virtue much better than others. He was the first to make a distinction between electrical conductors and insulators.

13-2
Two-Fluid Theory

In 1735, DuFay, a French scientist, discovered that there were two different kinds of electricity. One kind was produced when resinous materials were rubbed with wool and another kind when glassy or vitreous materials were rubbed with silk. He observed that *like kinds always repel each other while unlike attract.* Knowing from Gray's work that electricity could "flow" through materials, he proposed the two-fluid hypothesis of resinous and vitreous fluids. According to DuFay, an uncharged or neutral object possesses the same amounts of resinous and vitreous fluids. Rubbing simply removes one kind of fluid, leaving the other kind on the object being rubbed. Hence, the material used for rubbing is charged as well as the object being rubbed, but with the opposite charge. An amber rod rubbed with wool has some of the vitreous electricity removed, leaving a surplus of resinous fluid on the amber.

Several years later John Canton, a London schoolmaster, observed that when he rubbed a piece of clean glass tubing with silk, the glass was charged with the vitreous kind of electricity as predicted; but when it was rubbed with new flannel, the glass possessed resinous electricity. Since the glass was capable of producing both kinds of electricity, the term "vitreous" became meaningless.

13-3
One-Fluid Theory

In 1754, Benjamin Franklin, an eminent American, performed his famous kite experiment. While trying to determine the nature of lightning, he flew a kite into a thundercloud, and discovered that a spark jumped off a key, which was fastened to the kite string, to the knuckle of his finger. He observed that objects charged in this manner had the same kind of electricity as that produced by rubbing. This proved that lightning was electrical in nature instead of a combustion of the gases in the clouds as previously thought. Since then several experimenters have reproduced Franklin's experiment with wires woven in the kite string and were electrocuted. As a boy, Count Rumford tried Franklin's experiment, and according to his diary, he saw a medium of fire between his eyes and the kite that left him weak in the joints. It was sufficient to discourage him from flying any more kites into thunderheads. Franklin believed that matter was composed of one kind of electricity, and rubbing merely rearranged that electricity. He considered electricity to be a tenuous, invisible, weightless fluid that could pass through matter from one object to another. If an object has its normal amount of fluid, which is different for different substances, it is electrically neutral and shows no electrical effects. If it possesses an excess of this fluid, it has a *positive* (+) charge; and if it has a deficiency or less than normal amount, it has a *negative* (−) charge. He arbitrarily chose glass when rubbed with silk as having an excess of this fluid, thus calling the charge produced on the glass positive. Of course, the silk lost an amount equal to that gained by the glass, and so the silk became negatively charged. The amber, he believed, lost fluid, and he called it negative. These names are still used to designate those particular charges. As we shall see later, it would have been much simpler if he had selected the amber rod as having obtained an excess of the fluid or a positive charge. He imagined that if an object with an excess of this fluid were connected to one with a deficiency, the fluid would flow from the one with an excess of fluid, or the positive one, to the object with a deficiency, or the negative one. We still consider a conventional electric current as a flow from plus to minus. Some people still talk about electric "juice."

13-4
Forces Between Charges

Gilbert's versorium could detect the presence of electrical charges, but it could not measure their magnitudes. By 1777, an Italian scientist, Cavallo, had developed an instrument to measure charges, thus making it possible to study quantitatively the amount of charge on any object. This instrument, after a few refinements, is known today as the gold-leaf *electroscope* (see Fig. 13-1). It usually consists of a long, narrow, metal rod with a gold leaf *L* attached to the rod at approximately the length of the gold leaf from one end, and a metal ball *B* attached to the other end. The metal rod passes through an insulator in the top of a box with the gold leaf enclosed in the box. To observe the movement of the leaf, glass windows are placed on opposite sides of the box. If a negatively charged object *E* is placed in contact with the knob of the electroscope, some of the negative charge on the object flows onto the rod—or, if you are a one-fluid believer, the fluid flows off the elec-

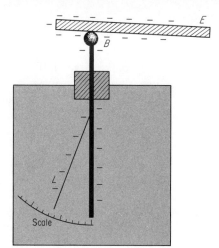

FIG. 13-1   Gold-leaf electroscope.

troscope onto the object E, where there is a deficiency of the fluid. In either case, the rod and gold leaf receive a negative charge, the same as that of the object E, thus forcing the leaf away from the rod. This is called "charging by contact." The larger the charge placed on the electroscope, the greater is the deflection of the gold leaf. By placing a scale in the instrument so that the deflection of the leaf can be accurately determined, the instrument is capable of quantitative measurements.

In 1784, Charles Coulomb, a French scientist and engineer, developed a torsion balance which was far more sensitive than the electroscope (see Fig. 13-2). With it he proved that the repelling force between two small equally charged metal spheres varied inversely as the square of the distance between their centers. Later experimenters showed that the force was also proportional to the product of two different amounts of charge Q_1 and Q_2 placed on the spheres. These two relationships were then combined into one statement known as Coulomb's law: *The force of attraction or repulsion be-*

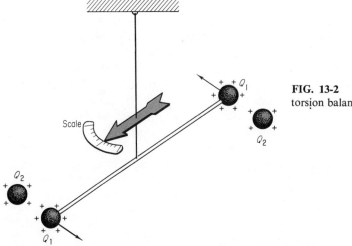

FIG. 13-2   Coulomb's electric torsion balance.

tween two electric charges is proportional to the product of the two charges and inversely proportional to the square of the distance between them. It is expressed symbolically as:

$$F = \frac{kQ_1Q_2}{d^2}$$

From this inverse-square law, a unit of charge can be precisely defined, and was first defined in the cgs system of units: If two identical charges are placed 1 centimeter apart in air and repel each other with a force of 1 dyne, we call each charge an electrostatic unit, or a *statcoulomb*. By defining a unit charge in this manner, we have made the value of the proportionality constant k equal to 1 dyne $\times$ cm²/statcoul².

We find that the electrostatic unit of charge defined above is too small for practical purposes, and so we have arbitrarily taken 3 billion statcoulombs as a more practical unit of charge. This amount of charge is called a *coulomb*. In the mks system of units, charges are expressed in this more practical unit of coulombs, the distances d in meters, the forces F in newtons, and the constant k in Coulomb's law becomes 9×10^9 newtons $\times$ m²/coul². We may now define a coulomb as that charge which when placed 1 meter in air from an identical charge will repel it with a force of 9 billion newtons.

To illustrate Coulomb's law, let us assume that a negative charge of 0.02 coulomb is 10 meters from a positive charge of 0.03 coulomb. The force of attraction each exerts upon the other is

$$F = \frac{9 \times 10^9 \text{ nt-m}^2/\text{coul}^2 \times 0.02 \text{ coul} \times 0.03 \text{ coul}}{(10 \text{ m})^2}$$

$$= 5.4 \times 10^4 \text{ newtons}$$

An interesting experiment illustrating electrostatic forces can be performed as follows. Place one end of a negatively charged ebonite rod in some saw-dust. Then remove the rod and observe the sawdust attracted to it. The sawdust will stick out from the rod like the hair on an angry dog's neck (see Fig. 13-3). After a few minutes the fibers, one at a time, will fly off the rod.

FIG. 13-3   Sawdust attracted to a charged rod. Soon the sawdust flies off the rod.

The behavior of the sawdust can be explained as follows: when the charged rod is put in the sawdust, it repels the negative charges in the wood fibers, and forces them to the farther ends of the fibers, leaving the nearer ends positive. Hence, the sawdust is held to the rod because the attractive force of the nearer positive charges is greater than the repelling forces of the negative charges at the farther ends. When the rod is removed from the sawdust, the fibers will stick out perpendicular to the rod, for the negative ends of the fibers are repelled by the negatively charged rod. While in this position, some of the negative charges on the ebonite rod slowly move through the points of contact onto the positive ends of the fibers, neutralizing the charges there. This leaves the sawdust with an excess of negative charges, like that of the rod, and the sawdust fibers are consequently repelled from the rod.

13-5
Electrical Energy

We are now able to measure electrical charge and express it in terms of stat-coulombs or coulombs, but what is it we are measuring? If we think of it as a measure of a certain amount of weightless fluid, then we must ask if there is a limit to the amount of fluid an object can possess. If not, where does all of the fluid come from? If there is a limit, what is left after all of this fluid is removed? Why should two objects, each with normal amounts of fluid, exert a gravitational attraction upon each other and, when all of the electric fluid is removed, repel each other? Hence, the fluid theory seems to raise more questions than it answers.

By studying the various effects produced by an electric current, scientists were better able to understand the nature of electricity. Michael Faraday studied the chemical effects of electric currents in solutions that were capable of conducting electricity. From his results, he concluded that there was a two-way flow of charges in the solution, and that these charges seemed to come in discrete amounts. In electroplating, he found that the copper appeared to have twice the charge of silver. Several years later, Joule observed a definite relationship between the heat produced and the amount of the electric current. Since heat is a form of energy, energy must be involved in the movement of charges. These two facts alone seemed to indicate that electricity is not a perfectly continuous, weightless fluid, but some finite thing in motion with a considerable amount of energy.

13-6
The Electron

A study of the conduction of electricity through gases produced many interesting facts. In 1874, William Crookes made a detailed analysis of

FIG. 13-4 Shadow on end of discharge tube of the cross inside the tube cast by a beam of cathode rays. Cathode is at far end of tube.

electrical discharges inside glass tubes from which most of the air had been removed, and he observed that the visible rays radiate from the negative terminal in straight lines, cast shadows of metal objects placed in the rays (see Fig. 13-4), heat objects upon which they are focused, deflect when a magnet is brought near, and repel other similar rays. Since they radiated from cathode, or negative terminal, they were called *cathode rays*. Crookes suggested that these rays might be streams of negatively charged molecules traveling at very high speeds, since such molecules would satisfy his observations. Later investigators placed thin sheets of aluminum foil in the path of the rays and some of the rays penetrated the foil. Since the foil was thick enough to stop all known molecules, it was concluded that the rays must consist of extremely small negative particles—perhaps subdivisions of the molecule.

In 1897, J. J. Thomson, another Englishman, made a very important discovery. From the amount these cathode rays were bent by a magnet (see Fig. 13-5), he determined that they consisted of streams of negatively charged particles. From the deflection of these rays by magnets and charges, he was able to determine that each has a charge-to-mass ratio of about 2,000 times that of a hydrogen ion. Of course, this might be due to either a large

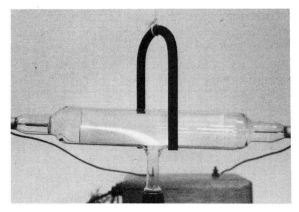

FIG. 13-5 Deflection of a beam of cathode rays by a magnet. The stream of electrons coming from the cathode to the left cause the fluorescent screen in the tube to glow, showing the path of the electrons. The magnetic pole on the observer's side of the tube is a north-seeking pole.

charge or a small mass. Since the particles could penetrate aluminum foil, Thomson assumed that they were less massive than the hydrogen atom, a subdivision of the hydrogen molecule. Further investigation showed that cathode rays were identical in nature regardless of the material of the cathode from which they were liberated. Hence, these extremely small negatively charged particles, called *electrons*, must be parts of all atoms. The electrons might be one of the fundamental "building blocks" of matter.

13-7
Natural Unit of Electrical Charge

Immediately after Thomson's discovery, physicists everywhere began devising methods for measuring the charge of this little electron. One of the most direct and accurate of these was the famous oil-drop experiment performed by Robert A. Millikan, an American physicist. He found that droplets of oil sprayed from an atomizer were electrified by friction as they went through the nozzle of the atomizer. By a very ingenious but simple method he determined that the charge each oil droplet received was some multiple of 4.8 $\times$ 10^{-10} statcoulomb or 1.6×10^{-19} coulomb, but never smaller. This amount of electricity is a natural unit of charge; if it is negative, it is the charge of an electron. We can better understand the smallness of this unit of charge when we realize that 1 statcoulomb of negative electricity, which in itself is extremely small, consists of the charges of 2.08×10^9 electrons. The practical unit, 1 coulomb, consists of 6.25×10^{18} electron charges. Hence, this natural unit of charge of the electron is incredibly small; it is difficult to imagine a quantity of electricity so minute.

13-8
Electrical Nature of Matter

In 1911, fourteen years after the discovery of the electron, Ernest Rutherford bombarded gold atoms with the high-speed alpha particles emitted from a certain radioactive material. (For details, see page 261.) From the manner in which the alpha particles were scattered, he concluded that the atom consists of a positive core, with electrons surrounding the core and out a small distance from it. The positive core of the simplest atom, which is hydrogen, is called a *proton*. Its charge is equal to that of the electron, or 1.6×10^{-19} coulomb, but opposite in sign. It has been found to be about 1,840 times as massive as the electron. The cores of all atoms contain a certain whole multiple of these protons. We now believe that there are two kinds of electricity, negative and positive, and that both kinds exist in discrete amounts, some multiple of that associated with the electron or proton. An object that has acquired an excess of electrons is negatively charged, while an object that has lost some of its electrons has an excess of protons and is positively charged. This theory of the electrical nature of matter accounts for the simultaneous appearance of equal and opposite charges. When amber is rubbed by wool, the amber rod gains electrons from the atoms in the wool. The amber becomes negatively charged while the wool is left positively charged. If molecules lose or gain electrons, they become positively or negatively charged particles, and are called positive or negative *ions.*

In solids, the positive cores of the atoms or their *nuclei* remain in relatively fixed positions, oscillating with only the thermal motions of the atoms. Some of the electrons, however, may move about from atom to atom. In metals they move about quite freely, like the molecules of a gas, and are easily forced to move from atom to atom through the metal. In liquids and gases, some of the molecules may gain or lose electrons, and both ions can be forced by some external charge to move through the liquid or gas.

13-9
Charging by Induction

When a negatively charged object is brought near the knob of a neutral electroscope, some of the free electrons are repelled from the knob and distribute themselves over the gold leaf and support rod, causing the leaf to be pushed away from the rod [see Fig. 13-6(a)]. If the electroscope is grounded by connecting the metal rod to the ground with a wire or by simply touching it with a finger, the repelled electrons will flow from the leaf and rod to the ground in order to get farther from the charged object. The leaf then collapses, as shown in Fig. 13-6(b). If the ground is then disconnected (c) and the charged object removed (d), in that order, the leaf will diverge again, indicating a charge on the electroscope. It will be left with a positive charge since it lacks the electrons that escaped to the ground and never got back. This method of charging any object is called *induction.* If an object is charged by contact, it receives the same charge as that of the charging body, but if it is charged by induction, it is given the opposite charge.

FIG. 13-6.   Charging an electroscope by induction.

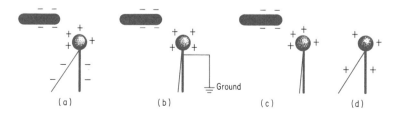

| (a) | (b) | (c) | (d) |

One charge can interact with another charge without coming in contact with it. One charge seems to act on another through some kind of a "field of influence," which we call an *electric field*. The field around a charge cannot be detected by sight, touch, or smell; but if a charge is placed in the field, we can feel a force acting upon that charge. When this charge is removed, we believe that the field is still there. The strength of an electric field is defined as *the force experienced by a unit positive charge placed in the field*. For example, the strength or intensity $\mathscr{E}$ of the electric field 1 meter from a $+600$-statcoulomb or $+2 \times 10^{-7}$ coulomb charge is

$$\mathscr{E} = \frac{F}{Q} = k\frac{Q_1}{d_2} = 9 \times 10^9 \text{ nt-m}^2/\text{coul}^2 \times \frac{2 \times 10^{-7} \text{ coul}}{1^2 \text{m}^2}$$

$$= 1.8 \times 10^3 \text{ nt/coul}$$

The direction of the electric field is the direction of the force on the unit positive charge, and is away from the $(+2 \times 10^{-7})$-coulomb charge.

As another example, let us determine the strength of the electric field midway between two charges of $+1 \times 10^{-7}$ coulomb and -3×10^{-7} coulomb, which are 40 cm apart. If a unit positive charge $(+1$ coul$)$ is placed midway between the two charges, the force on the test charge is

$$\mathscr{E} = 9 \times 10^9 \times \frac{1 \times 10^{-7}}{(0.2)^2} + 9 \times 10^9 \times \frac{3 \times 10^{-7}}{(0.2)^2}$$

$$= 2.5 \times 10^4 + 6.75 \times 10^4 = 9.25 \times 10^4 \text{ nt/coul}$$

The two forces were added because the $+1 \times 10^{-7}$ coulomb repelled the unit positive charge and the -3×10^{-7} coulomb attracted it. Hence, the direction of the electric field is away from the "$+$" charge and toward the "$-$" charge, and the total field strength is the sum of the two field strengths at that point.

If one moved a test charge so that it always moved in the direction of the electric field, the resulting line is called a *line of force*. Since the direction of the field varies from point to point, the lines of force are usually curved. These lines of force make up an electric field pattern as shown in Fig. 13-7. The field around a positive charge may be shown pictorially by lines radiating outward from the charge. These lines originate at the positive charge, but instead of stopping in space as shown in the figure, they may go great distances and terminate at some negative charge. Fields between unlike and like charges are illustrated in Fig. 13-7(c) and (d). At any point in the field, the force on a test charge can have but one direction. Consequently, lines of force cannot cross each other, for if they did, at the point of intersection the force on the test charge would be in two directions and this is impossible.

Unit + charge

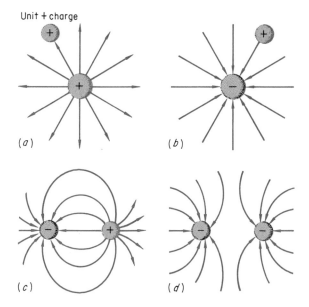

(*a*) (*b*)

FIG. 13-7   Electric fields around charged objects.

(*c*) (*d*)

Therefore, all lines of force originate at positive charges and terminate at negative charges, and never cross between charges.

In addition to giving the direction of the electric field, the number of lines of force can be made to give the magnitude of the field strength. By limiting the number of lines, we can make the number of lines per unit cross-sectional area proportional to the strength of the field. The more lines per unit area, the stronger is the electric field in that region. Hence, by looking at the figures in Fig. 13-7 one can see at a glance that the field strength, which is the force on a unit positive charge, becomes stronger as one approaches a charged object. Likewise, between the two like charges we see that there is a region where there is no electric field. If the field is uniform, we draw parallel lines of force uniformly spaced. Hence, a pictorial representation of an electric field helps us to understand electrostatic effects, as is the case with most physical models.

13-11
Electric Current

In solids the positive nuclei remain in relatively fixed positions, while the electrons are more or less free to move about. If a positive charge is placed on one side of a solid in which the electrons are relatively free to move and a negative charge on the other side, the electrons in the solid will drift from atom to atom opposite the electric field or away from the negative side toward the positive one. This drifting of the electrons through the material constitutes an electric current. In liquids and gases, the negative ions will move in one direction and, at the same time, the positive ions will move in the opposite direction. The net charge flowing through any cross section of the substance per second is called an *electric current*. If 6.25×10^{18} electrons pass through a cross section of a wire per second, we know that 1 coulomb of electricity per second passes through that area, and we call this 1 *ampere*, in honor of the French physicist André Ampère. Therefore, 1 coulomb/sec = 1 ampere. The amount of current (I) through a substance can be expressed in equation form as:

$$I = \frac{\text{Charge}}{\text{Time}} = \frac{Q}{t}$$

If 50 coulombs move through any cross-sectional area of wire in 10 seconds, the current is (50 coul)/(10 sec) or 5 amperes. *Ammeters* are connected in electric circuits to measure electric currents. An ammeter is merely a counting device which indicates the number of coulombs per second passing through the circuit.

If the electrons continue to drift in one direction all the time, we designate this as *direct current*, or d.c. If the electrons drift in one direction, stop, then drift back again, stop, drift forward again, and oscillate back and forth in this manner at a regular rate, we call this *alternating current*, or a.c. If the electrons move back and forth 60 times a second, this is a 60-cycle alternating current, the frequency most commonly used in the United States.

13-12
Electrical Potential Energy

To charge an object requires work. The first electron is easy to place on a neutral object, but the second electron is repelled by the first and a little work must be done on this electron to put it on the same object with the first electron. More and more work is required to overcome the electrostatic forces as more and more electrons are placed on the object. Therefore, the electrons "piled" on the object possess potential energy. When electrons are removed from a neutral object, work is required to pull the electrons away from the positive charges left on that object. As far as the electrons are concerned, the potential energy of the charged object has been lowered. If a wire connects a negatively charged object to a positively charged one, electrons will move from atom to atom through the wire away from the object with an excess of electrons toward the object which has a deficiency of electrons. In other words, the electrons move from the negative to the positive, or from high to low potential energies. Note that this is opposite the direction of the fluid flow suggested by Benjamin Franklin. If Franklin had taken the amber rod as possessing an excess of the electrified fluid, this would have made the electron a positive particle, and electron flow would satisfy the same conditions as fluid flow. The greater the potential energy difference between the ends of a conductor, the more electrons will move through the conductor per second, and the larger will be the current produced. We find that the amount of electric current flowing through a substance is directly proportional to the potential difference across that substance. (The term *energy* is usually omitted, but it cannot be forgotten, because it is the difference in energy that induces the electrons to move.) If a coulomb of charge moving through a conductor loses 1 joule of energy, we say that the potential drop across the conductor is 1 *volt*. Hence,

$$1 \text{ Volt} = 1 \text{ Joule/Coulomb}$$

We have devices that increase the potential energy of electrons the same as water pumps increase the level, or potential energy, of water. Electrostatic machines, batteries, generators, thermocouples, and photocells are a few examples of such devices. Through chemical reactions, a storage battery can remove electrons from one electrode and deposit them on the other electrode, thus developing a voltage difference between the terminals of the battery. A 12-volt battery is designated as such because it will give each coulomb it delivers 12 joules of energy. A 110-volt source gives each coulomb of electricity it delivers 110 joules of energy. As these charges flow through a solid or a solution, they lose energy. If each coulomb loses 5 joules of energy when it flows through a substance, the potential drop across that substance is 5 volts. Since we have conservation of energy, the sum of the potential drops around any closed circuit is equal to the sum of the potential boosts. A *voltmeter* is a device used to measure the amount of energy each coulomb gains in a source or loses in a conducting material. Whether it be a potential boost or potential drop, the difference of potential V can be expressed symbolically as:

$$V = \frac{\text{Energy}}{\text{Charge}} = \frac{E}{Q}$$

13-13
Electrical Resistances

We find that copper and silver are excellent conductors of electricity. Aluminum is also quite good, but lead is fairly poor. Glass, porcelain, rubber, and bakelite are very poor conductors, so they are called *insulators*. The conductivity of a material depends on how easily an electron can be moved from one atom to the next. In some materials electrons are relatively free to move, while in others, like glass, poreclain and rubber, the electrons are rather firmly bound to the atomic nuclei. Every substance, however, offers some opposition to the flow of an electric charge, and this opposition is called *resistance*.

The amount of current through most metals depends directly on the voltage across it, and inversely on its resistance. These quantities can be expressed as:

$$\text{Current} = \frac{\text{Potential difference}}{\text{Resistance}}$$

$$I = \frac{V}{R}$$

This is known as *Ohm's law*, one of the most important relationships in electricity. If I is measured in amperes and V in volts, the unit for the resistance, R, is expressed in *ohms*. Hence,

$$\text{amperes} = \frac{\text{volts}}{\text{ohms}}$$

To illustrate this law, let us examine two problems.

1. When a 20-ohm toaster is connected to a 110-volt line, what current is drawn by the toaster?

$$I = \frac{110 \text{ volts}}{20 \text{ ohms}} = 5.5 \text{ amperes}$$

2. What is the resistance of a lamp that draws 1.4 amperes when connected to a 110-volt source?

$$R = \frac{V}{I} = \frac{110 \text{ volts}}{1.4 \text{ amperes}} = 78.6 \text{ ohms}$$

13-14
Electrical Power

In electrical as well as mechanical devices, the rate at which work is done or energy is dissipated is very important. The amount of power delivered depends on two factors, the current and the voltage, and is directly proportional to the product of the two:

Power = Current × Potential difference

$$P = IV$$

$$P = \text{Amperes} \times \text{Volts}$$

$$P = \text{coul/sec} \times \text{joules/coul} = \text{joules/sec} = \text{watts}$$

1. What current is drawn by a 150-watt lamp when it is connected to a 115-volt line?

$$I = \frac{P}{V} = \frac{150 \text{ watts}}{115 \text{ volts}} = 1.3 \frac{\text{joules/sec}}{\text{joules/coul}}$$

$$= 1.3 \text{ coul/sec} = 1.3 \text{ amperes}$$

2. What is the resistance of a 1,000-watt flatiron that operates on a 115-volt line?

$$I = \frac{P}{V} = \frac{1{,}000 \text{ watts}}{115 \text{ volts}} = 8.7 \text{ coul/sec} = 8.7 \text{ amperes}$$

$$R = \frac{V}{I} = \frac{115 \text{ volts}}{8.7 \text{ amperes}} = 13.2 \text{ ohms}$$

or

$$P = IV = = \frac{V}{R}V = \frac{V^2}{R}$$

$$R = \frac{V^2}{P} = \frac{115^2 \text{ volts}^2}{1{,}000 \text{ watts}} = 13.2 \frac{\text{volts}^2}{\text{amp} \times \text{volts}}$$

$$= 13.2 \text{ volts/amp} = 13.2 \text{ ohms}$$

13-15
Electrical Energy—Kilowatt-Hours

From our definition of potential difference, we see that electrical energy is equal to voltage times charge:

$$\text{Energy} = \text{Voltage} \times \text{Charge}$$

$$E = VQ$$

$$\text{joules} = \frac{\text{joules}}{\text{coul}} \times \text{coul}$$

Another common unit for electrical energy is the *electron volt*. This is the amount of kinetic energy given an electron by a difference of potential of 1 volt, and is equal to 1 volt times the charge of an electron or 1.6×10^{-19} joule. It is written as ev; Mev means million electron volts.

The cost to operate electrical appliances is based upon the electrical energy used, and not just upon the amount of current or voltage. Since we do not normally have a coulomb meter, we can determine the charge Q by multiplying the current through the appliance by the time the charges are flowing. Hence,

$$\text{Energy} = \text{Voltage} \times \text{Current} \times \text{Time}$$

$$E = VIt = \text{watt-sec}$$

For practical purposes this is not a convenient unit for computing costs of operation of electrical appliances. It is simpler to express the electrical power (VI) in kilowatts and the time (t) in hours and to charge a certain amount for each *kilowatt-hour:*

$$\text{Energy} = \text{Kilowatts} \times \text{Hours} = \text{KWH}$$

To illustrate this, let us look at two problems.

1. At 4 cents per kilowatt-hour, how much does it cost to operate a 1,000-watt flatiron for 3 hours?

$$P = 1,000 \text{ watts} = 1 \text{ kilowatt}$$

$$\text{Energy} = 1 \text{ KW} \times 3 \text{ hr} = 3 \text{ KWH}$$

$$\text{Cost} = 3\text{KWH} \times 4 \text{ cents/KWH} = 12 \text{ cents}$$

2. How long can one operate a 250-watt television set for 25 cents if electricity costs 5 cents/KWH?

$$P = 0.250 \text{ kilowatt}$$

$$\text{Cost} = 0.250 \text{ KW} \times t \text{ hr} \times 5 \text{ cents/KWH} = 25 \text{ cents}$$

$$t = 20 \text{ hr}$$

13-16
Electrical Charges and the Nature of Matter

Electricity has made a significant contribution to our industrial develop-ment, and its use has made living conditions far more pleasant for all of us. We do not realize how much we rely upon electricity until power has been interrupted for an extended period of time. Then we are aware that almost everything we do in or around the home is run or controlled by electricity. Its importance in our daily lives is reason enough to study this form of energy, but in addition to its utilitarian value, a clearer concept of the basic electrical phenomena will help us to understand better the true nature of matter—a subject that we shall explore in the following chapters.

The modern theory of the structure of matter began with the idea that substances were composed of tiny, impenetrable spheres moving or jiggling about in a random manner. This concept was adequate to explain the be-havior of gases and the kinetic theory of heat, but it was not able to account for the experimental observations relating to the electrical nature of matter. Solid atoms were then replaced in theory by nebulous structures in which electrical charges are the fundamental quantities, electrons surrounding posi-tively charged cores called nuclei. "Solid" matter consists of empty space populated by electrically charged particles. This theory has been very success-ful in explaining the classification of elements, chemical reactions, the spectra produced by different substances, and the nature of certain electrical phenom-ena. The electrical properties most essential to an understanding of the charge concept of matter may be stated as follows: (1) Electricity comes in discrete amounts. (2) Charges cannot be destroyed. (3) Charges react with other charges through their electrostatic fields. (4) Like charges repel and unlike charges attract, according to Coulomb's inverse-square law.

QUESTIONS AND PROBLEMS

1. What is the origin of the word *electricity*?

2. Describe Franklin's kite experiment. What did he attempt to show and what did he show?

3. Can it be shown that there are two kinds of electrification?

4. Why do we designate charges as being positive and negative?

5. What happens to a negatively charged gold-leaf electroscope when a positive charge is brought near its knob?

6. An object having an unknown electrical charge is brought near a positively charged gold-leaf electroscope, and the leaf of the electroscope diverges farther from the central rod. What is the charge on the body? Give your reasons.

7. How did Coulomb arrive at his inverse-square law?

8. Why should metallic objects be attracted to a charged body regardless of the charge on that body?

9. Two positive charges of 4×10^{-6} and 5×10^{-7} coulomb are 10 cm apart. What is the force each exerts upon the other in newtons and in dynes?

10. It is found that a charge of 3×10^{-5} coulomb exerts a force of 2,000 newtons on another charge 40 cm from it. What is the magnitude of the second charge?

11. What is the strength of the electrostatic field 50 cm from a negative charge of 2×10^{-5} coulomb? What is the direction of the field?

12. If a negative charge of 0.005 coulomb is placed in an electric field of 2,000 nt/coul, what is the force on the charge? If the field is toward the right, what is the direction of the force on the charge?

13. What is the strength of the electric field halfway between two negative charges of 0.0002 and 0.005 coulomb which are 200 cm apart? What is the direction of that field?

14. What was the first convincing evidence that the electron is a fundamental constituent of all matter? Why are metals better conductors of electricity than wood?

15. Why, in winter, does a spark sometimes pass between a person's finger and a metal object he is about to touch, such as a light fixture? Why doesn't this occur in the summer?

16. In an electrical storm is it safer to be inside an automobile which has a steel top or standing alone in a field? Explain.

17. How can one determine whether an object is positively or negatively charged?

18. What advantage would have resulted if in formulating his one-fluid theory of electricity, Benjamin Franklin had assumed that the amber rod, when rubbed by wool, received an excess of electricity, or a positive charge?

19. In an electric lamp: (a) Is some current consumed? (b) Are some electrons transformed into heat? (c) Do electrons give up some charge? (d) Do electrons lose some of their energy? Explain.

20. What do you mean by (a) a current of 10 amperes? (b) a potential difference of 10 volts? (c) a resistance of 20 ohms? (d) a power dissipation of 20 watts?

21. What current will flow through a lamp whose resistance is 50 ohms when connected across a 120-volt line?

22. What is the electric current in amperes if 30 coulombs pass through a resistor in 10 seconds?

23. The resistance of an electrical appliance is 20 ohms. What power, in watts, is dissipated when the appliance is connected to a 120-volt line?

24. What is the resistance of a toaster that draws 6 amp from a 120-volt line?

25. What current is drawn by a 200-watt lamp when connected to 110 volts?

26. What current would expend 5 kilowatt-hours of electrical energy in a 10-ohm coil in 45 minutes?

27. The current drawn by a certain X-ray tube is 20 milliamperes when the voltage across the tube is 100 kilovolts. What power, in watts, is supplied to the tube?

28. What is the resistance of an electric lamp that takes 250 watts from a 115-volt line?

29. A 400-watt, 120-volt coffee pot contains 2 kg of water. If 80% of the heat developed by the electric current goes into the water, how long will it take to heat the water from 30°C to 100°C?

30. Suppose your home utilizes an average of eight 100-watt bulbs for an average of 5 hours each night. At 4 cents per kilowatt-hour, what would it cost to light your home for 30 days?

31. How much would it cost at 4 cents/KWH to operate a 2-watt electric clock for 30 days?

32. If a 1,500-watt, 110-volt air conditioner is in operation 10 hr a day during hot weather, what is the cost at 4 cents/KWH to use the air conditioner for 30 days?

33. A 3-cell flashlight operates at 4.5 volts and 0.4 ampere. If each cell costs 25 cents and the flashlight can operate for a total of 10 hours before the three cells must be replaced, what is the cost of this electrical energy per kilowatt-hour?

34. Describe the energy transformations that take place in an electric lamp, in a radio, and in an electric motor.

SUGGESTED REFERENCES

ASHFORD, T. A., *From Atoms to Stars*, Chap. 4. Holt, Rinehart & Winston, New York, 1960.

BEISER, ARTHUR, *The Mainstream of Physics*, Chaps. 12 and 13. Addison-Wesley Publishing Co., Reading, Mass., 1962.

PERLMAN, JAMES S., *The Atom and the Universe*, Chap. 15. Wadsworth Publishing Co., Belmont, Calif., 1970.

PRIESTLEY, HERBERT, *Introductory Physics*, Chap. 14. Allyn and Bacon, Boston, 1958.

14

Magnetism

14-1
Early Concepts of Magnetism

Magnetism dates further back than the electrification of amber, but the origin of the term *magnet* is questionable. According to the Roman scholar Pliny, a Greek shepherd, Magnus, observed that the nails in his shoes and the iron on the tip of his staff adhered to certain black stones, and those "magic" rocks were named after him. But the Roman poet Lucretius referred to those stones as magnets because they came from a large deposit of this black rock in Magnesia, a province of Asia Minor. Those rocks, which had the ability to attract iron, were also called *lodestone* (*lode* meaning "attract" or "lead"). The Greeks called this black mineral *magnetite*, which consists mainly of iron ore. The ability of a lodestone to communicate with iron and to transfer its power to iron was considered as a supernatural power, more like a spiritual behavior than a physical phenomenon. The Greeks could not see how a lodestone could attract iron without any visible connection between them unless it was spiritual, and they wondered why it showed its affection only for iron. Thales even thought that a lodestone possessed a soul. Plato once praised his friend by saying: "There is a divinity moving you like that in a stone which Euripides calls a magnet." Many fantastic stories were written about the powers of the lodestone. According to one story, Archimedes used a very strong lodestone to pull the nails out of a number of the enemy's ships, sinking them. These black rocks were also believed to possess the secrets of good health. They were ground into powder and then taken internally as medicine to improve one's physical condition. The Greeks thought that the magnets emitted invisible emanations that pushed the air away from the magnets, and then iron moved into this void. Because of its magic powers, magnetism was one of the first natural phenomena to be investigated.

244

The earliest users of magnets were the Chinese. According to a Chinese dictionary completed in A.D. 121, they observed that a lodestone when floated on a bit of wood in water assumed a north-south position. They also found that needles rubbed with magnetite pointed north-south when allowed to swing freely. Such magnetic compasses were employed by the Chinese for journeying over land as early as A.D. 900. By the twelfth century, compasses were used for maritime navigation in Europe as well as in China. In the thirteenth century, Pierre de Marincourt (Petre Peregrine), a French nobleman who was a friend of Roger Bacon, became interested in the magic powers of the lodestone, and wrote a remarkable document on the subject. He was the first to locate and identify the so-called poles of a magnet—the regions near the ends of a magnet where the magnetic property seemed to be concentrated. He also noticed that when a magnet was broken in two, new unlike poles appeared at the broken ends. These magnetic poles seemed to come in pairs, and the poles of a magnet are equal and opposite. Unlike electric charges, there seemed to be no single poles. It was later learned that unlike poles attract each other, and like poles repel. Marincourt was the first to shape a lodestone in the form of a sphere and have it retain its magnetic properties. He also introduced the idea that there is a "field of influence" around a magnet where it affects magnetic substances as indicated by sprinkling iron filings around a lodestone. This we now call a *magnetic field*.

The first real scientific study of magnetism was started by Dr. William Gilbert near the end of the sixteenth century. His work was published in 1600 in his *De Magneta Magneticique Corporibus*. He refuted most of the magnetic superstitions with experimental facts. For centuries man had wondered why lodestones or compasses always pointed toward the north. Some thought that the north end of a compass was attracted by the Pole-Star, Polaris, while others thought that it pointed toward a submerged magnetic island someplace near Greenland. Gilbert settled the problem when he, like Marincourt, shaped a lodestone in the form of a sphere, but he identified the magnetic properties of it with that of the Earth. He noticed that a compass placed anywhere around his so-called *terrella* ("little earth") (see Fig. 14-1) always pointed toward a fixed point on the sphere. He argued that the only difference between the Earth and his terrella was size. The end of the compass which pointed toward the north he called the north-seeking or north (N) pole and the end pointing south he called the south-seeking or south (S) pole. Before this time the poles of a magnet had not been named.

His view that the Earth acts like a big magnet is now universally accepted, but we feel that the magnetism is produced by some activity within the mantle or outer core of the Earth instead of the Earth being a big permanent bar magnet. We find that the Earth's magnetic poles are several degrees from the geographic poles; therefore, compasses at various places on the Earth do not

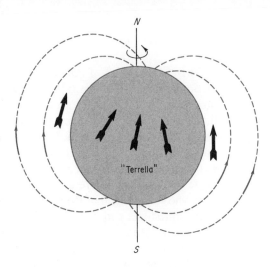

FIG. 14-1 Gilbert's terrella, or "little earth."

point directly north. Columbus, on his voyage across the Atlantic Ocean, observed that the compass pointed west of north as determined by Polaris when he left Europe, and east of north when he arrived in the New World. This deviation of the compass from true north is called the *angle of declination*. The Chinese knew about this phenomenon, but made no scientific study of it.

14-2
Magnetic Fields

As previously mentioned, Marincourt noted that iron filings sprinkled around a magnet formed curved paths from one pole to the other, clearly showing the "field of influence" or the magnetic field around a magnet. Such a field can be demonstrated quite easily as follows: Lay a glass plate or a peice of cardboard over a magnet, and then sprinkle iron filings upon it. When the glass or cardboard is gently tapped, the filings will arrange themselves in an orderly manner about the magnet. The filings lie end to end in lines from one pole to the other. The filings give us a picture of the "field of influence" around the magnet. The lines displayed by the filings represent the magnetic lines of force of the magnetic field [see Fig. 14-2(a)]. The more dense the lines of force, the stronger the field. The direction of a line of force has been arbitrarily chosen as the direction a N pole would move along that line of force. These lines of force never cross, and they are directed toward, or away from, the regions near the ends of the magnet. These regions are called magnetic poles. Observe the positions of the poles in Fig. 14-2.

The field can also be studied by using a small compass as follows: Place the magnet to be studied on a piece of paper. Put the compass near one end of the magnet, make a dot on the paper at each end of the compass needle. Slide the compass away from the magnet until the end nearest the magnet

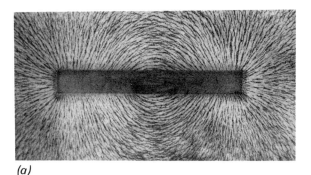

(a)

FIG. 14-2 The magnetic field around a bar magnet.

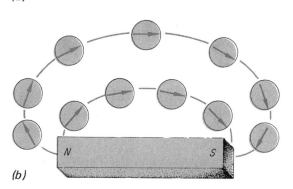

(b)

points at the dot previously made at the end of the needle away from the magnet, and again make a dot at the outer end of the compass. Continue the process until the other end of the magnet or the edge of the paper has been reached [see Fig. 14-2(b)]. A line drawn through these dots is a magnetic line of force, and its direction is the direction the north end of the compass points. With a little endurance, the complete magnetic field around the magnet can be plotted.

14-3
Electricity and Magnetism

The early pioneers worked with both electric charges and magnets, but at first saw no connection between them. Later scientists believed that there was some relationship between the two because charges could interreact with charges at a distance, and magnets could interact with magnets at a distance; they both followed the inverse-square law of force; and both produced fields of influence. The confusion, however, came in their differences. Electric charges could be isolated and a single charge obtained, but poles always come in pairs. We have never found a monopole, although some think that it might exist. Magnetism is very stable and remains in some substances for a long period of time, but electrical charges gradually leak off objects.

The long-sought connection between electricity and magnetism was discovered in 1819 by Hans Christian Oersted, a Danish physicist. While attempting to heat a platinum wire by sending a current from a galvanic cell through it, he and his students observed that a compass nearby took a position at right angles to the wire. When the current was reversed, the direction of the compass needle was revsersed and it again took a position perpendicular to the wire. Thus by accident he proved that a moving charge, which is a current, produces a magnetic field around itself. These magnetic lines of force he found to be concentric circles around the moving charge, and to lie in a plane perpendicular to its motion. The direction of the magnetic lines of force around a moving *negative* charge can be determined by encircling the moving charge, or wire, with the fingers of the *left* hand so that the extended thumb points in the direction of the moving charge; the fingers will point in the direction a N pole would be pushed, which is the direction of the magnetic lines of force. In other words, a compass would point in the direction of the fingers (see Fig. 14-3). A moving *positive* charge produces a magnetic field in the opposite direction. For a flow of *positive* charges, encircle the moving charge with the fingers of the *right* hand so that the extended thumb points in the direction of the moving charge; the fingers will point in the direction of the magnetic lines of force. The magnetic field produced by any moving charge is exactly the same as that produced by a magnet. If you could only detect the magnetic field without knowing its source, you could not tell whether it was produced by a moving charge or a permanent magnet.

A magnet is completely unaffected by a stationary charge placed near it. A charge at rest has an electric field, but no magnetic field. A moving charge has both electric and magnetic fields, and the more charges set into motion, the larger the field produced.

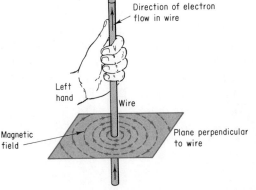

FIG. 14-3 . Magnetic field around wire carrying a current.

In 1825, William Sturgeon discovered that a coil of wire with a current flowing through it acts like a permanent magnet with one end a N pole and the other a S pole (see Fig. 14-4). André Ampère coined the name *solenoid* for this long coil, and formulated its theory of operation. Such an electromagnet attracts iron and produces a magnetic field exactly the same as a permanent magnet. Ampère also discovered that as the amount of current in the wire increases, the strength of the magnetic field becomes larger. Hence, there is a direct connection between moving charges and magnetism, and as you have noticed, the discovery of this relationship had to wait until man had developed the galvanic battery in order to produce the necessary current.

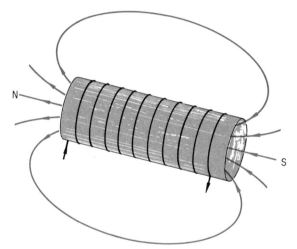

FIG. 14-4   Magnetic field produced by an electric current flowing through a solenoid.

The question one might now ask: is the Earth's magnetic field produced by moving charges within the Earth like a big coil of wire carrying a current, or is the Earth a permanent magnet that was formed during its condensation and cooling period? The answer is not fully known, but we believe that the Earth's magnetic field is due partly to the motion of electric charges in the Earth's mantle or molten core. The electric charges existing in the mantle may be weak, but due to the Earth's size they could produce a fairly large magnetic field. According to some scientists, another contributing factor may be the motion of the charges in the circulating electric currents of the ionosphere of our outer atmosphere. Hence, it appears that the Earth seems to be more like an enormous electromagnet instead of like a large bar magnet.

Force on a Charge Moving through a Magnetic Field

Since a moving charge has a magnetic field of its own, it must interact some-how with another magnetic field—but how? The simplest way of showing what effect a magnetic field has upon a moving electron is to place one pole of a long magnet beside the electron beam of a cathode-ray tube. The beam will not move toward or away from the pole, but it will be deflected sideways (see Fig. 13-5). If the other pole of the magnet is placed near the beam of electrons, the deflection will be reversed, but again will be perpendicular to the line between the pole and the beam of electrons. For any position of the magnet, the electrons will experience forces perpendicular to both their direction of motion and the magnetic field. Hence, the force, velocity of electrons, and magnetic lines of force are all mutually perpendicular to each other. If the stream of electrons is parallel to the magnetic lines of force, there will be no deflection of the electrons. Hence, it is only the velocity of a charge per-pendicular to the magnetic field that is relevant. The direction of the force acting upon a *negative* charge moving in a magnetic field can be found by using a left-hand rule. With the thumb of the left hand extended perpendicular to the fingers of an open hand and in the plane of the palm, point the thumb in the direction of motion of the negative charge and the straightened fingers in the direction of the magnetic lines of force; the force on the moving charge is in the direction the palm will normally push (see Fig. 14-5). Check the direction of the force on the wire carrying negative charges in Fig. 14-6. To find the direction of the force on a moving *positive* charge, repeat the above procedure using the *right* hand, and the direction the right palm pushes is the direction of the force on the positive charge.

If the magnetic pole is moved closer to the cathode-ray tube, the deflection of the electron beam will be greater, thus indicating that the deflecting force

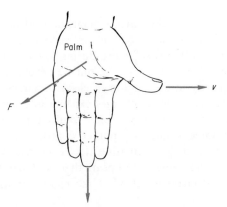

FIG. 14-5 Left-hand rule. Place thumb in direction of v, fingers in direction of B, and the direction the palm pushes is the direction of the force on the moving nega-tive charge.

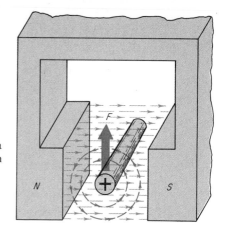

FIG. 14-6 Force on a wire which is carrying a current and in a magnetic field. With an electron current away from the observer, the force is up.

on the electrons is directly proportional to the magnetic field strength, which we shall designate by the letter B. From similar experiments where the speed of the electrons are caused to increase, the force on the electrons in a given magnetic field is found to be greater. Also, by varying the amount of charge moving through a magnetic field, we find that the deflecting force on the charge becomes larger as the amount of charge increases. By combining these three factors, the deflecting force on a moving charge is proportional to the product of the magnetic field strength B, the charge Q, and the velocity of the charge that is perpendicular to the magnetic field $v_\perp$. This relationship may be written as follows:

$$F = BQv_\perp$$

From this equation we see that the strength B of the magnetic field is equal to $F/Qv_\perp$. If 1 coulomb of charge moving through a magnetic field with a velocity of 1 meter/sec experiences a sideways force of 1 newton, the field strength is taken as 1 and its unit is nt/(coul/m/sec). Since we like to represent a magnetic field as so many lines per square meter, we call 1 nt/(coul/m/sec) a weber/m², where a *weber* (wb) is taken as 10^8 magnetic lines of force. Another common unit for measuring B is the *gauss*, which is the number of magnetic lines per square centimeter. Hence, 1 weber/m² $= 10^4$ gauss. The Earth's magnetic field strength is about 0.5×10^{-4} wb/m² or 0.5 gauss. By choosing these units, the proportionality factor in the force equation is 1.

As an example of the force on a moving charge, let us imagine an electron traveling at a speed of 2×10^5 meter/sec perpendicular to a uniform magnetic field of 5 webers/m². What is the deflecting force on the electron?

$$F = BQv_\perp$$

$$= 5 \text{ wb/m}^2 \times 1.6 \times 10^{-19} \text{ coul} \times 2 \times 10^5 \text{ m/sec}$$

$$= 5\frac{\text{nt}}{(\text{coul/m/s})} \times 1.6 \times 10^{-19} \text{ coul} \times 2 \times 10^5 \text{ m/sec}$$

$$= 1.6 \times 10^{-13} \text{ newton}$$

We are quite familiar with charges in motion such as the electrons in the cathode-ray tube, the electrons in the television tube, and cosmic particles entering our atmosphere from outer space, just to name a few. But at the time of André Ampère the only moving charges available were in wires set into motion by the galvanic cell. These current-carrying wires produced magnetic fields around themselves, but how did they interact with other magnetic fields? It was found that the left- or right-hand rules for moving charges still apply. Place the thumb of the *left* hand in the direction of the negative current, the straightened fingers pointing in the direction of the external magnetic field, and the direction the left palm pushes is the direction of the force on the wire. What is the value of that force? Since 1 ampere is 1 coulomb/sec, $(I = Q/t)$, $I \times t$ can be substituted for Q in the force equation. We also know that the velocity is equal to L/t. Hence, Qv is equal to $I \times t \times L/t$ or IL, and so

$$F = BIL$$

where in the case of the wire, L is the length of the wire carrying the current I that is in the magnetic field B. In the mks system of units, the unit of F is newtons; F, B, and I must all be mutually perpendicular to each other.

To illustrate this relationship, let us suppose that a current of 5 amperes is flowing through a wire 10 cm long which is perpendicular to a magnetic field of 0.5 wb/m². What is the force on the wire?

$$F = 0.5 \text{ wb/m}^2 \times 5 \text{ amp} \times 0.01 \text{ m}$$

$$= 0.5 \frac{\text{nt}}{\text{coul/m/sec}} \times 5 \text{ coul/sec} \times 0.10 \text{ m}$$

$$= 0.25 \text{ newton}$$

14-6
Mass of an Electron

If a beam of electrons is fired through a magnetic field, the electrons experience forces perpendicular to their motion. Hence, the force cannot change the speed of the electrons, but merely deflects them along a circular path. The resulting forces provide the centripetal forces to keep the electrons on a circular path. Therefore,

$$Bev_\perp = mv_\perp^2/R$$

If the field strength B, the charge of an electron e, the velocity of the electrons $v_\perp$, and the radius R through which the electrons are bent are all known or can be measured, the mass m of an electron can be determined. By performing this experiment, scientists have determined the mass of the electron to be 9.1×10^{-31} kilogram. Similarly the mass of a proton has been determined to be 1.67×10^{-27} kilogram.

We learned in the last chapter that matter consists of electrical charges. Now we know that in some substances the charge must be in some sort of motion to give the substance its magnetic property. This might be due to a linear motion and/or a spinning motion of the charges. With these electrical and magnetic properties in mind, we shall now be able to look at the finer structure of matter. We shall also find out that matter is not the ultimate reality of the physical world, but it is only a particular manifestation of energy.

QUESTIONS AND PROBLEMS

1. What are the poles of a magnet? What is a north-seeking or N pole? South-seeking or S pole?

2. A small magnet placed on a small piece of cork, which is floating in water, will take a north-south position. Will the cork and magnet then move north or south, if located in the Northern Hemisphere? Explain.

3. Two bars of iron are exactly alike except one is magnetized. How can you tell, without the aid of anything else, which is the magnet?

4. What is a magnetic field? What are magnetic lines of force?

5. How does a compass indicate direction? Why doesn't it point true north?

6. Can a magnet be used inside a steel submarine? Explain.

7. How would you determine whether a magnetic field is produced by a magnet or by a moving charge if you could not see the sources?

8. What is the direction of a magnetic field above an electron that is moving southward?

9. A phonograph record while running is rubbed with fur, charging the record negatively. When the record is turning in its clockwise direction as seen from above, what is the direction of the resulting magnetic field?

10. If a moving electron is deflected off its original path, how can we tell if it is deflected by a electrostatic field or by a magnetic field?

11. An electron is moving at a high horizontal speed in an easterly direction. If it enters a magnetic field which is vertically downward, what will be the direction of the force acting upon the electron?

12. A positive ion moves horizontally westward through a uniform horizontal magnetic field which is from south to north. In what direction will the ion be deflected?

13. A weight is hanging from the lower end of a vertically mounted spiral spring. If a large current were sent through the spring, what would happen to the weight? Explain.

14. A straight wire 20 cm long and carrying an electron current of 15 amperes is placed in a field where B is 0.50 weber/m². If the wire and field are perpendicular to each other, what is the force, in newtons, on the wire?

15. An electron has an energy of 500 electron-volts. What is the velocity of the electron?

16. What magnetic field is required to make a proton traveling at 5×10^7 m/sec follow a circular path of 30 cm radius?

17. An electron travels in a circular path of 2 cm radius in a magnetic field of 1.5×10^{-3} weber/m². Find the velocity of the electron.

18. Find the magnitude and direction of the force exerted on a wire 2 meters long suspended in an east-west horizontal direction and carrying an electron current of 25 amperes flowing from east to west in a region where there is a field of 6×10^{-3} weber/m² vertically downward.

SUGGESTED REFERENCES

FORD, KENNETH W., *Basic Physics*, Chaps. 15 and 16. Blaisdell Publishing Co., Waltham, Mass., 1968.

PERLMAN, JAMES S., *The Atom and the Universe*, Chaps. 14 and 16. Wadsworth Publishing Co., Belmont, Calif., 1970.

PRIESTLEY, HERBERT, *Introductory Physics*, Chaps. 17, 18, and 19. Allyn and Bacon, Boston, 1958.

TAYLOR, LLOYD W., *Physics: The Pioneer Science*, Chaps. 39 and 42. Houghton Mifflin Co., New York, 1941.

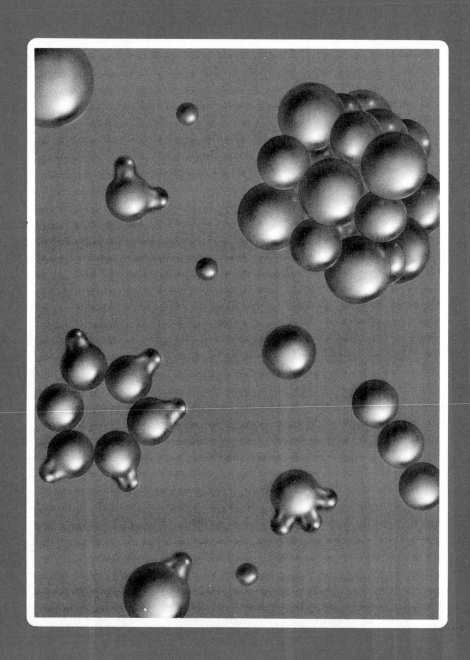

3

Matter and Change

Matter, though divisible in an extreme degree, is nevertheless not infinitely divisible. There must be some point beyond which we cannot go in the division of matter. The existence of these ultimate particles of matter can scarcely be doubted, though they are probably much too small ever to be exhibited by microscopic improvements.
—John Dalton

15

Inside the Atom

Speculations about the ultimate nature of matter are found in some of man's earliest writings. Democritus, a Greek philosopher who lived about 400 B.C., viewed matter as atomic in nature, and about 100 years later Epicurus founded a materialistic philosophy based on atomism. Greek science, however, did not develop along lines capable of providing any experimental evidence for the atomic concept. During the Middle Ages, the atomistic idea was actually considered subversive by religious authorities, who regarded it as an attempt to destroy religious faith. The atomic hypothesis did not achieve any respectability in the Western world until the seventeenth century, and it was not developed in any convincing form until the nineteenth century. The atomic concept has become so commonplace to our thinking today that it may be presented and accepted as dogma. It is very important that we understand the logical and experimental basis for the universal acceptance of this concept.

15-1
Dalton Concept—Atoms as Tiny Spheres

The modern atomic theory was first proposed in systematic form by John Dalton, who published it in his *New System of Chemical Philosophy* in 1808. There was, even at the beginning of the nineteenth century, little direct experimental evidence of the existence of atoms. The assumption that matter is atomic made many natural phenomena, such as the behavior of gases, much more understandable. In effect, it became easier to believe that atoms exist than to deny it, because of the usefulness of the concept in forming a rational picture of the world. These particles were really an invention of the mind of man, rather than a sensational discovery.

The chemical background for the atomic theory was provided by the introduction of careful weighing and measuring in the study of chemical reactions. The *law of conservation of matter* was developed by Lavoisier and other chemists who had shown that matter is neither created nor destroyed in chemical reactions. The *law of definite proportions*, the subject of a great controversey between two eminent chemists, Proust and Berthollet, was established by Dalton's time. According to this generalization, elements unite in definite proportions to form chemical compounds. For example, water always contains 11.1 % hydrogen and 88.9 % oxygen by weight. These quantitative relationships strongly suggest the existence of fundamental unit particles of matter.

Dalton's atomic theory consisted of five basic assumptions:

1. All matter consists of tiny, indivisible particles called *atoms*.

2. Every atom of a given element is exactly like any other atom of that element.

3. The atoms of different elements differ from each other in weight.

4. Atoms combine in definite whole-number ratios to form chemical compounds.

5. Atoms are neither created nor destroyed in chemical reactions.

This theory was not only able to provide reasonable explanations for known facts, but was also capable of predicting new facts. A successful scientific theory not only explains what is known, but also suggests new lines of investigation and predicts new relationships. The *law of multiple proportions* was predicted with the aid of the atomic theory and was soon verified experimentally. This law states that in the case of two elements combining to produce more than one compound, the different masses of one element which combine with a fixed mass of the second element may be expressed as a ratio of small whole numbers. Copper, for example, forms one oxide when 63.54 grams of copper unite with 15.999 grams of oxygen, and another when 127.08 grams of copper unite with 15.999 grams of oxygen. Thus the different masses of copper combining with a fixed mass of oxygen are in the ratio of 1 : 2.

Even though Dalton's concept of the distinction between an atom and a molecule was not clear and his determinations of atomic weights were erroneous, his theory was of primary importance in the development of chemistry. The Daltonian concept of the atom as a tiny, indivisible particle of matter was adequate for about 100 years. However, this simple picture of an atom was not satisfactory for the interpretation of the experimental evidence which had accumulated by the beginning of the twentieth century.

15-2
Electrical Nature of Matter

The decomposition of chemical compounds by means of an electric current was accomplished during the early part of the nineteenth century. This process, called *electrolysis*, led to the discovery of sodium and several other new elements. Faraday's laws, formulated in 1833, established a quantitative relationship between chemical change and the electric charge causing the change. These laws state:

> 1.   The mass of any element deposited at an electrode during electrolysis is directly proportional to the quantity of electricity used.
> 2.   The mass of any element deposited in electrolysis is proportional to the atomic weight divided by a small whole number.

These small whole numbers are the combining capacities of the elements. These relationships suggested, but did not prove, that electric charge exists only in multiples of a fundamental unit.

The work of Crookes and Thomson on electrical discharge through gases, in 1897, led to the discovery of the electron as the fundamental unit of negative charge (see Chapter 13). Positively charged electric particles were discovered by Goldstein and Wien in experiments similar to those by which electrons were identified. These unit positive electric charges are known as *protons*. Experiments on the deflection of rapidly moving protons in magnetic and electric fields show that they have a mass about 1,840 times as great as the electron mass. Electrons and protons seemed to be fundamental to all matter, since their properties were found to be independent of their source. Thus, by the early part of the twentieth century, the electrical nature of matter was established and the Daltonian concept of the atom as an indivisible particle was no longer satisfactory.

The realization that atoms are complex structures containing positive and negative particles of electric charge led, naturally, to the question of how these particles are arranged in atoms. One of the early theories of atomic structure was suggested by J. J. Thomson, the discoverer of the electron. This theory, sometimes called the "plum pudding" theory, suggested that an atom is a spherical structure with protons embedded uniformly throughout a matrix consisting of an equal number of electrons, as indicated in Fig. 15-1. Such an atom would be electrically neutral, but could become charged by the gain or loss of electrons or protons. The electrical conductivity of

FIG. 15-1   "Plum Pudding" atom model.

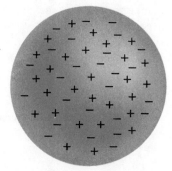

gases and solutions could be explained by this theory; however, it was not able to meet the challenge of a crucial experiment by Sir Ernest Rutherford in 1911.

15-3
Nuclear Atom

Rutherford's idea for a nuclear atom resulted from experiments in his laboratory on the scattering of alpha particles by thin metal foils. Alpha particles are positively charged particles ejected from radioactive elements (see Chapter 17). The experimental arrangement is shown in Fig. 15-2. The narrow beam of alpha particles, moving at about 2×10^9 cm/sec, is directed toward a gold foil 4×10^{-5} cm thick. The detector is a fluorescent screen which emits a flash of light when struck by an alpha particle. The detector is arranged to intercept particles deflected at various angles by moving around a circle.

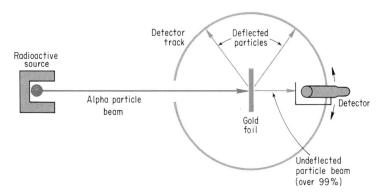

FIG. 15-2   Alpha particle scattering by metal foil.

These scattering experiments produced very unexpected results. Most of the high-speed alpha particles penetrated the foil with little or no deflection, but a small fraction were deflected through rather large angles and a very few were deflected backward. The results are indicated in Fig. 15-3. The "plum pudding" model of the atom could not account for these experimental results, since mathematical calculations indicated that backward scattering would be impossible unless the greater part of the atomic mass and charge were concentrated in a small part of the atomic volume. Rutherford's reaction to the results of the scattering experiments are best described by his own words:

It was quite the most incredible event that has ever happened to me in my life. It was almost as incredible as if you had fired a 15-inch shell at a piece of tissue

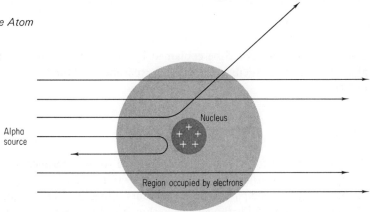

FIG. 15-3   Deflection of alpha particles by atomic nucleus (not to scale).

paper and it came back and hit you. On consideration I realized that this
scattering backward must be the result of a single collision, and when I made
calculations I saw that it was impossible to get anything of that order of magnitude unless you took a system in which the greater part of the mass of the
atom was concentrated in a minute nucleus. It was then that I had the idea of
an atom with a minute massive centre carrying a charge.*

The concept of a nuclear atom, suggested by those scattering experiments,
has been very successful in explaining a wide variety of phenomena and is
the basis for our modern concept of the atom. This theory pictures the atom
as mostly empty space with all of the positive charge and most of the mass
concentrated in a very small core, or *nucleus*. The electrons are distributed
in a relatively large volume outside the nucleus.

Rutherford's calculations indicated a nucleus with a diameter of approximately 10^{-12} cm at the center of a spherical atom having a diameter on the
order of 10^{-8} cm. Thus the nuclear diameter is only 1/10,000 that of the atom.
If an atom were expanded until its diameter was equal to the length of a football field, its nucleus, at the center, would have a diameter of 0.2 inch. The
penetration of gold foil by most of the high-speed alpha particles appears
quite reasonable in terms of this picture of the atom. The occasional alpha
particle making a direct hit on a nucleus would be deflected backward, or
through a large angle.

The deflection of alpha particles by the positively charged atomic nucleus
depends on the nuclear charge. The scattering experiments enabled Rutherford to estimate the charge on the nuclei of various atoms. These charges
were found to be the same for all atoms of a given element. H. G. J. Moseley
developed an X-ray method in 1913 for the determination of the nuclear

* Quoted in Alfred B. Garrett, *The Flash of Genius* (Princeton, N. J.: D. Van Nostrand Co., 1963),
p. 114. Copyright © 1963 by Litton Educational Publishing, Inc. Reprinted by permission of
Van Nostrand Reinhold Co.

charge. This method is based on the fact that X rays are produced by the impact of high-speed electrons on the target of an X-ray tube. Moseley found that the square root of the characteristic X-ray frequency was linearly related to the nuclear charge on the target element. Every element produces X rays of a characteristic frequency, and the higher the nuclear charge, the shorter the wavelength of the X rays. These nuclear charges are always integral numbers and increase progressively with the position of the element in the periodic table.

15-4
Atomic Number

The *atomic number* of an element has been defined as the number of unit positive charges in the nucleus of an atom of the element. Since atoms are electrically neutral, the atomic number is also equal to the number of electrons surrounding the nucleus. For example, the carbon atom, with atomic number 6, has 6 unit positive charges, or *protons*, in the nucleus and 6 *electrons* surrounding the nucleus. The chemical properties of elements are determined by the atomic numbers, and, as we shall see in Chapter 16, this is the basis for the periodic classification of the elements.

Rutherford's nuclear model for the atom implies that practically all the atomic mass is concentrated in the nucleus. The total mass of the electrons in an atom is negligible, since the mass of the proton is about 1,840 times that of an electron. Early determinations of atomic masses did not agree with the masses predicted from atomic numbers. The number of protons in each nucleus, equal to the atomic number, accounts for only about half of the experimentally determined mass. This discrepancy was explained by assuming that the number of protons in the nucleus is equal to the atomic mass, with a sufficient number of electrons present in the nucleus to reduce the nuclear charge to the atomic number. This raised the question: why are some electrons outside the nucleus and others inside the nucleus? The possibility of a neutral particle, having the same mass as a proton, was suggested in 1920 by Rutherford. This particle, called the *neutron*, was identified in 1932 by James Chadwick, a British physicist. Neutrons were produced experimentally by bombarding the element beryllium with alpha particles.

Although a large number of subatomic particles have been identified experimentally, only three particles—the proton, neutron, and electron—are essential to our present elementary theory of atomic structure. The protons and neutrons are contained in the nucleus, with the number of protons equal to the atomic number and the number of neutrons equal to the difference between the mass number and the atomic number. The mass number is the atomic mass rounded off to the nearest whole number. The electrons, equal

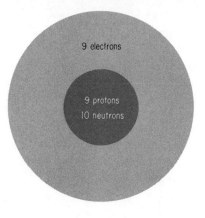

FIG. 15-4 Fluorine atomic structure.

in number to the protons, occupy the space around the nucleus. As an illustration, consider the fluorine atom with the atomic number 9 and the mass number 19. The fluorine nucleus, containing 9 protons and 10 neutrons, is surrounded by 9 electrons, as shown in Fig. 15-4.

15-5
Atomic Weights

Chemists use the term *atomic weight*, even though in a strict sense *atomic mass* would be a more appropriate term. John Dalton recognized the importance of a system of atomic weights as a part of his atomic theory. He realized that he could hope to determine only relative weights, since his atoms were far too small to be measured individually. Dalton saw the possibility of determining the relative sizes of atoms if the relative weights could be found, since the densities of different gases were known.

Dalton worked out a crude set of relative weights from relative combining weights of elements in compounds. These relative weights were in serious error because the ratios in which atoms combine to form compounds were not known. Dalton assumed that 1 atom of oxygen combined with 1 of hydrogen to form water, and his analysis of water indicated 1 part hydrogen to 6 parts oxygen. Thus, if the relative atomic weight of 1 is assigned to hydrogen, the atomic weight of oxygen is 6. Dalton would have arrived at a weight of 8 for oxygen with a more accurate analysis of water. However, if the combining ratio of hydrogen to oxygen atoms in water is known to be 2:1, then the weight of oxygen is 16.

More accurate experimental work and correct values for combining ratios of elements in compounds led to better values for atomic weights. Oxygen was later chosen as the standard for atomic weights and it was assigned a value of 16.0000. Since oxygen combines with so many different elements it was a very useful standard. However, it later developed that not all oxygen atoms have the same weight, and two atomic weight standards came into use.

There are three naturally occurring isotopes (see Section 15-6) of oxygen, with mass numbers of 16, 17, and 18. The physical scale was based on the oxygen isotope with mass number 16 as 16.0000 and the chemical scale was based on the average of all naturally occurring oxygen atoms as 16.0000. To get a universal standard for atomic weights, and for various technical reasons, the carbon-12 isotope (see Section 15-6) with a weight of 12.0000 was adopted as the standard for atomic weights in 1961. The adoption of this new standard makes very little change in the old weights based on oxygen. The change is only about 43 parts in 1 million and is insignificant for most purposes.

It is important to recognize that atomic weights are relative weights. When we say that sulfur has an atomic weight of 32.064, we mean that the sulfur atom is 32.064/12.0000 times as heavy as the carbon-12 atom. The units for atomic weights are *atomic mass units*, amu. The atomic mass unit is defined as $\frac{1}{12}$ the mass of a carbon-12 atom. The *gram atomic weight* is a unit of weight which is often convenient in the laboratory. This is simply the quantity of an element equal to its atomic weight in grams. Thus the gram atomic weight of copper is 63.54 grams, since the atomic weight of copper is 63.54.

15-6
Isotopes

Dalton considered all the atoms of a given element to be exactly alike. However, in 1912, J.J. Thomson obtained enough experimental evidence to suggest than not all neon atoms have the same weight, and by 1920, after methods for weighing atoms were developed, it became apparent that differences in weight exist among the atoms of many elements. The differences were detected by giving the atoms an electrical charge, accelerating them to high velocities in electric fields, and deflecting their paths in electric and magnetic fields. The particles having the greatest mass experience the smallest deflection, if all other factors are held constant. Figure 15-5 illustrates this idea, which is the basis for the modern mass spectrograph.

FIG. 15-5   Deflection of charged atoms by magnetic and electric fields.

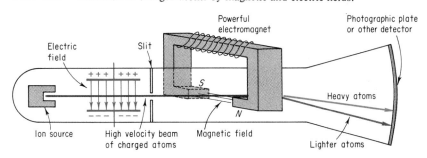

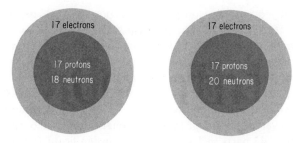

FIG. 15-6   Chlorine isotopes.

Atoms that have the same atomic number, but different masses, are called *isotopes*. Isotopes differ in the number of neutrons present in the nucleus. As shown in Fig. 15-6, chlorine atoms of mass 35 have 17 protons and 18 neutrons in their nuclei, and those of mass 37 have 17 protons and 20 neutrons. Naturally occurring chlorine consists of 75.4% chlorine-35 and 24.6% chlorine-37. This distribution results in an atomic weight of 35.46, which is the average weight of a large number of these two isotopes.

The isotope of krypton having a mass of 86, krypton-86, is used in the establishment of a standard of length. The wavelength of light produced by this isotope is the basis for defining a standard meter (see Chapter 7).

The atoms of some elements, such as fluorine, are all of the same mass; that is, there are no natural isotopes. The number of naturally occurring isotopes for a given element ranges up to 10 (for the element tin). Man has been able to produce artificial isotopes of most of the elements by bombardment of atoms with high-energy particles. Many of these man-made isotopes, such as iodine-131 and phosphorus-32, are radioactive and are useful in medicine and research.

15-7
Bohr Atom

With the acceptance of the nuclear atom, questions naturally arose concerning the arrangement of the electrons around the nucleus. One of the early theories pictured the atom as a static structure with electrons fixed at the corners of cubes around the nucleus. An obvious difficulty with such an arrangement is the question: if such an atom could exist, why are the electrons not pulled into the nucleus by electrostatic attraction?

Prior to 1913, there was no theory of atomic structure capable of explaining the radiation of electromagnetic waves by atoms. When heated sufficiently, or when excited by an electric arc, every element produces a unique set of light waves. When viewed or photographed through a spectroscope, this light appears as a series of bright-colored lines, called a *spectrum*. This provides a "fingerprint" for elements, since no two have identical spectra. A satisfactory theory of atomic structure should explain the spectra of elements as well as the chemical behavior of the atoms.

A dynamic atom would seem reasonable from the standpoint of keeping the positive and negative charges separated. Rutherford had suggested the idea of electrons moving around the nucleus in circular paths with electrostatic attraction keeping the electrons in the circular path and the inertia of the electrons preventing them from falling into the nucleus. This idea presented difficulties, since the principles of electrodynamics would predict the radiation of energy as electromagnetic waves by a revolving electron. A radiating electron would lose energy and eventually spiral into the nucleus.

Niels Bohr suggested, in 1913, that the laws describing the behavior of moving charges in ordinary electrical circuits are not applicable to atoms. Bohr proposed three hypotheses to describe the electronic structure of the nuclear atom:

1. Electrons revolve around the atomic nucleus in certain circular orbits with no gain or loss of energy. The electrons revolve in a manner analogous to the revolution of the planets around the Sun.

2. Electrons normally remain in the orbit of lowest energy, that is, the one nearest the nucleus. The energy of the electron orbit increases with distance from the nucleus.

3. Electrons may be forced into a higher energy orbit by absorbing a definite quantity of energy, but they will soon fall back to the lower energy orbit and give up the extra energy as electromagnetic radiation. (This hypothesis was based on the quantum theory, developed in 1900 by Max Planck, which states that radiant energy comes in discrete packages or *quanta*.)

The electron orbits, or *energy levels*, for hydrogen are represented in Fig. 15-7. The solid circle represents the lowest energy level and the dotted circles

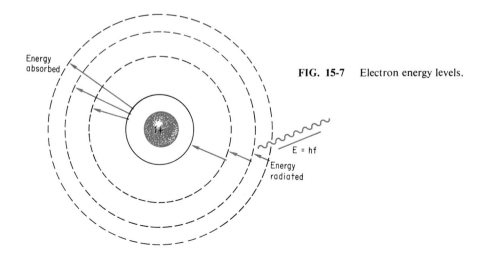

FIG. 15-7   Electron energy levels.

represent higher energy levels. The single electron of hydrogen is normally found in the lowest energy level, but can be raised to higher levels with the absorption of energy. When the electron drops from a higher level back to a lower one, the excess energy is radiated as an electromagnetic wave. The energy associated with these electron jumps comes in packages of definite size called *quanta*. The energy of a quantum is directly proportional to the frequency of the radiation associated with it and is expressed as $E = hf$, where E is the energy of the quantum, h is Planck's constant with a value of 6.6×10^{-27} erg-second, and f is the frequency of radiation. Thus it can be seen that a line in the spectrum of an element corresponds to an electron jump between two energy levels, and the frequency of the line is a measure of the energy difference between these two levels. As the energy difference becomes greater, the frequency increases and the wavelength decreases.

The measurement of ionization energy provides experimental evidence for electron energy levels within atoms. The *ionization energy*, which is the energy required to remove an electron from an atom, increases as successive electrons are removed from an atom. This indicates that the electrons in an atom are not all held with the same energy. Those nearest the nucleus are in the lowest energy levels and are most difficult to remove.

The Bohr theory was very successful in describing the spectrum of the hydrogen atom. Equations were developed for the calculation of the energies and radii of the various electron orbits. The calculated frequencies of the lines in the hydrogen spectrum were in very good agreement with the measured frequencies of these lines. Calculations for other atoms proved to be very difficult and the results were much less satisfactory.

15-8
Modern Theory of Atomic Structure

Bohr's original theory of the electronic structure of atoms has been modified drastically since its introduction in 1913. First, the idea of circular orbits for all electrons was abandoned when it was shown that the spectra of elements could be better explained by assuming that some orbits might be elliptical. The Heisenberg uncertainty principle has shown that it is impossible to make a precise determination of the location and momentum of an electron simultaneously. Modern atomic theory concerns itself with the probability distribution of electrons in certain regions of space around the nucleus. The modern chemist is interested in the energy of a given electron rather than the exact path it follows in moving around the nucleus.

The modified Bohr model of the atom and the study of spectra and chemical properties have enabled scientists to determine the distribution of electrons in the various energy levels of atoms. The term *energy level* is used to

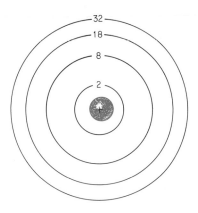

FIG. 15-8   Electron capacities of energy levels.

indicate the total energy of the electron, or the work required to remove it from the atom. The electrons in low energy levels are relatively close to the nucleus and tightly bound to it, whereas those in high energy levels are relatively easy to remove.

The principal energy levels of an atom, designated by $K, L, M, N, \ldots$, or by $1, 2, 3, 4, \ldots$, have a limited electron capacity. The maximum number of electrons that may be accommodated in each of the first four levels is shown in Fig. 15-8. *The energy levels are represented as circles, but it should be understood that electrons move in three-dimensional space, and that the space occupied by the electrons of a given energy level is in some cases spherical and in other cases more complex.*

The distribution of electrons in several of the lighter atoms is shown in Fig. 15-9. The total number of electrons is, in each case, equal to the number of protons in the nucleus. The number of neutrons in the nucleus of the most common isotope of each of these elements is also shown. Protons are designated by a "$+$" and neutrons by an "n".

The principal energy levels, with the exception of the K level, are made up of two or more energy sublevels. These sublevels, differing only slightly in energy, are designated by the letters $s, p, d,$ and f. The capacity of a sublevel is two electrons and the region of space occupied by each of these electron pairs is called an *orbital*. The K level contains only an s orbital and thus is limited to two electrons. The L level contains an s orbital and $3 p$ orbitals with

FIG. 15-9   Electron distribution in light atoms.

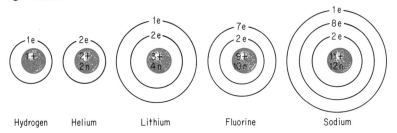

Hydrogen   Helium   Lithium   Fluorine   Sodium

a total capacity for 8 electrons. The orbitals and electron distributions for the first four principal energy levels are shown in Table 15-1.

TABLE 15-1
Electron Population for Principal Energy Levels

| | Orbitals | | |
Principal Energy Level	Number and Type	Electron Capacity	Total Electron Capacity
K or 1	1 *s*	2	2
L or 2	1 *s*	2	
	3 *p*	6	8
M or 3	1 *s*	2	
	3 *p*	6	
	5 *d*	10	18
N or 4	1 *s*	2	
	3 *p*	6	
	5 *d*	10	
	7 *f*	14	32

The relative energies of the electrons in the chlorine atom are shown in Fig. 15-10. This diagram shows the electron population of each sublevel in the order of increasing energy. The electrons in any given atom will normally occupy the lowest possible energy levels.

Since the exact determination of an electron orbit is no longer considered possible, the energy levels may be visualized as electron "clouds," or regions in which there is a high probability of finding an electron. The electron itself behaves in some ways as though it were a wave instead of a particle. For example, the acceleration of an electron in an electric field suggests a charged particle, whereas the diffraction pattern produced by high-speed electrons passing through a narrow slit is similar to the behavior of light waves. The

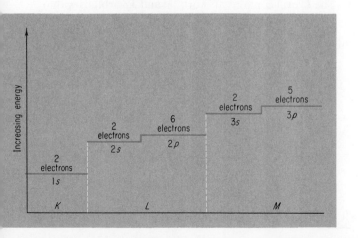

FIG. 15-10 Electron distribution in chlorine.

suggestion that electrons might act like waves was first made by Louis de Broglie in 1924, and a mathematical equation describing the electron as a wave was developed by Erwin Schroedinger in 1926. The wave properties of electrons are utilized in an instrument called the *electron microscope*, which has enabled man to go far beyond the magnification of the optical microscope.

The relative shapes of high-electron-density regions in atoms have been determined by the calculations of quantum mechanics. These electron-density calculations agree with experimental evidence and contribute to our understanding of the geometry of molecules. Even though the method for obtaining these electron-probability distributions is highly mathematical, a qualitative picture is useful as an aid to the understanding of chemical bonding between atoms. The shapes of the *s* and *p* orbitals are shown in Fig. 15-11. These diagrams represent regions around the nucleus where the probability of finding an electron is high. The *s* orbitals, with a capacity of 2

FIG. 15-11   *s* and *p* orbital shapes.

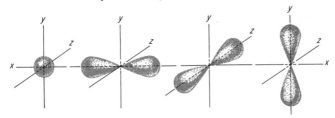

electrons each, are spherical; the probability of finding an electron is equally good in any direction from the nucleus. The electron distribution in the *p* orbitals is not uniform in all directions. The three orbitals are mutually perpendicular and the electron density is maximum along the directions of the X, Y, and Z axes, as shown in Fig. 15-12. The *d* and *f* orbitals are somewhat more complicated, so we shall not consider them. The understanding of

FIG. 15-12   Model of p_x, p_y, p_z orbitals.

molecular geometry is simplified by the fact that a very large proportion of all chemical bonds involve atoms with bonding electrons in *s* and *p* orbitals.

Dalton's concept of an atom as a fundamental unit of an element is as valid today as it was in 1808. Even though no man has seen an atom, the concept is indispensable to our understanding of the physical world, and the experimental evidence for the existence of atoms is completely convincing. Dalton's simple picture of the atom as a small, impenetrable particle is, of course, no longer adequate. This picture has become increasingly complex as men have developed more sophisticated means of exploring the behavior of atoms under various experimental conditions. This change in our physical model of the atom is a good illustration of the development of a theory in science. Theories are seldom abandoned completely and abruptly. Rather, they are gradually modified as new experimental evidence forces change to make them fit the facts. Science is a dynamic activity which is always unfinished. Our present theory of atomic structure provides a reasonably satisfactory explanation for the behavior of matter. Even now, this theory suggests new experiments, the results of which will very likely bring about further changes in the theory.

QUESTIONS AND PROBLEMS

1. What evidence did John Dalton have for the existence of atoms in 1808 that Democritus did not have in 400 B.C.?

2. What experimental discovery forced a change in Dalton's assumption that all atoms of a given element are *exactly* alike?

3. How much greater is the volume of an atom than the volume of an atomic nucleus? Assume the nuclear diameter to be 10^{-12} cm, the atomic diameter to be 10^{-8} cm, and the atom and nucleus to be spherical.

4. Hydrogen combines with oxygen in the ratio of approximately 2 grams to 16 grams to form water. What possible ratios would you suggest for other compounds of hydrogen and oxygen?

5. What difference would you expect in the results of Rutherford's scattering experiment if it were performed with aluminum foil instead of gold foil? The atomic weight of gold is 197 and that of aluminum is 27.

6. How would the deflection of alpha particles compare with that of high speed electrons in a magnetic field? Explain. (Assume that the alpha particles and the electrons are moving across the magnetic field at the same velocity.)

7. Why do you think most of the alpha particles in Rutherford's scattering experiments went through the gold foil with no deflection?

8. How many protons are there in the nucleus of a silicon atom with atomic number 14? How many electrons in this atom?

9. How many neutrons are present in the nuclei of each of the neon isotopes (mass numbers 20, 21 and 22)? The atomic number of neon is 10.

10. How is it possible for some silver atoms (atomic number 47) to have greater mass than some cadmium atoms (atomic number 48)?

11. Which end of the visible spectrum is associated with the highest energy quanta? Show how you reach this conclusion.

12. Calculate the atomic weight of an element with the following isotopes: mass number 24, 79%; mass number 25, 10%; mass number 26, 11%.

13. How many electrons are present in the third principal energy level (*M* level) of the element with atomic number 20?

14. How many electrons are present in each principal energy level of the potassium atom with atomic number 19? How many neutrons are in the nucleus of this atom if the mass number is 39?

15. One gram of oxygen is known to combine with 3.70 grams of element *X* and it is known that element *X* and oxygen combine in the ratio of 1 atom of *X* to 2 atoms of oxygen. Find the approximate atomic weight of element *X* from these facts. What atomic weight would be determined for *X* if this element combined with oxygen in a 1-to-1 ratio?

SUGGESTED REFERENCES

BOOTH, VERNE H., *The Structure of Atoms*, Chaps. 1, 2, and 3. The Macmillan Co., New York, 1964.

GAMOW, GEORGE, *The Atom and its Nucleus*, Chaps., 1, 2, 3, 4, and 5. Prentice-Hall, Englewood Cliffs, N.J., 1961.

KIEFFER, WILLIAM F., *Chemistry: A Cultural Approach*, Chap. 2. Harper & Row, New York, 1971.

16

Order in the World of Atoms

A casual look at the world around us does not reveal much evidence of an orderly structure in the great variety of material objects. We encounter such diverse things as water, coal, apples, the air, and the soil. Primitive man learned that some natural materials are complex and can be separated into simpler things or converted into more useful forms. Metallurgical processes, glass, textiles, and dyes were developed by empirical methods some 4,000 years ago in the civilizations of the Middle East, and perhaps in China. As men worked with matter in its various forms, they quite naturally wondered if the number of natural substances is limited. Chemists have shown that the many varied materials found in nature are really made up of a relatively small number of fundamental substances. The accomplishments of modern chemistry have resulted from an understanding of these fundamental substances and the ways in which they combine with one another.

16-1
Chemical Elements

The idea of a world made up of a few fundamental substances, or *elements*, was considered seriously by the Greeks. Aristotle taught that all matter consists of four elements—fire, earth, water, and air—an idea which had originated about 100 years earlier with Empedocles. This idea seemed to be quite logical on the basis of common experience. When green wood burns, fire is produced, water is given off, gases go into the air, and ash is left as a part of the earth. According to Aristotle, these four elements originate when fundamental matter is combined with the qualities of heat, cold, wetness, and dryness. Water, for example, would result when the qualities of cold and wetness are combined with fundamental matter. These elements could

274

be combined in varying proportions to form different familiar substances. Matter could be changed from one form to another by altering the proportions of the four elements.

The forerunner of chemistry was a pseudoscience called *alchemy*, which originated during the first century after the birth of Christ and flourished for more than 1,500 years. One of the principal goals of alchemy was to find the primary component of all matter, called the *materia prima*, and the "philosopher's stone." The philosopher's stone, also called the "elixir of life," was expected to work many miracles, such as changing lead into gold and restoring youth.

The fundamental matter of Aristotle was probably related to the alchemist's *materia prima*. The alchemists generally recognized Aristotle's fire, earth, water, and air as elements, but they added others to the list, particularly mercury, sulfur, and salt. The elements bearing these names were not the substances now commonly known by these names. Mercury represented the metallic and volatile character in general, sulfur the property of combustibility, and salt the earthy property of resistance to fire. The property of combustibility became the foundation of the phlogiston theory early in the eighteenth century (see page 386).

Jan Baptista Van Helmont considered water the primary element as late as the seventeenth century. His conclusion was based on an experiment in which a small tree was weighed and planted in a weighed quantity of soil. The tree was watered for five years, after which time the earth was carefully removed from the roots. The tree had gained about 164 pounds, while the soil weight was essentially unchanged. Van Helmont concluded that the weight gain was due to water, which changed into other elements in the growth process. Strangely enough, Van Helmont discovered carbon dioxide, the substance responsible for the deceptive result of his experiment. We now know that carbon dioxide, obtained through the leaves, and water, obtained through the roots, are the basic raw materials for photosynthesis, the process by which a plant manufactures carbohydrates.

The modern concept of an element was developed by Robert Boyle. His book, *The Sceptical Chymist*, published in 1661, greatly influenced the development of chemistry. Boyle challenged the concept of an element advanced by Aristotle and the alchemists. He defined elements as

> ... certain primitive and simple, or perfectly unmingled bodies; which not being made of any other bodies or of one another, are the ingredients of which all those called perfectly mixt bodies are immediately compounded, and into which they are ultimately resolved.*

Lavoisier later restated this definition in the form of a concise experimental test for an element: "An element is a substance that has not been decomposed

*Robert Boyle, *The Sceptical Chymist* (New York: Everyman's Library, 1911 [first published 1661]).

into simpler substances." We shall define an element *as a substance in which all the atoms have the same atomic number.*

16-2
Chemical Symbols

The use of symbols as a shorthand representation for the elements dates back to the early alchemists. They generally used certain symbols to represent indefinite amounts of elements. John Dalton devised a system of symbols to represent a single atom of each element. He represented compounds by a combination of the symbols of the atoms in the compound. Dalton's symbol for oxygen was O, for nitrogen ⓘ, and for hydrogen ⊙.

Berzelius, the Swedish chemist, proposed a system of symbols in 1819, consisting of a one or two letter abbreviation of the element name. This is the system we use today, although some of the symbols have been changed since the time of Berzelius. Many names for elements were in Latin at the time. Thus we have symbols such as Pb (*plumbum*) for lead, Fe (*ferrum*) for iron, and Cu (*cuprum*) for copper.

A symbol may be thought of as representing 1 atom of an element. However, the chemist also uses a symbol to represent 1 gram atomic weight of an element. When this practice is followed, the symbol O for oxygen represents 15.999 grams of oxygen and H represents 1.008 grams of hydrogen.

16-3
Relative Abundance of the Elements

The number of known elements has grown from 26, at the end of the eighteenth century, to the present number of 105. Most of the elements up through atomic number 92 occur naturally; the remaining elements are man-made. The naturally occurring elements are not distributed uniformly in the Earth. Ten elements account for a total of more than 99% of the weight of the Earth's crust to a depth of 10 miles. (The crust of the Earth includes the atomsphere and the water on the surface.) Oxygen is the most abundant element in the Earth's crust, but hydrogen is the most abundant element in the universe. Stars, such as our Sun, consist mainly of hydrogen under very high pressure. The relative abundance of the ten most common elements in the crust of the earth is shown in Table 16-1.

16-4
Classification of Elements

As the number of known facts accumulates in any activity of man, some sort of classification system becomes necessary. A system for organizing informa-

TABLE 16-1
Relative Abundance of Elements in the Earth's Crust
(including water and atmosphere)

Order of Abundance	Element	Weight, %
1	Oxygen	49.2
2	Silicon	25.7
3	Aluminum	7.5
4	Iron	4.7
5	Calcium	3.4
6	Sodium	2.6
7	Potassium	2.4
8	Magnesium	1.9
9	Hydrogen	0.9
10	Titanium	0.6

tion makes the information more readily available, simplifies learning for students in the field, and often reveals relationships that lead to new principles or generalizations. The search for these relationships is the primary concern of the scientist. As the number of known chemical elements increased and chemists learned more about their properties, the need for a classification system became evident.

A look at the properties of the elements will reveal certain groups of elements which show quite pronounced resemblances in physical and chemical properties. About 1850, chemists began serious attempts to find a classification system which would best show these group resemblances. Various schemes of classification were suggested, but the one in use today, called the *periodic table*, was devised independently by Lothar Meyer in Germany and Dmitri Mendeleev in Russia. The name of Mendeleev is usually associated with the periodic table, since his ideas were published in 1869, about a year ahead of Meyer, and he predicted the existence of many elements not known at that time.

The classification scheme worked out by Mendeleev and Meyer is based on the arrangement of elements in the order of increasing atomic weight. Elements with similar chemical and physical properties reappear at definite intervals in such an arrangement. This principle is illustrated for a few of the lighter elements in Table 16-2. The atomic weight for each element in the table is given directly below the symbol.

TABLE 16-2

Li	Be	B	C	N	O	F	Ne
(6.94)	(9.01)	(10.81)	(12.01)	(14.01)	(15.999)	(18.90)	(20.08)
Na	Mg	Al	Si	P	S	Cl	Ar
(22.99)	(24.31)	(26.98)	(28.08)	(30.97)	(32.06)	(35.45)	(39.95)

The elements appearing in the same column of Table 16-2 show striking resemblances in properties. For example, lithium (Li) and sodium (Na) are very similar in many ways. They are both light metals and very readily enter into chemical reactions with other elements or with compounds. Similar relationships exist between the elements in other columns of this table.

Sixty-three of the 105 elements currently known were known in the time of Mendeleev, a fact which greatly complicated the construction of a periodic table. The remarkable insight of Mendeleev led him to leave gaps in his periodic table in those places where the known element in the atomic weight sequence did not have properties similar to the elements in the same column. The element germanium (Ge) was unknown to Mendeleev. Table 16-3 will show that if he had followed the sequence of increasing atomic weights, arsenic (As) would have followed galium (Ga). However, Mendeleev knew that arsenic is not chemically similar to carbon (C) and silicon (Si), but resembles nitrogen (N) and phosphorus (P). Therefore, he left the space below silicon blank, and predicted the discovery of a new element with properties intermediate between silicon and tin (Sn). The discovery of this element and others, predicted in a similar manner, led to the rapid acceptance of this scheme of classification. None of the elements in group VIII were known in the time of Mendeleev, so he could not have predicted the existence of any of these elements.

The periodic arrangement served some very useful purposes in the era immediately following its development. There were a few places where the arrangement in order of increasing weight did not seem to place the elements in the proper groups on the basis of properties. For example, iodine (I), element number 53, would appear ahead of tellurium (Te), element number 52, in an arrangement based on increasing atomic weight. However, iodine is similar to chlorine (Cl) and bromine (Br), and tellurium is similar to selenium (Se) and sulfur (S). Those apparent inconsistencies stimulated efforts toward more careful determinations of atomic weights. There was also a great interest in the search for new elements and new relationships between elements. The periodic table also proved to be very valuable in the coordination of chemical knowledge, and thus a useful tool in the study of chemistry.

Many advances in chemical knowledge have resulted from the use of the periodic table to predict chemical behavior. The discovery of the compounds of boron and hydrogen resulted from use of the periodic table. Boron was first isolated in 1807, by Sir Humphry Davy. By 1900 very little was known about the chemistry of this element and very few compounds of boron were known. Alfred Stock began to study boron in 1901 and reasoned that an element adjacent to carbon in the periodic table might be expected to form similar compounds. Since carbon forms many compounds with hydrogen, Stock attempted to make compounds of boron and hydrogen. He succeeded in this attempt and discovered many of these compounds, called *boranes*. These studies have led to many uses for boron and its compounds and much has been learned about the chemistry of this element.

The periodic table proved to be much more than a useful method for the classification of chemical information. The basic principle behind this classification scheme, often called the *periodic law*, has become one of the most important generalizations in science. This generalization, as understood by Mendeleev, may be stated in the following form: *the properties of the elements and their compounds are periodic functions of the atomic weights of the elements.* Mendeleev and other chemists of his day had no understanding of the reasons behind this orderly arrangement of the elements. The search for the cause of this order was an important motivating factor in the development of our present physical model of the atom. Our knowledge of atomic structure gives us a logical explanation for the order we find in the periodic table.

16-5
Modern Periodic Table

The basis for our modern periodic table is *atomic number* rather than atomic weight, a change which removed many inconsistencies in the original table. Hydrogen does not fit well into any group, but has some resemblance to both group IA and group VIIA. The *lanthanides* and *actinides* are separated from the main body of the table, since they have very similar chemistry and their inclusion would expand the table to 32 spaces.

Three major classes of elements may be found in different sections of the table. Approximately 75 of the elements are metals, located to the left of the heavy stairstep line. The metals usually have from 1 to 3 electrons in their highest occupied energy levels. The transition metals have partially filled *d* or *f* orbitals, while the representative metals have no partially filled *d* or *f* orbitals. The nonmetals, located to the right of the stairstep line usually have from 4 to 7 electrons in their highest occupied energy levels. The noble gases have all their occupied *s* and *p* orbitals filled to capacity; consequently, they have no unpaired electrons.

16-6
Periodic Properties of Elements

An examination of the properties of the elements will reveal that these properties are indeed periodic functions of the atomic number. We see very active metals on the left side of the table, and as we progress to the right in a horizontal row, or period, we come to very active nonmetals and, finally, to

TABLE 16-3
Periodic Table of the Elements*

1	1 H 1.00797

	IA	IIA	III B	IV B	V B	VI B	VII B		VIII B	
(shells)										
2,1	3 Li 6.939	2,2 / 4 Be 9.0122								
2,8,1	11 Na 22.9898	2,8,2 / 12 Mg 24.305								
2,8,8,1	19 K 39.102	2,8,8,2 / 20 Ca 40.08	2,8,9,2 / 21 Sc 44.956	2,8,10,2 / 22 Ti 47.90	2,8,11,2 / 23 V 50.942	2,8,13,1 / 24 Cr 51.996	2,8,13,2 / 25 Mn 54.9380	2,8,14,2 / 26 Fe 55.847	2,8,15,2 / 27 Co 58.9332	
2,8,18,8,1	37 Rb 85.47	2,8,18,8,2 / 38 Sr 87.62	2,8,18,9,2 / 39 Y 88.905	2,8,18,10,2 / 40 Zr 91.22	2,8,18,12,1 / 41 Nb 92.906	2,8,18,13,1 / 42 Mo 95.94	43 Tc (99)	2,8,18,15,1 / 44 Ru 101.07	2,8,18,16,1 / 45 Rh 102.905	
2,8,18,18,8,1	55 Cs 132.905	2,8,18,18,8,2 / 56 Ba 137.34	57-71 See Lanthanide Series	2,8,18,32,10,2 / 72 Hf 178.49	2,8,18,32,11,2 / 73 Ta 180.948	2,8,18,32,12,2 / 74 W 183.85	2,8,18,32,13,2 / 75 Re 186.2	2,8,18,32,14,2 / 76 Os 190.2	2,8,18,32,15,2 / 77 Ir 192.2	
2,8,18,32,18,8,1	87 Fr (223)	2,8,18,32,18,8,2 / 88 Ra 226	89-100 See Actinide Series	(104)	(105) Ha					

Lanthanide Series (Rare Earth Elements)

2,8,18,18,9,2 / 57 La 138.91	2,8,18,19,9,2 / 58 Ce 140.12	2,8,18,21,8,2 / 59 Pr 140.907	2,8,18,22,8,2 / 60 Nd 144.24	2,8,18,23,8,2 / 61 Pm (147)	2,8,18,24,8,2 / 62 Sm 150.35

Actinide Series

2,8,18,32,18,9,2 / 89 Ac (227)	2,8,18,32,18,10,2 / 90 Th 232.038	2,8,18,32,20,9,2 / 91 Pa (231)	2,8,18,32,21,9,2 / 92 U 238.03	2,8,18,32,22,9,2 / 93 Np (237)	2,8,18,32,23,9,2 / 94 Pu (244)

NOTE: A value given in parentheses denotes the mass number of the isotope of the longest known half-life, or of the best known one.

*Adapted from "Periodic Chart of the Elements," published by Merck and Co., Rahway, N.J., 1967.

Representative Metals

Transition Metals

Periodic Table (partial)

	IB	II B	III A	IV A	V A	VI A	VII A	V III
								2 / **2 He** / 4.0026
			2,3 / **5 B** / 10.811	2,4 / **6 C** / 12.01115	2,5 / **7 N** / 14.0067	2,6 / **8 O** / 15.9994	2,7 / **9 F** / 18.9984	2,8 / **10 Ne** / 20.179
			2,8,3 / **13 Al** / 26.9815	2,8,4 / **14 Si** / 28.086	2,8,5 / **15 P** / 30.9738	2,8,6 / **16 S** / 32.064	2,8,7 / **17 Cl** / 35.453	2,8,8 / **18 Ar** / 39.948
2,8,16,2 / **28 Ni** / 58.71	2,8,18,1 / **29 Cu** / 63.546	2,8,18,2 / **30 Zn** / 65.37	2,8,18,3 / **31 Ga** / 69.72	2,8,18,4 / **32 Ge** / 72.59	2,8,18,5 / **33 As** / 74.9216	2,8,18,6 / **34 Se** / 78.96	2,8,18,7 / **35 Br** / 79.904	2,8,18,8 / **36 Kr** / 83.80
2,8,18,18 / **46 Pd** / 106.4	2,8,18,18,1 / **47 Ag** / 107.868	2,8,18,18,2 / **48 Cd** / 112.40	2,8,18,18,3 / **49 In** / 114.82	2,8,18,18,4 / **50 Sn** / 118.69	2,8,18,18,5 / **51 Sb** / 121.75	2,8,18,18,6 / **52 Te** / 127.60	2,8,18,18,7 / **53 I** / 126.9044	2,8,18,18,8 / **54 Xe** / 131.30
2,8,18,32,17,1 / **78 Pt** / 195.09	2,8,18,32,18,1 / **79 Au** / 196.967	2,8,18,32,18,2 / **80 Hg** / 200.59	2,8,18,32,18,3 / **81 Tl** / 204.37	2,8,18,32,18,4 / **82 Pb** / 207.19	2,8,18,32,18,5 / **83 Bi** / 208.980	2,8,18,32,18,6 / **84 Po** / (210)	2,8,18,32,18,7 / **85 At** / (210)	2,8,18,32,18,8 / **86 Rn** / (222)

| 2,8,18,25,8,2 / **63 Eu** / 151.96 | 2,8,18,25,9,2 / **64 Gd** / 157.25 | 2,8,18,26,9,2 / **65 Tb** / 158.924 | 2,8,18,28,8,2 / **66 Dy** / 162.50 | 2,8,18,29,8,2 / **67 Ho** / 164.930 | 2,8,18,30,8,2 / **68 Er** / 167.26 | 2,8,18,31,8,2 / **69 Tm** / 168.934 | 2,8,18,32,8,2 / **70 Yb** / 173.04 | 2,8,18,32,9,2 / **71 Lu** / 174.97 |
| 2,8,18,32,24,9,2 / **95 Am** / (243) | 2,8,18,32,25,9,2 / **96 Cm** / (247) | 2,8,18,32,26,9,2 / **97 Bk** / (247) | 2,8,18,32,27,9,2 / **98 Cf** / (251) | 2,8,18,32,28,9,2 / **99 Es** / (254) | 2,8,18,32,29,9,2 / **100 Fm** / (253) | 2,8,18,32,30,9,2 / **101 Md** / (256) | 2,8,18,32,31,9,2 / **102 No** / (254) | 2,8,18,32,32,9,2 / **103 Lw** / (257) |

Nonmetals

Noble Gases

a noble gas. This sequence is repeated in each period of the table. Thus we can say that metallic or nonmetallic character is a periodic function of atomic number.

Atomic size is also a periodic function of atomic number. Starting on the left with a metal such as lithium (Li), we find a relatively large atom with a diameter of about 3 angstrom units. One angstrom unit (Å) is equal to 10^{-8} centimeter. As we progress through this period, the size decreases until we reach fluorine (F), with a diameter of about 1.3 Å. The size increases sharply with neon (Ne), which has a diameter of approximately 2.2 Å. Generally, the metal atoms are relatively large and the nonmetals are small, with the inert gases being intermediate in size. The periodic variation in atomic size for the first 57 elements is illustrated in Fig. 16-1, which shows the variation in atomic radius with atomic number.

As we go down a vertical column, or group, in the table we find that atomic size increases. This is due to the addition of electrons to another main energy level as we progress from one period to the next. Therefore, we would expect to find the largest atoms among the metals in the lower left section of the table and the smallest atoms in the nonmetals at the upper right.

Ionization energy is another important periodic property of atoms. This is the energy required to remove the most loosely held electron from an atom.

FIG. 16-1   Periodic variation in atomic size.

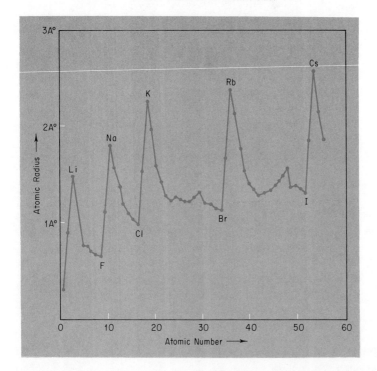

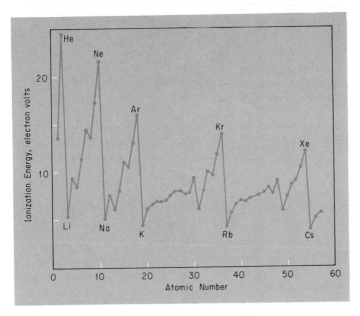

FIG. 16-2   Periodic variation of ionization energy.

The ionization energy depends on atomic size and nuclear charge, or atomic number. There are certain other less obvious factors which are beyond the scope of this discussion. The larger the atom, the farther the outer electrons are from the positively charged nucleus and the smaller the attractive force between the two. As the nuclear charge, or atomic number, becomes larger, the attractive force for electrons would be greater and the ionization energy would tend to be higher. The atomic size apparently exerts more influence than nuclear charge since the ionization energy increases with a decrease in atomic size. Therefore, as we go from sodium (Na) to chlorine (Cl), we find increasing ionization energy. The energy decreases sharply at potassium (K) and then shows an increasing trend in the next period. The ionization energies of the inert gases are influenced by other factors which will not be discussed here. Figure 16-2 shows the periodic variation of ionization energy for the first 57 elements.

One of the most significant periodic variations, from the standpoint of understanding the meaning of the periodic classification, is that of the number of outer-energy-level electrons in the atoms. These electrons are often called *valence electrons*, a term which will be discussed in more detail in Chapter 19. We find that the number of outer electrons increases from 1 to 8 as we progress across each of the periods from left to right. This increase is quite regular for the main groups of the table (the groups with numbers followed by A). There is no regular increase for the transition metals in the center of table. Thus we see that all elements in each of the main groups (vertical columns) have the same number of outer electrons. The elements of group

IA all have 1 outer electron, those of group IIA have 2, etc. This fact would definitely indicate some connection between number of outer electrons and chemical properties, a connection that we shall explore in more detail later.

16-7
Families of Elements

The vertical columns of the periodic table contain elements which exhibit very definite similarities in chemical and physical properties. These groups of elements are called *groups* or *families*. While the elements in a given family are very much alike, there are also differences. These differences increase as we proceed down a given group from top to bottom.

The elements in group IA make up the *alkali metal family*. They are all light, soft metals and are very active chemically. Their tendency to unite with other elements is so great that they are difficult to obtain and keep in pure form. For example, they all react violently with water. The chemical activity of these elements increases from the top to the bottom of the group. The atoms of these elements have a single valence electron and they always combine with other elements in the same ratio. These elements give up their single valence electron when they enter into chemical combination with other elements. Since they each give up a single electron, they all have the same combining capacity.

The *alkaline earth* metals are found in group IIA. These are also relatively light and quite active metals. There are 2 valence electrons in the atoms of these elements and they all combine in the same ratio with other elements. The 2 valence electrons of the elements in this family are given up to other elements in chemical combination, and thus they all have the same combining capacity. The differences among the elements within a family are more pronounced here than in the alkali metal family. The chemical activity increases from the top of the group toward the bottom. For example, barium (Ba) reacts very rapidly with water, while beryllium (Be) does not react at all with cold water.

Group VIIA contains a family of nonmetallic elements known as the *halogens*. This name, meaning "salt formers," is related to the type of compounds formed by these elements. Common table salt results from the chemical combination of sodium and chlorine, and has the chemical name *sodium chloride*. The other elements of the family form similar compounds. Here we find a change in physical state from a gas to a solid as we go down the group from fluorine (F) to iodine (I). These elements are all quite active and form similar compounds. However, fluorine at the top of the family is the most active of these elements and we find the activity decreasing as we go down the column. All the halogen atoms have 7 valence electrons. The atoms of these elements share their valence electrons when combining with other nonmetals. When combining with metals, each halogen atom gains a single electron and, therefore, each has the same combining capacity.

The family at the extreme right of the table is made up of gaseous elements having very little tendency to undergo any chemical change. Therefore, these elements are often called the *inert gases* or the *noble gases*. Prior to 1962, these elements were thought to show no chemical activity and, consequently, to form no compounds. However, during that year it was shown that xenon (Xe) will unite chemically with fluorine and we now know that these elements are not totally inert. In addition to such compounds as xenon difluoride, xenon tetrafluoride, and xenon hexafluoride, xenon trioxide has also been prepared. Compounds of krypton and fluorine have also been made, but are very unstable. Helium (He) has 2 valence electrons and all the other members of the family have 8. These facts suggest that an atomic energy level containing 8 electrons is relatively stable and would have little tendency to undergo any change.

Thus we see that the vast array of material objects around us is really composed of a relatively small number of fundamental substances, which we call "elements." Even though there are 105 known elements, most of the materials we encounter are composed mainly of 10 elements. Chemists have found that the elements can be arranged logically into a pattern which reveals a periodicity in their physical and chemical properties. This arrangement lends support to our theories of atomic structure and aids our understanding of the way in which elements are joined in chemical compounds, a topic which we shall investigate in a later chapter. We shall turn next to a discussion of the atomic nucleus and nuclear reactions.

QUESTIONS AND PROBLEMS

1. In what ways would you expect zinc (Zn) and cadmium (Cd) to resemble one another? Upon what general principle do you base your answer?

2. Which of the 10 most abundant elements in the crust of the earth are metals? How can you determine whether or not a given element is a metal without knowledge of its properties?

3. Which of the atomic "building blocks" are present in equal numbers in the nuclei of all atoms of a given element?

4. Arrange the following elements in order of *increasing* atomic size: sodium (Na), chlorine (Cl), magnesium (Mg), fluorine (F), potassium (K), and cesium (Cs). What general principles are involved in this arrangement?

5. Arrange the following elements in order of *increasing* ionization energy: fluorine (F), calcium (Ca), chlorine (Cl), potassium (K), and cesium

(Cs). What general principles enable you to arrange these elements in the proper order?

6. What simple experimental observations will show that Aristotle's four elements are not elements in the light of our present concept of an element?

7. What structural feature of the atoms of elements in a given family (vertical column) of the periodic table accounts for the chemical similarity of these elements?

8. Arrange the following elements in order of *increasing* chemical activity: copper (Cu), potassium (K), magnesium (Mg), and cesium (Cs). What simple experimental test would enable you to check the accuracy of your arrangement?

9. Consider elements number 3 and number 9 in light of general principles related to the periodic table. What predictions would you make about the relative properties of these elements?

10. Photoelectric cells require a cathode surface from which electrons may be easily removed by the energy of incident light. What elements would you suggest for this purpose? Explain.

11. How would you expect magnesium (Mg) and barium (Ba) to compare in ionization energy? What is the basis of your prediction?

12. Sodium is quite difficult to obtain in pure form, despite the fact that it is one of the 10 most abundant elements in the crust of the earth. How do you account for this fact?

13. What features of our present physical model of the atom are most useful in explaining the orderly arrangement of elements in the periodic table?

14. How do you relate the number of elements in period 4 (fourth horizontal row) of the periodic table to the information in Table 15-1?

15. How is the information in Fig. 15-11 related to the relative ionization energies of group IA of the periodic table?

SUGGESTED REFERENCES

Dingo, Gustav P., "The Elements and the Derivation of Their Names and Symbols," *Chemistry*, 41, no. 2 (1968), 20.

Seaborg, Glenn T., "From Mendeleev to Mendelevium and Beyond," *Chemistry*, 43, no. 1 (1970), 6.

Sisler, Harry H., *Electronic Structure, Properties, and the Periodic Law*, Chap. 1. Reinhold Publishing Corp., New York, 1963.

Zimmerman, Joan, "The Strange World of Helium," *Chemistry*, 43, no. 2 (1970), 14.

17

The Atomic Nucleus

Before the nineteenth century the building blocks of matter were molecules. Later it was shown that molecules are made of atoms. At the beginning of the twentieth century Rutherford proved experimentally that the atom consists of outer electrons and a positively charged core, or nucleus. We find that this nucleus can be subdivided into smaller pieces of matter called protons and neutrons. Before studying how atoms can be combined to form compounds, let us investigate the composition of the nucleus to gain a better understanding of the atom itself. We shall first look at spontaneous nuclear disintegrations called radioactive decay, and then look at nuclear reactions and nuclear energies. We hope that this will lead us to a better understanding of the nuclear structure.

17-1
Discovery of Radioactivity

In 1896 A. H. Becquerel, a French physicist, discovered a new radiation while experimenting with fluorescent material. After Roentgen reported his discovery of X rays, Becquerel thought that he could produce the same effect by exposing fluorescent materials to the sunlight. To do this he wrapped a photographic plate in several layers of heavy black paper, laid a coin on the paper, placed a small amount of fluorescent material (sulfate of uranium) on top of coin, and laid the whole thing in the sunshine for several hours. When the plate was developed, a silhouette of the coin appeared on the negative. It did indeed seem that the fluorescence of the material caused by the sunshine produced the X rays. Later on he prepared a similar arrangement, but the Sun did not shine, and so he put it in the drawer of a case to keep it dark. After several days of cloudy weather, he decided to develop the film to see if some phosphorescence had produced a small amount of X rays, and to his amazement, the silhouette appeared on the negative stronger than before. He then kept some uranium salts in the dark for several months, and they continued to emit radiations similar to those of X rays. He also found that uranium compounds placed near an electrically charged object caused the charge to leak off that object. Many other uranium compounds were tested as well as the uranium metal itself, and they all showed the same effect. Becquerel felt that this could be understood only if the atoms of the uranium element spontaneously emitted rays that could penetrate paper, darken photographic plates, and ionize the air through which they passed. This was the first instance ever observed of the phenomenon we now call *radioactivity*.

Uranium did not especially appeal to the popular imagination. But two years later, Pierre and Marie Curie separated from several tons of pitchblende about $\frac{1}{100}$ ounce of a substance that was a million times as active as uranium. Then the whole world was interested. Because of its remarkable radiation activity, the new element was called *radium*.

The rays that caused the fogging of Becquerel's photographic plates proved to be of the same nature as X rays—electromagnetic waves of very short wavelength. Ernest Rutherford, then a professor of physics at McGill University in Canada, soon found that rays of other kinds were also emitted by both uranium and radium. To test for the different kinds of rays, he inserted a little radioactive material into a small hole drilled in a lead block, and several centimeters above the hole he mounted a photographic plate as a detector. When a strong magnetic field was applied across the beam of rays radiating from the hole, he discovered that the beam divided into three parts, as indicated in Fig. 17-1. One ray was slightly deflected in one direc-

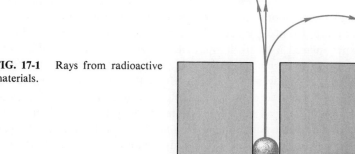

FIG. 17-1 Rays from radioactive materials.

tion, another ray was strongly deflected in the opposite direction, and the third was not bent at all. For convenience the three component parts were called *alpha particles*, *beta particles*, and *gamma rays*, respectively.

From the direction the *alpha beam, A*, was deflected, Rutherford knew that it consisted of positively charged particles. To determine the nature of these charged particles, he placed an alpha emitter inside a thin glass tube which, in turn, was sealed inside an evacuated discharge tube. After several days, he detected a gas pressure in the outer tube, and enough gas had been formed to allow an electrical discharge within the tube. An analysis of the spectrum of the light produced by the discharge revealed that the newly formed gas was helium. Evidently, some of the positively charged alpha particles had penetrated the thin walls of the inner glass tube, picked up orbital electrons from the surroundings, and became neutral helium atoms. This was conclusive evidence that the alpha particle was identical to the helium nucleus, which we now know consists of 2 protons and 2 neutrons. All alpha particles have exactly the same charge and mass, but have different energies, depending on the elements from which they are emitted. Some radioactive atoms emit them with speeds as high as 3×10^7 m/sec, or $\frac{1}{10}$ the speed of light. In general, alpha particles are very energetic, but, because of their size and mass, they cannot penetrate very deeply into matter. A sheet of ordinary writing paper will stop most of them.

From the direction the *beta beam, B*, was deflected, Rutherford knew that it was a stream of negatively charged particles; and from the amount it was deflected, he knew that the particles were not very massive. It was later proven that betas have the same charge and mass as electrons. Most of them are emitted from radioactive nuclei with much higher speeds than the alphas; some have speeds almost equal to that of light. They are slightly more penetrative than alpha particles because they are scattered about by the molecules of the material. Most of them can be stopped by a few millimeters of lead or by an ordinary glass plate.

The undeflected *gamma ray, G*, was found to be the same in nature as an X ray, but with a shorter wavelength and much more energy. We find that these gamma rays do not have as much energy as most alpha particles, but, because of their wave-like nature, they are far more penetrative. Several inches of lead or several feet of concrete are required to absorb most of the more energetic ones. The penetrative power of the gamma rays emitted by radium is very important in the treatment of disease.

17-2
Detection of Radioactive Rays

The first investigators used photographic films and fluorescent screens to detect these radioactive rays, because the rays darkened unexposed films and made fluorescent screens glow. Alpha particles that strike a fluorescent material produce tiny flashes of light. With the aid of a magnifying glass or a microscope these flashes, or *scintillations*, can be seen and counted. From this count and the solid angle the screen subtends at the source, we can determine the number of alpha particles emitted per second by a given radioactive element—a rather tedious task, to say the least. You can observe the little flashes of light produced by alpha particles if you look at the radium dials of a watch in a completely darkened room. The hands and numerals of such a watch are coated with a mixture of radium bromide and zinc sulfide. The alpha particles from the radium strike the zinc sulfide and produce a glow. If you carefully observe the hands of the watch through a magnifying glass, you will be able to see the little flashes of light as soon as your eyes have become accustomed to the darkness. These flashes make the hands and numerals appear to twinkle. You will notice that counting these scintillations is rather difficult, if not impossible.

For a more quantiative analysis of radioactivity, a gold-leaf electroscope (Fig. 13-1) can be used. When a radioactive material is brought near a charged electroscope, the leaf slowly returns to its uncharged position. From the rate the gold leaf falls, the intensity of the radiation can be determined. The rays entering the electroscope ionize the air by dislodging the outer electrons from the atoms of the air molecules. This produces pairs of ions, the dislodged electrons and the positive molecules. These ions make the air conductive, and the charges on the electroscope leak off. The more ion pairs produced by the rays, the faster the electroscope discharges, thus giving a measure of the intensity of the radiation. An electroscope cannot detect a single particle or a single gamma photon, a unit of electromagnetic energy. It measures the average effect of a large number of ionizing rays.

In 1908, Rutherford and Geiger described a method for detecting individual ionizing particles. Their original device was very slow-acting; but after years of research and many improvements by Geiger and others, we now have an instrument which can detect and count ionizing particles up to about 10,000 per second. This useful instrument is commonly known as the *Geiger counter* (see Fig. 17-2). It consists of a Geiger-Müller tube,

FIG. 17-2   A Geiger counter.

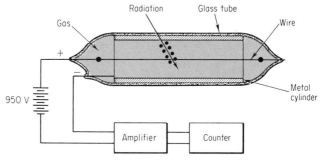

FIG. 17-3 A Geiger-Müller tube.

Labels on figure: Radiation, Glass tube, Gas, Wire, +, −, 950 V, Metal cylinder, Amplifier, Counter

an amplifier, and some type of counting device. The tube, which is the heart of the apparatus, has a fine wire running along the axis of a hollow, thin, metal cylinder (see Fig. 17-3). Some tubes use this metal cylinder as their outer wall, while others mount the cylinder inside a thin glass tube. The cylinder contains a mixture of a gas, usually argon, and a vapor of some organic compound, such as alcohol, at a total pressure of about 10 centimeters of mercury. The wire is connected to the positive side of a high-voltage power supply and the cylinder is grounded, making it safe to handle. When an ionizing particle enters the cylinder, it produces several ion pairs. The dislodged electrons are attracted to the positively charged wire and, in their mad rush toward it, they knock electrons off other atoms. These electrons also head for the wire and soon gain enough energy to knock more electrons from other atoms. This process quickly results in an avalanche of electrons moving toward the center. When they strike the wire, its voltage drops slightly, causing an electrical pulse in the circuit. This pulse is amplified and made to operate a neon tube, a speaker, and a mechanical counter. Before any other particle can be detected, the massive positive ions, which were produced in the ionization, must move out to the metal cylinder and be neutralized. This process requires from 50 to 100 millionths of a second. Any particle entering the tube during this "dead time" will not be counted. Thus there is an upper limit to the number of particles such a device can count per second.

Gamma and X-ray photons can also be counted with a Geiger counter. Upon entering the tube, each photon produces a photoelectron which starts the avalanche of electrons necessary to produce a count. Neutrons cannot be detected by an ordinary Geiger-Müller tube because they produce no ions. A special tube, however, has been designed to detect them (see page 316).

With today's interest in radiation, the Geiger counter has become a very familiar instrument; anyone searching for deposits of uranium must use either a Geiger counter or a *scintillation counter*. The latter, which is far more sensitive, consists of a small crystal of a fluorescent phosphor, a layer of photosensitive material, and an electron multiplier (Fig. 17-4). When a

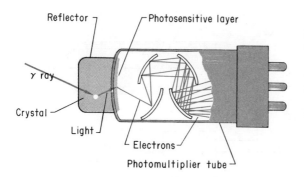

Reflector ⌐ ⌐ Photosensitive layer

γ ray

Crystal

Light ⌐

⌐ Electrons ⌐

Photomultiplier tube ⌐

FIG. 17-4 Cross section of a scintillation tube. The light to the tube is proportional to the gamma energy. If 1 electron ejects 5 electrons from each electrode, 11 electrodes result in 5^{11} or about 50 million electrons output. (Courtesy U.S. Atomic Energy Commission, Isotopes Division.)

charged particle or a photon enters the crystal, it produces a tiny flash of light. This light strikes the photosensitive material and releases photoelectrons, which are increased in number several million times by the electron multiplier. The resulting surge of electrons is amplified and made to operate a speaker and a counting device. Scintillation counters are gradually replacing Geiger counters in most work because they are far more sensitive to weak radiations.

In 1911, C. T. R. Wilson, an English physicist, demonstrated an instrument which made it possible to see and photograph the "track" of any individual ionizing particle. Such an instrument consists of a cylinder containing air, enough water to saturate the air, and a piston which can be lowered rapidly (Fig. 17-5). The top of the cylinder is covered with a glass plate for viewing the tracks. When the piston is raised, the compressed air becomes warmer, and some of the water evaporates. When the piston is lowered suddenly, the air in the cylinder expands, cools, and becomes supersaturated. It now contains more water vapor than it can hold at the reduced temperature, and this vapor condenses on any ions present. If at this time a charged particle passes through the chamber, it will produce a path of ion pairs, and the vapor condenses on these ions, forming a fog track. A light entering one side of the chamber illuminates the fog and makes the tracks visible.

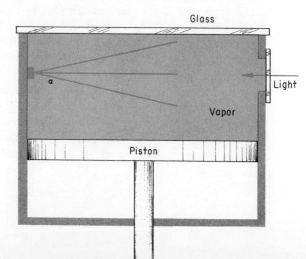

Glass

α

Light

Vapor

FIG. 17-5 The Wilson cloud chamber.

Piston

With the *Wilson cloud chamber*, the various ionizing particles can be identified by the kind of tracks they produce (Fig. 17-6). For example, an alpha particle makes an intense, straight track which is several centimeters long. A beta particle leaves a long, thin, crooked trail. If the chamber is placed in a strong magnetic field, the tracks become curved. From the direction they curve, the charges on the particles can be determined. The amount of curvature indicates the speeds and masses of these particles. With the addition of this magnetic field, the Wilson cloud chamber has become a very useful instrument in the field of nuclear research.

A bubble chamber, invented in 1952 by D. H. Glaser, has become more valuable than the cloud chamber for studying high-energy ionizing particles. Instead of droplets of water forming on the ions produced by charged particles passing through a gas-filled chamber, vapor bubbles are formed around the ions produced as the charged particles pass through a liquid. In this device, a chamber is filled with a liquid under very high pressure, usually liquid hydrogen or liquid isopentane, and the temperature is raised above its normal boiling point. When the pressure is suddenly reduced, the liquid becomes superheated and vapor bubbles are formed around the ions left along the paths of the charged particles. Thus tiny vapor bubble trails

FIG. 17-6 A cloud-chamber photograph of alpha and beta ray tracks. The heavy tracks were formed by alpha particles while the fainter ones were formed by beta particles. (Photo courtesy of Central Scientific Co.)

are formed in the liquid. These tracks are visible for only a very short time because the vapor bubbles grow rapidly in size as the liquid begins to boil. Fast particles may produce only a few ions in traversing a gas chamber, but they produce many ions per centimeter in a liquid, making a well-defined trail. Such a device may be more valuable than the cloud chamber, but it is less convenient to use.

17-3
Measurement of Radioactivity

To indicate the activity of a radioactive substance, a unit of measurement had to be established. The activity of 1 gram of radium was arbitrarily chosen as the standard because radium could be obtained in a purified state and remain usable for fairly long periods of time without very much variation. One gram of radium was observed to decay at the rate of 37×10^9 (37 billion) disintegrations per second. This value was taken as the measuring unit and was called a *curie* in honor of Madam Curie, who discovered radium. The curie is an extremely large unit. Microcuries, which are more commonly used, represent 37,000 (3.7×10^4) disintegrations per second. Ten microcuries of phosphorus-32 means that 370,000 of its atoms are disintegrating per second; hence, it emits 370,000 beta particles per second. In hospitals and research laboratories, quantities measured in millicuries are often used. Such activities must be handled with extreme care and must be stored in thick lead containers.

The curie indicates the number, but not the energy, of the emitted radiations. The more energetic a ray is, the more penetrative it is, and the more damage it can do to living tissues. A unit for measuring the amount of radiant energy *absorbed* was first adopted for X rays and was called the *roentgen*, after the discoverer of X rays. It represents the ionizing ability of the rays. A beam of radiation which can dislodge 2.08×10^9 (2.08 billion) electrons from the atoms in 1 cubic centimeter of dry air under standard conditions has an energy of 1 roentgen unit, 1 r. To get a clearer concept of this unit, let us look at some of its biological effects. A whole-body exposure of 700 r at one time is fatal to humans, while an exposure of 450 r is fatal to about 50% of humans. A whole-body exposure of 100 r in a very short time may cause leukemia or cancer. Small areas, especially in the arms, hands, and legs, can be exposed to large amounts of radiation without serious damage. A dose of 5,000 r can be used to treat small skin cancers. It scars the tissue, but has no other permanent effect. A fluoroscope exposes a small section of the body to about 10 r without any ill effects. A chest X ray exposes the chest to 0.1 r. Normally we are all exposed to about 0.0015 r per week by radiations entering our atmosphere from outer space. The safe upper limit for a whole-body exposure is considered to be 0.3 r per week. However, an exposure of 0.3 r spread over a week is less harmful than a dose of 0.3 r in one day and then none for the rest of the week. People working with X rays and radioactive materials wear film badges or dosimeters to determine their exposure per week. The average person receives in a lifetime less than 10 roentgens from both the natural radiations and medical doses, and this is well within the safe limit.

17-4
Transformation of Radioactive Elements

What effect does the emission of an alpha particle, a beta particle, or a gamma ray have upon the atom itself? Let us first consider what happens when an alpha particle leaves an atom. Since it is identical to the helium nucleus, it removes 2 protons and 2 neutrons from the nucleus. This reduces the original nucleus by 2 positive charges and 4 nucleons. (A *nucleon* is a particle in the nucleus, either a proton or a neutron.) The atomic number of the atom decreases by 2 and its nucleon number by 4. Let us take an example to illustrate an alpha transformation. The radium atom emits an alpha particle and disintegrates into a lighter element. Since radium has an atomic number of 88 and a nucleon number of 226, its nucleus consists of 88 protons and 138 neutrons, a total of 226 nucleons. When the radium atom discards an alpha particle (2 protons and 2 neutrons), it becomes an atom with 86 protons and 136 neutrons, or an element with an atomic number of 86 and a nucleon number of 222. This is radon, an inert gas. Radon is also radioactive and emits another alpha particle. It disintegrates into a different atom which has 84 protons and 134 neutrons in its nucleus. This is polonium-218. Such an atom has more neutrons and a greater mass than the polonium listed in the periodic table (see Table 16-3). It is called an *isotope* of polonium. Since it is radioactive, we call it a *radioisotope*.

Now let us consider what happens when beta particles are emitted from a radioactive material. Since beta particles are known to be electrons, and nuclei are composed of protons and neutrons, what part of the atom emits them? Experimental data proves that some of these betas come from the orbitals around the nucleus, but most of them originate in the nucelus. Another fact which adds to the confusion is that the beta particles emitted from any element have a wide range of energies or speeds (see Fig. 17-7). This means that one nucleus may emit a slow beta particle, while another nucleus of the same substance may emit a fast one. Since all the atoms of a given beta-emitting material disintegrate into exactly the same element, it seems as though the energy released ought to be a definite amount, thus producing beta particles with the same speed. The distribution of speeds is

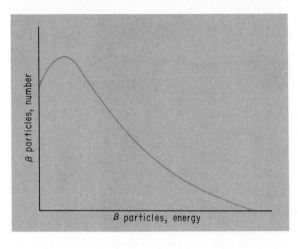

FIG. 17-7 Energy distribution of beta particles.

very puzzling. After a considerable amount of research, it was suggested that the neutrons (n) in the nucleus actually disintegrate into protons (P^+), electrons (e^-), and neutral particles of negligible rest mass which are called *neutrinos* (v).

$$n^0 \longrightarrow P^+ + e^- + v$$

The electrons and neutrinos leave the nucleus. The possible existence of neutrinos was introduced to explain beta disintegration about 20 years before they were actually detected. Scientists were in dilemma for years because they could detect only one of the released particles—the electron. In some cases, the electron receives most of the released energy, leaving very little for the neutrino; and in other cases, the neutrino receives the lion's share, leaving only a small amount for the electron. Hence, the beta particles can have a range of energies from a certain maximum value to practically zero. The sum of the energies of the two emitted particles must be a definite amount for a given element. We find that in the beta decay the neutral particle is antimatter, and so it is an antineutrino, $\bar{v}$. Hence,

$$n^0 \longrightarrow P^+ + e^- + \bar{v}$$

When a beta particle is emitted from an atom, we know that an internal change has taken place within that nucleus; a neutron has been changed to a proton and has released an electron and an antineutrino. This process increases the number of protons in the nucleus by 1, but keeps the mass approximately the same. The atomic number of the element increases by 1, but the nucleon number remains unchanged. For example, the nucleus of thorium 234 consists of 90 protons and 144 neutrons; when a beta particle is emitted, there will be 91 protons and 143 neutrons left in the new nucleus. This is protactinium 234, which is an isotope of protactinium.

Gamma rays accompany the emission of some alpha and beta particles. After either particle flies out of the nucleus, the remaining nucleons may undergo a rearrangement and release energy in the form of gamma rays.

A rearrangement of the parts of the nucleus does not alter the character of the atom; its atomic and nucleon numbers do not change.

17-5
Radioactive Series

Many natural radioactive elements belong to one of four radioactive series. The "family tree" of such an element can be traced back through transformations to its original parent element, and all its descendants finally become some stable isotope of lead. There are three such natural radioactive series—uranium (see Fig. 17-8), thorium, and actinium—and one man-made series, plutonium, which ends in a stable isotope of bismuth instead of lead.

FIG. 17-8   The uranium series of natural radioactive transformations terminating with a stable isotope of lead (Pb).

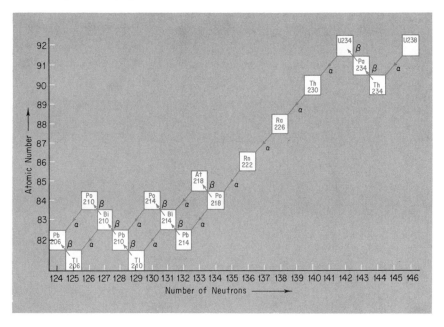

17-6
Half-Life of Radioactive Elements

We have noted that radium disintegrates into radon, but how long does each radium atom exist as radium before it emits the alpha particle and changes into the new element? To predict when any single atom will disintegrate is impossible. It may happen in the next second, or it may not happen for years. For a large number of atoms, however, there is a definite rate of transformation. This rate of decay is different for different elements. It cannot be changed in the slightest by intense heat, extremely large pressures, violent electrical discharges, ultraviolet lights, or chemical combinations with other elements, because radioactivity is a nuclear process. The same fractional part of a large number of atoms will undergo a change in every second, every year, and every century. If half of the atoms disintegrate in a certain time, we find that half of the remaining atoms will undergo decay in that same length of time. In every following equal interval of time, half of the remaining atoms will disintegrate (see Fig. 17-9).

This interval of time is known as the *half-life* of the radioactive element. By always halving the remaining quantity ($\frac{1}{2}$, $\frac{1}{4}$, $\frac{1}{8}$, $\frac{1}{16}$, $\frac{1}{32}$, and so forth), we never run out of material, but it reduces to a very minute amount. The half-life of radium is 1,612 years, whereas the half-life of its daughter product, radon, is only 3.8 days. If we have 10 micrograms of radon (2.7×10^{16} atoms, which is a large number of atoms), its emission of alpha particles

FIG. 17-9   The meaning of half-life. Rate of decay of a radioactive material. (Courtesy U.S. Atomic Wnergy Commission, Isotope Division.)

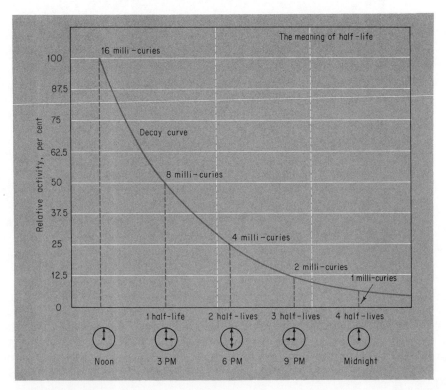

to become polonium-218 will leave us in 3.8 days with only 5 micrograms of radon left; in 7.6 days (3.8 days more) we will have half of that, or 2.5 micrograms. After 19 days (5 half-lives) there will remain only 0.31 microgram of radon. The activity of a substance may be used in place of its mass because the activity is directly proportional to the number of atoms present. The longer the half-life of an element, the more stable is its nucleus. Table 17-1 gives the half-lives of the elements in the uranium series.

17-7
Applications of Radioactivity

Radioactive material, if properly handled or used in very minute quantities, can be extremely useful to mankind. If handled improperly, it can be very dangerous. In 1934, it was discovered that any atom could be made radioactive. Since then we have found many uses for radioactive elements in medicine, agriculture, industry, and the various fields of science. There are hundreds of applications, but only a few will be cited here.

TABLE 17-1
Uranium Series

Atomic Number	Element	Nucleon Number	Half-life	Radiation Emitted
92	Uranium	238	4.5×10^9 yr	alpha
90	Thorium	234	24.5 days	beta, gamma
91	Protactinium	234	68 sec	beta, gamma
92	Uranium	234	2.67×10^5 yr	alpha
90	Thorium	230	8×10^4 yr	alpha, gamma
88	Radium	226	1,612 yr	alpha, gamma
86	Radon	222	3.82 days	alpha
84	Polonium	218	3 min	alpha
82	Lead	214	26.8 min	beta, gamma
83	Bismuth	214	19.7 min	beta, gamma
84	Polonium	214	1.5×10^{-4} sec	alpha
82	Lead	210	22 yr	beta
83	Bismuth	210	4.8 days	beta
84	Polonium	210	138 days	alpha, gamma
82	Lead	206	Stable	—

Becquerel left a small amount of uranium in a vest pocket and discovered that it produced a burned spot on his body similar to that of a sunburn. This suggested that the rays it emitted could destroy cells and might be used in the treatment of certain diseases. After the powerful radium had been produced in large enough quantities, it was used to destroy tumors and certain cancer tissue. Such regenerative or fast-growing tissue is far more sensitive to gamma rays than healthy tissue; hence, tumor and cancer cells can be damaged faster than normal cells. The problem is to "burn up" such growths without damaging the adjacent healthy tissue beyond recovery. This has been successfully accomplished. Some persons have been cured of cancer by irradiation of the cancerous area. In certain cases, the fast-growing cells can be "fed" a radioactive element and irradiated from within. The diseased cells are killed without seriously damaging the surrounding healthy tissue. This is done by determining the element that the growth readily absorbs, making that element radioactive, and giving it to the patient in the form of a "radioactive cocktail." Overactive thyroid glands have been treated in this manner, using radioactive iodine. Ninety percent of the thyroid cases treated have been brought under control in 2 to 4 months and have required no surgery.

Radioactive atoms make ideal "tracers." Any element can be made radioactive and traced through a body process without much difficulty. Dyes were first used as tracers, but the dye merely followed the process without taking part in it. In fact, so much dye was usually needed that it affected the condition being studied. Radioactive atoms, on the other hand, take part in the functions of the body exactly as normal atoms and can be traced with a Geiger counter or a scintillation counter. By using about 1 microcurie, this type of tracing is perfectly safe and far more sensitive than any other tracing technique. Salt can be followed through the body by using a sample containing some radioactive sodium atoms. We find that after a little of this kind of salt has been placed on the tongue, it can be detected in the fingers in about 75 seconds. Since sodium is very important in body fluids, these "tagged" sodium atoms are used to measure the rate of sodium transfer through blood-vessel walls. The blood itself can be studied by using radioactive iron. Since 65% of all iron in the body is in the red blood cells, "tagged" iron atoms can be used to study blood diseases. Germs and viruses have also been "tagged" and traced through the body to determine their distribution before any diseases develop. This has increased our knowledge of the different diseases and in many cases has aided us in planning better controls.

In a similar manner, radioactivity may be used in diagnostic work. If a person is suspected of having a brain tumor, he is given a "cocktail" of radioactive gold and, after several hours, the tumor, if present, can be accurately located with a scintillation counter before any surgery is undertaken. Sometimes after a thyroid cancer operation, a doctor wishes to determine if all of the diseased tissue has been removed. To do this, he feeds the patient some radioactive iodine and locates the cancer "offshoots" with a Geiger counter. Many of these offshoots would not be found in time by any other method.

The geologist has found natural radioactivity useful in checking his time scale for the various geological ages. By determining the amount of lead-206 in a given amount of uranium ore and by knowing the uranium series, he can calculate the age of that ore. Knowing the layer of rock in which the ore was deposited, he can estimate when that layer of rock was formed. Using the ore in the earliest rock formations, he has learned that the Earth is about 4.5 billion years old. This corresponds very closely to his previous estimate based upon the length of time required to form the various layers of rocks.

Radioactivity has also helped the farmer. The use of phosphorus-32 in artificial fertilizers has given him a better understanding of their effectiveness upon plants without waiting a season to observe the foliage and the crops (see Fig. 17-10). Tracer studies have shown that nutrients applied in a solution to the leaves of a plant show a 95% uptake; but if applied to the soil, only a 10% uptake results. Thus the farmer can utilize plant nutrients better by spraying a weak solution of the fertilizer on the leaves. This has been done with some trees and has proven successful. However, the nutrient taken in by the leaves does not go to the roots; therefore, fertilizer is also needed in the soil. In agricultural research, powerful rediations have been applied to various plants with the intent of altering the genes in the cells and changing their hereditary characteristics. When a change occurs in the germ cell, the alteration will be passed on to future generations. This is called *mutation*, and some success has been achieved in this field. A rust-resistant oat has been produced and, when further developed, should save farmers millions of dollars. In North Carolina, such a process has produced a new peanut plant which has a 30% higher yield and gives a more uniform shape and size to the peanuts. The farmer has also made use of tracers to understand better

FIG. 17-10   Study of phosphate fertilizer uptake. (Courtesy U.S. Atomic Energy Commission, Isotopes Division.)

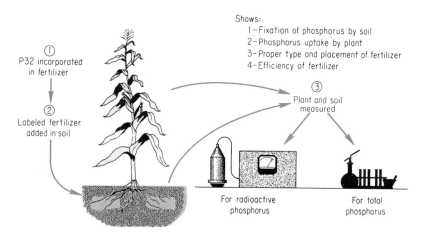

the feeding of livestock. It has been known for some time that cattle and sheep need more cobalt in their food to remain healthy than do other animals. Why do they need this excess cobalt? To answer the question, some cows were fed a small amount of radioactive cobalt with their regular food, and it was discovered that the cobalt combined with bacteria in the first stomach to form vitamin B_{12}, which is essential in the maturing of the red blood cells.

Radioactivity has made its contribution to industry as well. Penetrative gamma rays are used to detect flaws in thick castings which ordinary X rays cannot penetrate. A *radiograph* of the casting is taken by placing a film below the casting and a gamma emitter above it. The photograph produced will indicate dark lines in areas where there are defects in the casting. Furthermore, if a casting in a piece of equipment is suspected of having a crack or a flaw, it can be detected by radioactive means without dismantling the equipment. A gamma source is lowered into the casting, and a radiograph of the questioned region is taken. The developed film will show any defects that may exist. The automobile industry can test piston rings in a relatively short time by putting some radioactive iron in the rings and placing them in a test motor. After the motor has run a few hours, the crank case is drained and the oil is tested for radioactivity. From the activity in the oil, the amount of material worn off the rings can be determined. From this, the life of similar piston rings can be estimated.

In general, scientists have used radioactivity to diagnose and cure diseases, produce mutations in plants and animals, make radiographs, and trace elements through many possible reactions. Radioactive tracing is ranked in scientific importance with the discovery of the microscope. It is a powerful research tool.

After mentioning many of the wonderful uses of radioactivity, we must caution the reader that improper handling of such material might lead to health problems and possible death. Overexposure first leads to reddening of the skin followed by blisters which are hard to heal. For full-body overexposure, the early symptoms are nausea and vomiting accompanied by fatigue. After several days one loses his appetite, runs a high fever, and experiences diarrhea. A more severe exposure might result in bleeding gums and loss of hair in patches. An excess exposure may produce genetic defects, leukemia, or cataracts. As we have seen, controlled radiation can cure cancer, but too much radiation may induce it. Radioactive material taken internally by eating or breathing it is extremely hazardous. Too much radiation can be harmful to plants as well as animals. Hence, the use of radioactive materials had better be left to experienced persons who have instruments available to measure dosages to see that they remain within the tolerance of the human body.

We have been studying unstable nuclei which emit alpha or beta particles with accompanying gamma rays and disintegrate into other kinds of nuclei. There are, however, many stable nuclei that make up the atoms of the world we live in. What makes some nuclei stable and others unstable? For instance why is lithium-7 stable while lithium-8 is unstable and disintegrates into beryllium-8 in a half-life of 0.81 second? When a neutron and a proton approach to within 10^{-15} meter of one another, a new force of attraction becomes effective. This force is extremely strong and is called the *short-range nuclear force*. It is 10^{39} times as strong as the gravitational attraction of their masses. It is this force that holds the nucleus together. Then we ask, since all nuclei consist of neutrons and protons, why don't the short-range forces hold all nuclei together equally well? As the atomic number of the atoms increase, there are more protons and neutrons in the nuclei. If there were no electrostatic repelling forces between the protons, there would be an infinite number of different kinds of atoms instead of only the presently known 105. Since the atomic number represents the number of protons in the nucleus, the larger the atomic number, the greater the electrostatic force tending to blow the nucleus apart. Hence, additional neutrons are needed to produce the extraattractive short-range force to overcome the repelling forces of the protons. For small atomic numbers, the nuclei consist of equal numbers of neutrons and protons because the repelling electrostatic force is relatively small. For example, the nucleus of helium consists of 2 protons and 2 neutrons. As the atomic number increases, additional neutrons must be added to produce stable nuclei (see Fig. 17-11). Nuclei with more than 83 protons cannot be held together for any length of time regardless of the number of neutrons added. Hence, atoms with atomic numbers greater than 83 are all unstable, and those with atomic numbers above 100 have very short lives. Below 83, some of the elements may have several stable and several unstable isotopes. For example, the element tin (Sn) has 10 stable and about 15 unstable isotopes, all with an atomic number of 50.

To better understand the nucleus, let us look at the isotopes of the element carbon. This element has 2 stable nuclei, C-12 and C-13, and 6 unstable ones: C-9, C-10, C-11 with too few neutrons; and C-14, C-15, and C-16 with too many neutrons. Carbon-14, for example, has a nucleus with more neutrons than required to overcome the repelling forces of the 6 protons. Hence, in due time some of the excess neutrons will disintegrate into protons, electrons, and antineutrinos. The negative beta particle and the antineutrino escape from the nucleus leaving it with 1 less neutron and 1 more proton. The new nucleus is left with 7 protons and 7 neutrons, the nucleus of stable nitrogen.

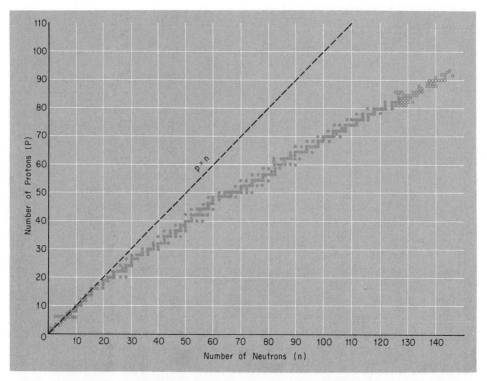

FIG. 17-11 Nuclear chart. Dark circles indicate stable nuclei; open circles indicate radioactive nuclei found in nature.

Since carbon-14 has a fairly long half-life of 5,730 years, and disintegrates into a stable atom, it is a good isotope for determining the ages of objects made from substances that during their life span took in carbon dioxide for their growth cycle. Since carbon dioxide in the air contains a small amount of carbon-14, one can determine from the activity of the carbon-14 approximately when the living plant was cut down and stopped receiving new carbon dioxide. For example, knowing the activity of carbon-14 in a tomahawk handle, one can tell how long ago the Indians cut down the tree that furnished the handle for the tomahawk. The Dead Sea Scrolls were dated in this manner from the activity of the carbon-14 left in the parchment. Carbon-15 and -16 are also unstable with too many neutrons. They emit beta particles and disintegrate into nuclei with 1 more proton and 1 less neutron. The carbon nucleus, with its 6 protons and 6 neutrons, is stable, and so is carbon-13, with its 6 protons and 7 neutrons. Of all the stable carbon occuring in its natural form 98.9% is C-12 and 1.1% is C-13. The nuclei with less than 6 neutrons do not have enough binding force to hold the nucleus together very long, and the fewer the neutrons the shorter is the half-life of the isotope. For example, the half-life of C-11 is 20.5 minutes, that of C-10 is 19 seconds, and that of C-9 is 0.13 second. In each of these three known unstable carbon nuclei, one of the protons absorbs some nuclear energy and transforms into a neutron, a positive electron called a *positron*, and a neutrino. The nucleus emits the positron and neutrino and is transformed into a nucleus with 1 less proton and 1 more neutron:

$$_6C^{11} \longrightarrow e^+ + \,_5B^{11} + \nu$$

In this relationship the subscripts represent the number of protons in the nuclei and the superscripts represent the number of particles in the nuclei. As we have noticed, those nuclei with more neutrons than is necessary for stability emit beta particles, and the number of protons increases by 1. Those nuclei that lack sufficient neutrons emit positrons, and the number of protons decreases by 1.

We must now explain how some radioactive nuclei emit gamma rays (see Table 17-1). Whenever a neutron changes to a proton, or vice versa, the remaining nucleus might be left in an excited state; in other words, the remaining nucleons are not in their lowest energy state. When these nucleons drop to a lower energy level, the energy loss is released in the form of an electromagnetic wave or a gamma ray. This is analogous to the photon emitted when an electron drops from a high- to a low-energy level. The nucleons, like the electrons, may drop in steps, emitting several different wavelengths of gamma rays, or in one big step emitting one wavelength of a gamma ray.

17-9
Structure of the Nucleus

At first the nucleus was thought of as being a very small positively charged core at the center of the atom. It was considered to be like a spherical drop of liquid with all of the nucleons within a short range of each other. Each nucleon moved throughout the nucleus volume under the attraction of the other nucleons. This model of the nucleus was very successful in explaining nuclear fission (see page 317), but it could not explain the different wavelengths of gamma rays emitted by a nucleus, nor the unusual stability of nuclei containing 2, 8, 20, 28, 82, and 126 protons or neutrons. These are called "magic numbers." The orbital electrons follow a similar pattern of 2, 8, 18, 36, etc., which indicates the maximum number of electrons that can exist in each energy level. Hence, the magic numbers must somehow represent the energy levels of the neutrons and protons within the nucleus. At a magic number, a certain energy level is filled, and the nucleus takes a spherical shape like a drop of liquid. During some disintegrations, the remaining nucleons are left in a high-energy level, and when the nucleons drop to a lower-energy level, a gamma ray is emitted. A nucleus model of energy levels has helped explain more nuclear phenomena than has the liquid-drop model, but the structure of the nucleus is still questionable.

Although we do not have a precise idea of the structure of the nucleus, we do know enough about it to understand certain nuclear reactions, which we shall study in the next chapter.

QUESTIONS AND PROBLEMS

1. Describe how Becquerel discovered radioactivity. What is meant by *radioactivity*?

2. What is spontaneous disintegration?

3. Describe the physical properties of alpha particles, beta particles, and gamma rays.

4. Describe how an electroscope can measure the intensity of charged-particle radiation. Can it be used to measure the intensity of gamma-ray radiations?

5. How does a Geiger counter really count ionizing particles? Does the scintillation counter work on the same principle? Explain.

6. How does a Wilson cloud chamber detect ionizing particles? Is the principle the same for a bubble chamber? What are the differences between the two?

7. What kind of particles do not leave tracks in a Wilson cloud chamber, and why not?

8. Curies and roetgens are units for measuring what quantities? What is meant when we say that we have a 10-millicurie source of radioactive material? Would it be correct to say that one has a 30-milliroentgen source? Explain.

9. What happens to an atom that has emitted an alpha particle? A beta particle? A gamma ray?

10. The following radioactive elements emit alpha particles and disintegrate into what substance?
    (a) Americium, Am-243.　　(d) Protactinium, Pa-231.
    (b) Thorium, Th-230.　　　(e) Polonium, Po-219.
    (c) Radium, Ra-223.

11. Can the activity of a radioactive material be increased by heating it to very high temperatures? Explain.

12. Can radium be neurtralized by combining it chemically with chlorine, forming radium chloride? Explain.

13. The following radioactive elements emit beta particles and disintegrate into what substance?
    (a) Thorium Th-234.   (d) Tritium, H-3.
    (b) Uranium, U-240.   (e) Phosphorus, P-34.
    (c) Francium, Fr-223.   (f) Silver, Ag-115.

14. What is a neutrino? Why was such a particle proposed? What did it turn out to be? Explain what happens in a beta decay.

15. Carbon-14 disintegrates into nitrogen-14. What does the carbon-14 nucleus emit to become nitrogen-14?

16. Why is the half-life of a radioactive substance so important? Do two half-lives equal a whole-life? Explain.

17. If the half-life of radioactive iodine-131 is 8 days, how long will it take for 128 milligrams to disintegrate into 1 milligram?

18. A certain laboratory receives 24 microcuries of phosphorus-32 (P-32) for some experimental work. The experiment is repeated 28 days later. Since the half-life of P-32 is 14 days, how many microcuries are left for the repeated experiment?

19. If the activity of a radioactive sample drops to $\frac{1}{32}$ of its initial value in 1 hour and 20 minutes, what is its half-life?

20. A radioactive material disintegrates from 160 micrograms to 5 micrograms in 40 days. What is the half-life of the material?

21. Americium-241 (Am-241) disintegrates into neptunium-237 (Np-237). What does the Am-214 nucleus emit to become Np-237?

22. An atom of uranium-238 (U-238) disintegrates into lead-206 (Pb-206) after a series of disintegrations in approximately 2 billion years. In the process, it emits 8 alpha particles and how many beta particles?

23. How long will it take for a sample of radon-222 (Rn-222), which has a half-life of 3.8 days, to decrease to 25% of its original amount?

24. Why do radioisotopes make better tracers than do those made by dyes?

25. How close must particles get to have the short-range nuclear forces take over? How much stronger are these forces than gravitational forces?

26. Why does stable cobalt consist of 27 protons and 32 neutrons instead of 27 protons and 27 neutrons? Why is cobalt-60 radioactive?

27. Would you expect boron-8 (B-8) to emit a beta particle or a positron when it disintegrates? Explain. What would B-13 emit upon disintegration?

28. The following radioactive substances emit positrons and disintegrate into what substances?
    (a) Iodine-119.   (d) Silver-102.
    (b) Chlorine-33.   (e) Sodium-21.
    (c) Aluminum-24.

29. What is the significance of the "magic number" of the nucleus?

30. When a nucleus emits a gamma ray, what takes place inside the nucleus?

SUGGESTED REFERENCES

FORD, KENNETH W., *Basic Physics*, Chap. 25. Blaisdell Publishing Co., Waltham, Mass., 1968.

GAMOW, GEORGE, *Matter, Earth, and Sky*, Chap. 14. Prentice-Hall, Englewood Cliffs, N.J., 1958.

GLASSTONE, S., *Sourcebook on Atomic Energy*, Chaps. 5 & 12. D. Van Nostrand Co., Princeton, N. J., 1958.

WHITE, HARVEY E., *Introduction to Atomic and Nuclear Physics*, Chaps. 23, 24, 25, and 32. D. Van Nostrand Co., Princeton, N. J., 1964

18
Nuclear Reactions and Energy

For centuries, the alchemists tried in vain to transform one element into another. Their great hope was to find some method of changing the baser metals into gold. At the same time, unknown to them, nature was transforming many of the heavier elements into other substances, but not into gold. The naturally radioactive elements were emitting alpha or beta particles and changing to other elements.

During the past 50 years, scientists have been able to achieve at least a part of the great dream of the alchemists. With the aid of "atom-smashing" machines, they have been able to change one element into another. Such a transformation we call *transmutation*. They have actually changed a substance into gold. Such a change will not yield the fabulous riches that fired the imaginations of the alchemists, because the substance transmuted was not one of the baser metals, but platinum, a metal more valuable than gold. Man can now duplicate the work of nature. Not only can he transform atoms, but he can make any element radioactive, and can even make new elements that do not exist in nature. The smashing of atoms has given us a much better understanding of their structure and has led us to a new source of energy called *nuclear energy*, which is sometimes incorrectly called *atomic energy*.

18-1
Discovery of Nuclear Transmutation

In 1919, while measuring the maximum distances that alpha particles could travel through various gases (see Fig. 18-1). Rutherford discovered an interesting phenomenon. He observed that in pure nitrogen the alpha particles had an unusually long range of about 40 centimeters. This was very surprising because their range in air, which is 77% nitrogen, was only about 7 centi-

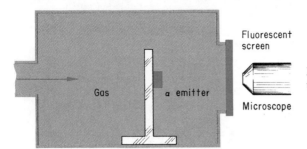

Fluorescent
screen

FIG. 18-1 Apparatus for measuring the range of alpha particles in a gas.

Gas   α emitter

Microscope

meters. At first he thought that perhaps the alpha particles struck the nitrogen molecules and propelled them 40 centimeters, but further experimentation with other gases proved definitely that this assumption was not valid. He then concluded that a bombarding alpha particle must have struck a nitrogen nucleus and knocked a smaller particle out of it. He reasoned that if it were a smaller particle, it could pass more easily between the nitrogen molecules, collide with them less frequently, and thus go farther through the gas before losing its forward motion. It seemed to him that the particle ought to be a proton. Later experiments, using magnetic deflections, proved that his assumption was correct. Rutherford also discovered that he could knock protons out of all the lighter elements from boron to potassium, with the exceptions of carbon and oxygen. This seemed to verify the theory that protons exist in all nuclei and are one of the fundamental "building blocks" of matter.

By using a Wilson cloud chamber, it was later shown that the nitrogen nucleus actually captured the alpha particle and immediately emitted a proton. The following nuclear reaction must have taken place: The nitrogen nucleus, consisting of 7 protons and 7 neutrons, "swallowed" the alpha particle, and became a nucleus with 9 protons and 9 neutrons. This temporary nucleus, which was that of fluorine-18, soon discarded a proton and became a nucleus with 8 protons and 9 neutrons, the resulting element being oxygen-17, one of the stable but less abundant isotopes of oxygen. Nitrogen had been changed to oxygen. Such a transmutation can be written symbolically as:

$$_7N^{14} + \,_2He^4 \longrightarrow (_9F^{18})^* \longrightarrow \,_1H^1 + \,_8O^{17}$$

The subscript to the left of each symbol is its atomic number, and the superscript to the right is its nucleon number; $(_9F^{18})^*$ is an exited nucleus which soon goes through some kind of transformation before emitting the proton.

18-2
Discovery of the Neutron

In 1930, W. Bothe and H. Becker of Germany noticed that when beryllium was bombarded by alpha particles, intensely penetrating radiations were emitted instead of protons. These radiations they believed to be gamma rays. The Curies found that such rays could, in turn, knock protons out of hydrogen-rich paraffin. From the range of these protons in air, it was possible to calculate the energy of the rays producing them. This energy, however, did not correspond with the energy determined directly from the original nuclear reaction that produced the rays. The whole problem became very confusing. In 1932, Chadwick, an Englishman, showed that everything worked out beautifully when he assumed that the beryllium nucleus emitted a neutral particle with a mass number of 1 instead of the gamma rays previously suggested. This new particle he called the *neutron*. Hence, the correct nuclear reaction was

$$_4\text{Be}^9 + {}_2\text{He}^4 \longrightarrow ({}_6\text{C}^{13})^* \longrightarrow {}_0n^1 + {}_6\text{C}^{12}$$

We make use of such a reaction to produce free neutrons. By coating some beryllium metal with a very thin layer of an alpha-emitting substance, such as polonium, thousands of neutrons may be produced per second.

Since neutrons possess no charge, they cause no ionization; therefore, they cannot be detected by the instruments described in the preceding chapter. These neutral particles can penetrate nuclei quite easily and produce transmutations. They are particularly harmful to living tissue because they destroy the cells which they strike; hence, we must protect ourselves from an excess amount of them. Ordinary water, paraffin, or cadmium sheets make excellent shields. When neutrons strike the hydrogen nuclei in the water or paraffin, they impart most of their kinetic energy to them. This slows down the neutrons and increases the vibrational energy of the atoms of the shield; the kinetic energy of the neutrons is converted into thermal energy of the atoms of the shield. The remaining neutrons have lost enough energy to make them harmless. The cadmium nuclei absorb neutrons leaving less neutrons to do harm.

18-3
"Atom-Smashing" Machines

During the 1930's, physicists searched for methods to smash the tiny atom other than using naturally occurring alpha particles. They needed some means of producing an intense beam of bombarding particles at high, controllable energies. Since charged particles can be accelerated to high speeds in strong electrostatic fields, it was quite logical that scientists should try to employ high voltages. Early investigators thought that lightning might be a convenient way of securing the necessary voltages, but it proved too difficult to control and far too dangerous. Then various types of high-voltage transformers were tried, but the insulation used in them limited their voltage output.

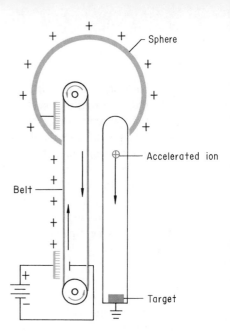

FIG. 18-2   Van de Graaff generator.

In 1931, Van de Graaff, an American physicist, developed an electrostatic generator capable of producing a steady output of several million volts. This generator is basically an electrostatic machine (Fig. 18-2). To produce the high voltage, electrons are removed from a moving fabric belt, leaving the belt with a positive charge. As the belt enters a large metal sphere, it attracts electrons, and by means of a series of properly arranged sharp metal points the electrons "leak" off the sphere onto the belt, neutralizing it. This continues until the sphere is charged positively with a very high voltage. To retain this accumulated charge, the sphere must be well insulated from the rest of the equipment. An evacuated discharge tube is placed between this positively charged sphere and the base of the machine, which is electrically grounded. The atoms to be smashed are introduced at the grounded end of the tube. Then hydrogen, helium, or deuterium ions are sprayed into the top of the tube. They are repelled by the large positive charge on the sphere and are accelerated as they stream down the tube. By the time they reach the lower end of the discharge tube, they have received enough kinetic energy to penetrate some of the nuclei of the atoms placed there. The energy of these bombarding particles is usually expressed in *electron volts* (ev), millions of electron volts (Mev), or billions (giga) of electron volts (Gev). One electron volt is the kinetic energy given 1 electron by a difference of potential of 1 volt. It is equivalent to 1.6×10^{-19} joule.

Van de Graaff generators, unless placed in tandem, are limited to less than 7 million electron volts (7 Mev). At that voltage, the charges attract negative ions from the surrounding air as fast as the positive charges are produced on the sphere by the moving belt. If, however, the entire equipment

312

is placed inside a large metal enclosure which contains a gas, such as Freon, at a high pressure, the charges on the sphere will not be neutralized as readily, and a much higher voltage can be obtained.

About the same time that Van de Graaff was developing his generator, E. O. Lawrence, of the University of California, invented a different type of accelerator, called the *cyclotron*. In order to impart to any electrically charged particle enough energy to enable it to penetrate a nucleus, one can give it the energy in one big wallop, or in smaller amounts repeated many times. The former method is that used by the Van de Graaff generator. It has the disadvantage of requiring the use of very high voltages. These voltages, running into the millions, are not hard to generate, but are very hard to control. The second method was not thought feasible until Lawrence, in 1932, showed how it could be done. The cyclotron applies a moderate voltage to a particle but applies it many times. By applying 50,000 volts to the particle there is no difficulty in the insulation needed, and by applying that voltage 100 times, the energy imparted to the charged particle is equal to that of a 5,000,000 volt drop.

Now let us see how the cyclotron accomplishes this feat. The heart of the cyclotron is a powerful electromagnet. The pole pieces of the magnet are located one above the other, a few inches apart. In the space between them is placed a broad, shallow, evacuated, cylindrical chamber (C, in Fig. 18-3). Inside C are two semicylindrical copper chambers, D_1 and D_2, $1\frac{1}{2}$ to 2 inches deep, which are open along the edges facing each other. The *dees*, as they are called, are insulated from each other and from C. Hydrogen, deuterium (heavy hydrogen), or helium gases are ionized and sprayed between the dees at their center. The kind of gas used determines whether the charged particles shall be protons, deuterons, or alphas.

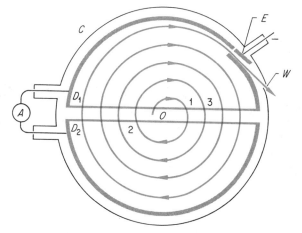

FIG. 18-3 The path of a charged particle in a cyclotron.

The dees are connected to the terminals of a high-frequency generator *A*. This is an oscillator very similar to a radio transmitter, minus the modulator and antenna. The electrified particles are produced at *O*, near the center of the magnetic field, by ionization of the gas entering between the dees. During an instant when D_1 is negative and D_2 positive, each positive particle is drawn into D_1. In this time it acquires a speed corresponding to the voltage delivered by the generator. Once it is inside D_1, the electrostatic force ceases to act, but the particle continues to move at its acquired speed. It does not move in a straight line, however. When in motion, the charge has all the properties of an electric current. The magnetic field exerts a force upon it in a direction perpendicular to the motion of the particle and to the lines of force of the field. The particle thus follows a circular course, which quickly brings it to point 1. At that instant D_1 is made positive and D_2 negative, and the particle is speeded up again by a pull into D_2. With its increased speed, it travels in a larger semicircle to the point 2, where it arrives just as the dees again change polarity. At that moment they give it another pull, now into D_1. After many such additions to its energy, the particle approaches the rim of its spiral racecourse. There it comes close to a negatively charged electrode *E*, which draws it into a larger circle and brings it out through the window *W*. It is at this point, in a suitably constructed chamber, that its energy is utilized.

Many of the universities of our country have built cyclotrons (see Fig. 18-4), either to carry on research on the structure of atomic nuclei or to artificially

FIG. 18-4   A beam of particles emerging from the Argonne 60-in cyclotron. (Argonne National Laboratory.)

produce radioactive materials for medical use. Some of these require hundreds of tons of steel and several tons of copper in the construction of the electromagnet, and employ a high-frequency electric generator several times more powerful than most of our larger radio transmitters. The energy they impart to protons and other positively charged particles ranges up to 30 Mev.

Cyclotron improvements led to synchrocyclotrons, which are capable of imparting energies to protons up to 600 Mev. To produce even higher voltages, giant accelerators called proton-synchrotrons, were developed. These machines have no fundamental limitations on the energies they can impart to charge particles, but since they contain such huge magnets, economics and engineering problems become the limiting factors.

The first of this type, called the *cosmotron*, was built at the Brookhaven National Laboratory on Long Island, N.Y., and produced 2.3 billion electron volts (Gev) on its first run. The same year the bevatron was put into operation developing energies up to 6 Gev. The Soviet Union has built one that produces 10 Gev. An internationally owned proton-synchrotron is now operating a 30 Gev in Geneva, Switzerland. The National Accelerator at Batavia, Illinois, operates at 200 Gev, and is capable of producing 500 Gev. With a few adaptations it might be able to produce energies of 1,000 Gev. Then they will be able to match the energies of some of the cosmic particles that enter our atmosphere from outer space, which have energies between 10 Mev and 10^{11} Gev.

18-4
Nuclear Reactions

The type of transmutation that takes place after a nucleus is smashed by an energetic particle depends on the structure of the nucleus, the kind of bombarding particle, and the energy of that particle. The common projectiles used for smashing atoms are alpha particles (helium nuclei), protons, deuterons, and neutrons. The first three can be accelerated in atom-smashing machines; but since neutrons possess no charge, they cannot be accelerated in this manner. Energetic neutrons are obtained from certain nuclear reactions (see p. 311). Whenever one of these particles enters a nucleus, a reaction usually takes place within that nucleus. After a short interval of time, the nucleus discards some kind of particle and changes to another element. Thousands of nuclear reactions are known, but we need consider only two such reactions to obtain a general idea of what happens when a nucleus is smashed.

When sodium is bombarded by high-speed protons, we observe alpha particles being ejected. We immediately ask: what kind of element remains? The sodium nucleus consists of 11 protons and 12 neutrons. When 1 proton is added, the temporary nucleus has 12 protons and 12 neutrons. After an alpha particle with its 2 protons and 2 neutrons is discarded, the remaining nucleus consists of 10 protons and 10 neutrons—the nucleus of neon. Such a nuclear reaction can be written as:

$$_{11}\text{Na}^{23} + {}_1\text{H}^1 \longrightarrow ({}_{12}\text{Mg}^{24})^* \longrightarrow {}_2\text{He}^4 + {}_{10}\text{Ne}^{20}$$

A useful and interesting transmutation takes place when boron-10 is bombarded by energetic neutrons. The boron nucleus absorbs 1 neutron and becomes boron-11. Shortly thereafter an alpha particle is ejected and the remaining nucleus has 3 protons and 4 neutrons, which is the nucleus of the lithium atom:

$$_5\text{B}^{10} + {}_0n^1 \longrightarrow ({}_5\text{B}^{11})^* \longrightarrow {}_2\text{He}^4 + {}_3\text{Li}^7$$

Neutrons themselves are not ionizing particles; but when they penetrate the nuclei of boron-10, ionizing particles are produced. If a small quantity of boron-10 in the form of a boron trifluoride (BF_3) gas is placed in a Geiger-Müller tube, the instrument can now detect and count neutrons. The neutrons entering the tube penetrate the boron nuclei and produce alpha particles which are actually counted by the Geiger counter. This is an indirect method, but it works.

18-5
Mass-Energy

In the nuclear reaction described above, it first appears that there is no change in the total mass; but if the exact masses are taken into consideration, there seems to be a discrepancy:

> *Before:*
> Boron-10 = 10.0161 atomic mass units
> Neutron = 1.0089
> Total   11.0250 amu
>
> *After:*
> Helium   = 4.0038 atomic mass units
> Lithium-7 = 7.0182
> Total   11.0220 amu

Does this represent a loss in mass, or does it represent an inaccuracy in the measured masses of the elements used?

In 1905, Einstein predicted that mass might disappear and change into some form of energy, and, conversely, that energy might also change into mass. He also derived a simple expression for the conversion from one to the other:

$$\text{Energy} = \text{Mass} \times (\text{Speed of light})^2$$
$$E = mc^2$$
$$\text{joules} = \text{kg} \times (\text{m/sec})^2$$

where E is the energy released, m is the amount of mass that disappeared, and c represents the velocity of light.

In 1920, this equation was verified experimentally and its position is now considered secure. The simplest experimental proof of this mass-energy relationship is the forming of *positron* (positive electron) and electron pairs. Cloud-chamber photographs show that, when extremely energetic gamma rays pass through a thin piece of lead foil, positron-electron pairs are formed. Some of the gamma rays disappear and matter appears in their place; electromagnetic energy has been converted into matter. Other experiments show the reverse to be true. When positrons and electrons come near each other, they spin around each other for a short time, and then combine to form two energetic gamma rays. In this case, matter has disappeared, and an equivalent amount of electromagnetic energy has been formed. Mass is not a distinct and independent entity, as was once believed, but is merely another form of energy. The line of distinction between the two has been obliterated.

In the boron reaction, there was no discrepancy in the atomic weights. The difference was real; mass actually disappeared. The lost mass was converted into kinetic energies of the alpha particle and lithium nucleus. In some transmutations, the loss in mass is only a few thousandths of 1 % of the total mass, while in others it may be almost 1%. However, a very small loss in mass when multiplied by the speed of light squared (900,000,000,000,000,-000,000) becomes a significant increase in energy. If 1 gram of matter were completely converted into energy, the heat produced would be $0.001 \times (3 \times 10^8)^2 / 4.186 \times 10^3$, or 2.15×10^{10} kilocalories. This is the same amount of heat that would be produced by the burning of 3.09×10^6 kg or 3,400 tons of high-grade coal. In many nuclear transmutations the opposite effect is noticed: the total mass after the reaction is larger than the mass before. In each of these cases, the bombarding particle must penetrate the nucleus with sufficient kinetic energy to supply the mass increase. Atom-smashing machines are needed for such reactions in order to give the bombarding projectiles enough energy to make the transmutations possible.

18-6
Nuclear Fission

In 1934, Enrico Fermi, an Italian physicist who later came to America, believed that he and his coworkers could make new elements with atomic numbers greater than 92 by bombarding uranium with neutrons. After such a bombardment, he detected beta activities different from any of those in the uranium series. Knowing that whenever a substance emits a beta particle it transforms into another element with a greater atomic number, he concluded that a "transuranic" element with an atomic number of 93 had been produced.

Chemical tests were made to verify this hypothesis, but working with the minute amounts of the newly formed radioactive material was so difficult that results were not very conclusive.

Many workers, including two Germans, Hahn and Strassman, became interested in this field of research. In 1939, these two scientists discovered, as the result of chemical experiments, that one of the radioactive elements formed by the bombardment of uranium with neutrons was an isotope of barium (atomic number 56). They suggested that, instead of forming a transuranic element, the uranium nucleus was split into two nuclei of roughly comparable masses. If the one element so formed was barium, the other was krypton (atomic number 36), their atomic numbers adding up to that of uranium (see Fig. 18-5). This splitting of a heavy nucleus into two lighter nuclei is called *nuclear fission*, commonly erroneously called *atomic fission*. As soon as this remarkable discovery was announced, physicists all over the world repeated the experiment and verified the results. It was later discovered that the nuclei being split were those of uranium-235, and not uranium-238. Normally a small amount of U-235 is found in any uranium metal, about 1 part in 137. The reaction for the particular nuclear fission discovered by Hahn and Strassman can be written as follows:

$$_{92}U^{235} + _{0}n^{1} \rightarrow (_{92}U^{236})^* \rightarrow _{56}Ba^{141} + _{36}Kr^{92} + 3_{0}n^{1}$$

This is only one of many ways in which the uranium nucleus can split. Each fission forms a pair of lighter fragments and releases some mass energy and, generally, two or three fast neutrons.

In discussing any nuclear fission process, there are three important factors to be stressed. First, there is a loss of mass in the reaction. In the foregoing case, it is approximately one-tenth of 1% (0.1%) of the original mass. Hence, considerable energy is released. Second, several neutrons are emitted by each neutron-producing fission. This means that under proper conditions

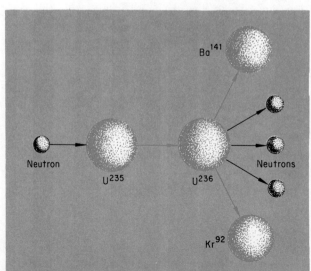

Neutron

U^{235}

U^{236}

Ba^{141}

Neutrons

Kr^{92}

FIG. 18-5 One mode of nuclear fission of uranium 235.

the reaction can be self-sustaining, a process which is known as a *chain reaction*. Third, the fragments formed are very radioactive. They emit beta particles and powerful gamma rays as they disintegrate into more stable elements.

Let us consider each of these three factors in a little more detail. The amount of energy released in this type of a nuclear reaction staggers the imagination. If 1 kilogram of uranium-235 were to experience fission, 1 gram of matter would be converted into 2.15×10^{10} kilocalories of thermal energy. This is equivalent to the heat produced by approximately 3.09×10^6 kg or 3,400 tons of coal, 7.6×10^6 kg or 8,360 tons of TNT, 2.4×10^6 liters or 605,000 gallons of gasoline, or 2.49×10^7 kilowatt-hours of electricity. The last value is enough electricity to supply 165,000 families for 1 month. Many interesting illustrations can be derived from these figures. For example, if 2.5 grams of uranium-235 were to experience fission, 2.5×10^{-3} grams of mass would be converted to thermal energy. This is enough energy to heat an average home for 1 year, or run an automobile for 161,000 km or 100,000 miles. At present, these two applications are not feasible, but they are very intriguing.

Since there are usually two or three fission neutrons released by every bombarding neutron, the number of nuclear reactions could increase very rapidly, provided the neutrons formed are not lost or absorbed by nonfissionable material. If, however, there are too few atoms present, the fission neutrons formed might escape from the material without splitting any more atoms; thus the fission process stops. The smallest amount of material needed to guarantee a continued nuclear reaction is called the *critical mass*. If an amount of pure uranium-235 larger than its critical mass experiences uncontrolled fission, the reaction will occur in a very short time—about one-millionth of a second. The release of so much energy in such a short time makes this type of nuclear reaction highly explosive. Fortunately, the emission of some neutrons is delayed for a fraction of a second, making it possible to control the reaction by removing, through absorption, the proper number of neutrons. Thus the number of reactions per second can be varied and even stopped, if the operator so desires, by sliding neutron absorbers in and out of the fissionable material. Cadmium and boron nuclei readily absorb neutrons; therefore, they make excellent control rods. Nuclear energy sources, called *nuclear reactors*, are built and properly controlled with very little danger of explosions.

It was mentioned that the fragments, or by-products, of a fission reaction are extremely radiactive, which makes this form of energy very hazardous if proper protection is not provided. After an A-bomb explosion, the radioactive material falls out of the air and irradiates the plants and animals upon which it settles. These radiations may cause mutations of the germ or reproductive cells and produce harmful effects upon the generations that follow. They also damage other living cells and, if too intense, will kill the plants and animals upon which they fall. Therefore, in case of a nuclear-bomb attack, those outside the blast area must seek fallout shelters to be protected from the harmful radiations emitted by the radioactive dust formed by the bomb. Nuclear reactors are surrounded by several inches of lead and several feet of lead or concrete to protect the people working near the installation from the harmful radioactive rays. We have been able to shield our nuclear furnaces, but what are we to do with the radioactive waste materials, some of which have very long half-lives? If one barrel of waste material from a nuclear reactor were dumped into Lake Michigan, it would seriously contaminate the entire lake and slowly kill all of its animal and vegetable life. At the present time, these useless "radioactive ashes" are either buried deeply in isolated regions or sealed in concrete containers and dropped to the bottom of the ocean. The latter isn't done too extensively, but such procedures cannot continue indefinitely without polluting our environment. Making chemical compounds out of the by-products is not the answer to the problem because chemical reactions do not affect the nuclei of the atoms, and the newly formed compounds will remain radioactive. The disposal of radioactive waste materials is a serious problem.

A number of other elements experience fission when bombared by neutrons. Some require neutrons of thermal speeds, called *slow neutrons*, whereas others are split by either fast or slow ones. Uranium-235 is far more fissionable by slow neutrons. Since fission usually produces high-speed neutrons of about nine-tenths the speed of light, the neutrons must be slowed down to thermal speeds in order to be efficiently captured by the uranium-235 nuclei. This is accomplished by passing the neutrons through a material which has atoms slightly heavier than the neutrons but does not absorb them. When the neutrons strike these atoms, they impart some of their kinetic energy to the atoms, and after successive collisions, slow down to the average kinetic energy of the atoms. Such a material is called a *moderator*. The best moderator is heavy water, but it is rather expensive. The next best is carbon in the form of pure graphite. Ordinary water is fairly effective. If uranium rods are properly placed throughout the moderator, the neutrons released by fission in one location will pass through the moderator and be sufficiently slowed down by the time they reach the uranium atoms in another location to split those atoms. To control the reaction, cadmium or boron rods are moved in or out of the reactor core.

18-7
Discovery of Transuranic Elements

It has been found that only a small proportion of the uranium-238 nuclei experience fission when struck by neutrons. Most of them capture the neutrons of medium energies and form uranium-239. This isotope of uranium has a short half-life of 24 minutes, emits a beta particle, and disintegrates into a new transuranic element with atomic number 93. This element is called *neptunium*. It, in turn, emits a beta particle and changes into another new element called *plutonium*, atomic number 94. Perhaps these were some of the beta activities that Fermi observed when he bombarded uranium with neutrons. Plutonium-239 is a fissionable material that can be split by either fast or slow neutrons; therefore, it makes a more efficient bomb than uranium-235, because no moderator can be used in the bomb. This isotope of plutonium is radioactive and has a half-life of 24,000 years. It disintegrates slowly, emitting an alpha particle, and yielding uranium-235. Since the discovery of plutonium and prior to 1972, man has made eleven more elements. They are:

95	Americium	Am
96	Curium	Cm
97	Berkelium	Bk
98	Califormiun	Cf
99	Einsteinium	Es
100	Fermium	Fm
101	Mendelevium	Md
102	Nobelium	No
103	Lawrencium	Lw
104	Unnamed	—
105	Hahnium	Ha

These elements are also listed in Table 16-3. They have short half-lives; therefore, they do not exist in nature. Some scientist claim to have discovered element 112, a superheavy nucleus.

18-8
Nuclear Reactors

Now let us consider the construction and operation of a nuclear reactor. The fuel for such a "furnace" is a metal—uranium-238 enriched in uranium-235 (1.4% U-235). This is done by removing U-238 from the natural uranium until the enrichment is of the desired amount. This uranium is formed into rods or plates and sheathed in aluminum or zirconium to keep the fuel from contaminating the rest of the reactor. These rods are properly spaced throughout a moderator of pure graphite or heavy water. When the uranium-235 atoms in the fuel experience fission, heat is produced and fast neutrons are released. Some of these neutrons are slowed down as they go through the moderator and are captured by other U-235 nuclei, producing more fissions.

Other neutrons are captured by U-238 nuclei, which are converted to plutonium. Some neutrons are lost or absorbed in the control rods or by impurities in the fuel and moderator. Some neutrons also drift away from the reactor core, or "leak" out. As this process continues, heat is produced by the split ting of the U-235 atoms and plutonium is formed from the U-238. Control rods of cadmium or boron-steel are arranged throughout the core and are automatically pushed in or out of the core to absorb the neutrons and keep the reactor operating at a desired power level. The uranium, as well as the moderator, must be cooled by circulating a liquid or a gas through the heating unit. If either heavy water or ordinary water is used as the moderator, it also functions as the coolant. In some graphite reactors, the cooling agent is liquid sodium or potassium; in others, it is helium or air. Since most coolants become strongly radioactive, they must be pumped through an exchange chamber where they transfer their heat, but not their radioactivity, to some water which is pumped through another part of that chamber (see Fig. 18-6). This water, which is not radioactive, boils and the steam produced can be used to heat buildings, generate electricity, or perform other functions. The reactor and exchange chamber must be adequately shielded to protect the working personnel. Care must be taken in the disposal of the waste material. We must also be sure that the reactors do not produce thermal pollution in our rivers and lakes above the tolerance of aquatic life.

There are many nuclear reactors of various kinds in operation throughout the world today. The first were used for research purposes and the production of plutonium, but now many are being built for generating electricity and heating buildings. The first nuclear power plant devoted entirely to civilian use was built at Shippingport, Pa., which is on the Ohio River, about 25

FIG. 18-6   Harnessing atomic energy for power. This reactor uses a gas as a coolant, and its heat is transferred to the water in an exchange chamber. (Courtesy U.S. Atomic Energy Commission, Isotopes Division.)

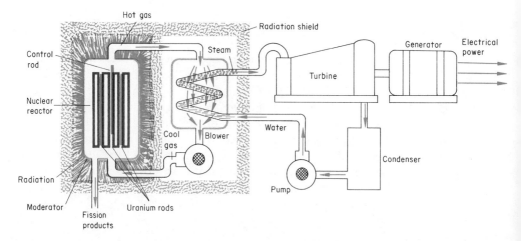

FIG. 18-7 The Enrico Fermi Atomic Power Plant, built, owned and operated by Power Reactor Development Company, utilizes the fast breeder reactor concept and is designed to produce heat from the splitting of uranium atoms for the generation of electric power and, at the same time, breed a better nuclear fuel, plutonium, in quantities greater than the uranium consumed. Reactor in the dome covered building. (Power Reactor Development Company.)

miles from Pittsburgh. It is operated by the Duquesne Power and Light Company and produces electrical energy at the rate of 60 megawatts. Many nuclear power plants for the production of electrical power are now being built in the United States (see Figs. 18-7 and 18-8) and the world. Small

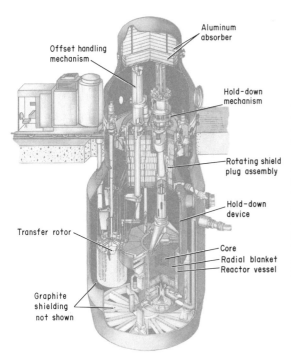

FIG. 18-8 Cutaway model of the Enrico Fermi reactor vessel contained inside of a primary shield tank. The core of the reactor is only 30 in. high and 30 in. in diameter. Ninety percent of the heat is generated in the core. Liquid sodium flows into the lower chamber of the reactor, is forced up through the core at 32 ft/sec, and leaves the top at 800°F. Plutonium is produced in the areas of radial and axial blankets. The reactor vessel does not extend above ground or floor level. (Power Reactor Development Company.)

reactors are being used to power a fleet of U.S. submarines, the *U.S.S. Nautilus* being the first of this kind. Nuclear power plants are especially suitable for submarine use because they require no oxygen, and the reactor can run for long periods of time without refueling, thus permitting longer periods of maneuvering below the ocean surface and the polar icecap.

18-9
Nuclear Fusion

For ages, man thought that the Sun and stars were heated to incandescence by combustion. He considered the stars as merely some kind of celestial coal piles. In 1853, Helmholtz tried to explain the tremendous amounts of heat developed by the contraction of gases, but failed. After the discovery of radioactivity, some thought that the energy released by the atoms upon disintegration contributed to the stars' energies, but this idea proved unsatisfactory. In 1920, Eddington suggested the possibility of the hydrogen in the Sun and stars combining to form helium with a release of energy. This hypothesis assumed that complex atoms could be made from hydrogen. Simple calculations show that the temperature necessary for the hydrogen nuclei to have sufficient kinetic energy to run into and react with other hydrogen nuclei, producing a *nuclear fusion*, would have to be approximately 4 million degrees Kelvin. Since stars are not known to be that hot, his suggestion was questioned. Others argued that, since gas molecules have a wide range of velocities at any given temperature, a few of the hydrogen nuclei near the center of the Sun must have high enough velocity to produce fusion. In 1939, H. A. Bethe of the United States proposed the following carbon cycle as the method by which hydrogen might be converted into helium in the Sun releasing energy and gamma rays:

$$_1H^1 + {_6}C^{12} \longrightarrow {_7}N^{13} + \gamma + \text{Energy (released)}$$
$$_7N^{13} \longrightarrow {_6}C^{13} + {_{+1}}e^0 + \text{Energy}$$
$$_1H^1 + {_6}C^{13} \longrightarrow {_7}N^{14} + \gamma + \text{Energy}$$
$$_1H^1 + {_7}N^{14} \longrightarrow {_8}O^{15} + \gamma + \text{Energy}$$
$$_8O^{15} \longrightarrow {_7}N^{15} + {_{+1}}e^0 + \text{Energy}$$
$$_1H^1 + {_7}N^{15} \longrightarrow {_6}C^{12} + {_2}He^4 + \text{Energy}$$

In this series of reactions, 4 hydrogen nuclei combine to form a helium nucleus with the release of tremendous amounts of energy. The carbon nucleus acts similar to a catalyst in chemical reactions.

Another thermonuclear reaction may also account for the stellar energies. It is the proton-proton cycle, which is:

$$_1H^1 + {_1}H^1 \longrightarrow {_1}H^2 + {_{+1}}e^0 + \nu - \text{Energy}$$
$$_1H^2 + {_1}H^1 \longrightarrow {_2}He^3 + \gamma + \text{Energy}$$
$$_2He^3 + {_2}He^3 \longrightarrow {_2}He^4 + {_1}H^1 + {_1}H^1 + \text{Energy}$$

Astronomers believe that both nuclear reactions take place concurrently in the stars, with the *p-p* cycle predominating at the lower stellar temperatures and the carbon cycle more significant at the higher temperatures. In the cool, red stars on the main sequence (see page 117) most of the heat is developed by the proton-proton cycle, while in the bright, blue-white stars the heat is produced by the carbon cycle. At the temperature of our Sun, both probably take place in approximately equal amounts.

18-10
Evolution of Stars

Astronomers believe that a star starts as a large cloud of hydrogen gas and interstellar dust. This cloud contracts as the cosmic matter is pulled together by gravitational attraction. The atoms and dust particles lose gravitational potential energy, and much of this energy is radiated into space. However, as the cloud contracts, some of it becomes dense enough to absorb part of the energy, causing the temperature of the cloud to rise. This process continues until the temperature at the center of the cloud reaches approximately 4 million degrees, at which temperature thermonuclear reactions begin; protons run into protons and form helium. The energy released by the mass loss causes more protons to react with protons, resulting in a self-sustaining reaction. The cloud then rapidly contracts, astronomically speaking, to the size of a regular star. It contracts until the internal pressure, due to the increase in temperature, is equal to the gravitational attraction of the dense core. The newly formed star is in equilibrium, and is on the main sequence of the H-R diagram (see Fig. 6-7). A spacious cloud contains a large amount hydrogen and cosmic dust and requires a higher temperature to develop an internal pressure great enough to counteract the greater attractional forces. This results in a bright, hot star on the upper part of the main sequence. A small cloud does not require as high a temperature to produce equilibrium, and so it becomes a dim, cool star. If the mass is much less than one-tenth the mass of the Sun, the gravitational attractions would not be sufficient to produce, through compression, a temperature high enough to start nuclear reactions of self-sustaining proportions, and a star would not be formed. If the mass of the cloud were over 100 Suns, chances are that the cloud would be blown apart before a star were born. Maybe a double star would be formed. From the cloud to the star requires millions and sometimes billions of years.

A star remains on the main sequence, or in equilibrium, until about 12% of the hydrogen near its center has been exhausted. Then the hydrogen nuclei nearer the surface start combining and the star gets brighter. The outer layers expand, producing a much larger star. As the lateral area increases, the radiation per unit area becomes less. The surface of the star becomes cooler, redder, and brighter as it departs from the main sequence, and moves into the red-giant and supergiant regions of the H-R diagram. A massive, blue-white star requires the use of its hydrogen at a faster rate in order to maintain its equilibrium, and so it stays on the main sequence for a relatively short time, perhaps a few hundred million years. A small star does not have to use its hydrogen very fast to maintain a balance, and it stays on the main sequence for billions of years. The Sun will remain on the main sequence, or remain stable, for about 6 billion more years before becoming a red giant.

Nuclear fuel is the lifeblood of a star, and the fate of a star depends upon how fast it is exhausting its fuel. Stars with masses less than that of 1.4 Suns die the gentlest of deaths. As their fuel is depleted, they gradually shrink, due to gravitational attraction, from the bright, red giants to dim, white stars, called *white dwarfs*. They contract until the pull of gravity has been balanced by the pressure produced by the fast-moving electrons. White dwarfs are stars roughly the size of the Earth, and with densities in the order of 10^8 gm/cm³. After billions of years, these stars cool into black cinders drifting through interstellar space. Stars with larger masses than 1.4 Suns die a more violent death. After those supergiants have used most of their fuel, they start to contract, but overcontract. Then they expand and contract in pulsating manner, as if trying to become stable. Suddenly the outer layers of hydrogen ignite and explode, blowing the outer gases into space forming novas and occasionally supernovas. The rest of the star collapses, due to the large gravitational pull of the heavy material at its core, and forms a star with a diameter of about 20 kilometers and a density of approximately 10^{14} gm/cm³. At this pressure the electrons are forced into the nuclei with the protons, forming a neutron star. Today we can see the result of such an explosion in the Crab nebula (see Fig. 18-9), which has a neutron star at its

FIG. 18-9 "Crab" nebula in Taurus. Remains of supernova of 1054 a.d. (Photograph from the Hale Observatories.)

center. Some of these neutron stars are rotating at very high rates of several turns per second, and send out beams of radiation which we detect each time a beam passes us. Since we receive the energy in pulses, we call these stars *pulsars*. The remaining star in the Crab nebula astronomers believe to be a pulsar. Some think that perhaps a quasar is a collection of supernova remnants with their pulsars at the centers of distant galaxies, but this is only speculation.

It has been suggested that some stars collapse so violently that they reach a diameter of only a kilometer or so before stopping. Such a remaining star would be so dense that not even the light it emits could escape its gravitational pull. Since it cannot be seen, it is called a "black hole." If black holes really exist, they ought to produce some visual effect upon the surrounding stellar objects, but no such effect has been observed. Hence, the black-hole theory is questionable.

To produce the amount of energy the Sun is radiating per second, it must be losing mass at the rate of 4,100,000 metric tons/sec (1 metric ton = 1000 kg). This seems like a terrific amount, but when compared with the total mass of the Sun, which is about 2×10^{27} metric tons, it is relatively small. In 1 million years, the Sun should lose about one ten-millionth of its mass.

18-11
Uses of Nuclear Fusion

As we have seen the most common reaction in the universe is nuclear fusion. Every star is a furnace that uses hydrogen as its fuel and produces helium and more massive elements as its "ashes." The possibility of producing thermonuclear reactions on Earth has attracted considerable attention because man realizes that his supply of fossil fuels (coal, oil, and natural gas) will probably last him at the most only another hundred years, if he continues using them at the present rate. Nuclear fusion seems to be the answer to the problem because 454 grams (1 lb) of water has the potential energy equivalent to about 1,100 liters (300 gal) of gasoline. The oceans possess an almost inexaustible supply of hydrogen and deuterium. However, man must first learn to control nuclear fusion before he can use it to heat his home, run his machines, and generate his electrical power.

We know that we can reach temperatures high enough to start a fusion process with nuclear fission. Once the thermonuclear reactions are started, they become self-sustaining, but the rapid release of energy produces a terrific explosion since there is not enough mass for the attractional forces to counteract the expansional forces. This is the case in the H-bomb or fusion bomb. Fusion bombs are not limited in size, as are A-bombs (fission bombs).

If the hydrogen reaction could be started by some means other than the A-bomb, it would be relatively free of radioactive fallout and would be considered a "clean" bomb. If, however, the fireball of even a clean bomb touches the ground, the earth will be made radioactive by the neutrons and beta particles in the fireball, and this radioactive material will go up into the cloud to fall out later on some unsuspecting human beings.

18-12
Complexity of the Nucleus

The study of nuclear transformations has led to many important results, one of which has been an increased knowledge of the interior structure of the nucleus. We know that it consists of protons and neutrons, because they seem to account for the observed charges and masses of the atoms. However, we cannot explain certain nuclear properties in terms of these particles alone. What holds all of the protons and neutrons together in such a small region? What produces the short-range nuclear forces? Why are neutrons fairly stable inside the nucleus, but unstable on the outside? A free neutron disintegrates with a half-life of about 12 minutes. We know that atoms are held together by the electromagnetic interaction between the orbital electrons and the protons in the nucleus, but electromagnetic or gravitational interactions are far too small to hold the nucleus together. In 1935, Hideki Yukawa, a Japanese theoretical physicist, predicted that a *pi meson* must be the nuclear glue that holds the particles together in the nucleus. According to the theory, the protons and neutrons inside the nucleus emit and absorb pi mesons, or pions, continually. The interchange of these pions is what supplies the strong nuclear binding force. The range of such interactions is of the magnitude of 10^{-15} meter, which is the diameter of the nucleus. Years after his prediction, the pi meson was discovered, and Yukawa was given the Nobel Prize for his theoretical work on the pion. We no longer have to rely upon cosmic rays to produce pions for we can produce them in the laboratory by bombarding protons or nuclei with energetic protons:

$$P^+ + P^+ \longrightarrow P^+ + n + \pi^+$$

These pions, however, come in three varieties, π^+, π^0, and π^-. The $+$ and $-$ pions carry a charge equal in magnitude to that of the electron, but with masses of about 273 times the mass of the electron. The neutral pion has a mass of about 264 times that of the electron. We know that it takes 13.6 electron volts of energy to pull the electrons away from the nulceus of the hydrogen atom, but it takes 135 million electron volts to generate a pi meson. This indicates how much stronger a pion interaction is than an electrostatic interaction. In the nucleus the neutron emits and absorbs pions from other nucleons and remains in a stable exchange pattern. Outside the nucleus or at a distance greater than 10^{-15} meter, the neutron can no longer exchange pions with other protons or neutrons and it disintegrates into a proton, electron, and an antineutrino.

The physicist has continually bombarded nuclei with higher-and-higher-energy particles. As the energy of the bombarding particles has increased, more and more different kinds of particles have come out of the nucleus—in fact, more than 100 different kinds have been produced and detected either directly or indirectly. These "elementary" or subatomic particles vary from the weightless neutrinos to the heavy omega particles, which have masses 3,276 times that of an electron. So far we have electrons and electron neutrinos in the electron family; muons and nuom neutrinos in the muon family; pions, kaons, and eta particles in the meson family; and protons, neutrons, and lambda, sigma, xi, and omega particles in the baryon (heavy-particle) family. Many of these come in the positive, negative, and neutral variety. The positron not only neutralizes the charge of the electron when they come in contact with each other, but they annihilate each other. Therefore, the mass of the positron must be different than the mass of the electron. We say that the positron consists of *antimatter*. The positron is really an antielectron. All of the subatomic particles have antiparticles which are identical in mass to the ordinary particles, but have opposite charges and consist of antimatter, which is ready and willing to annihilate its ordinary matter counterpart. To enhance the complexity of the situation, most of the subatomic particles disintegrate into other particles of lower mass. For example, the negative pion disintegrates in a very short time (2.6×10^{-8} sec) into a negative muon, an antineutrino, and a neutrino. Of all of these, the proton, the electron, and the neutrino are stable particles. As you clearly see, the nuclear physicist has quite a task ahead of him to unravel the mysteries of the nucleus. This new knowledge may bring good or evil to the world, depending upon how man uses it. The knowledge is good, but the use might be bad.

The one thing we have noticed is that the nucleons are tied together so strongly that neither heat nor chemical reactions can pull them apart. Hence, we may now study chemical reactions without questioning as to how this reaction might change the nucleus, for it has no effect whatsoever upon the nucleus of any of the atoms being combined. In the following chapters, we shall study the various ways of combining elements to form compounds.

QUESTIONS AND PROBLEMS

1. What is meant by *nuclear transmutation?* Give an example.
2. What led Rutherford to think that he had knocked protons out of the nitrogen nucleus?

3. Chadwick has been given credit for discovering the neutron, but he merely explained the results of other workers. What difficulties did they encounter, and how did his idea of a neutron correct them?

4. How does the Van de Graaff generator produce high voltages? What limits its voltage output?

5. Explain how a cyclotron accelerates charged particles.

6. What is the basic difference between the Van de Graaff generator and the cyclotron?

7. Can neutrons be accelerated in either machine in question 6? Explain.

8. What is an electron volt? Is the electron volt a larger or smaller unit of energy than the erg? Than the joule?

9. A molecule of oxygen (5.3×10^{-23} gm) when traveling at a speed of 0.5 km/sec has an energy of how many electron volts?

10. An alpha particle, which has a mass of 6.6×10^{-24} gm, is traveling at a speed of 2×10^9 cm/sec. What is its energy in million electron volts (Mev)?

11. An alpha particle, which has a mass of 6.6×10^{-24} gm, is emitted from a radioactive substance with 3.6 Mev of energy. How fast is the alpha particle traveling when emitted?

12. When an aluminum nucleus is bombarded by a neutron, an alpha particle is produced. What is the remaining nucleus?

13. When an alpha particle penetrates the nucleus of lithium-7, a neutron is released. What is the remaining nucleus?

14. When a sodium-23 nucleus is penetrated by a deuteron, a neutron is released. What is the nucleus that remains?

15. When an alpha particle penetrates an aluminum-27 nucleus, a proton is emitted. What is the remaining element?

16. When a fluorine-19 nucleus is bombarded by a proton, an alpha particle is released. What is the remaining nucleus?

17. When a carbon-12 nucleus is penetrated by a proton, a gamma ray is emitted. What is the remaining substance?

18. An oxygen-16 nucleus bombarded by a deuteron produces nitrogen-14. What particle was emitted in the process?

19. A boron-11 nucleus penetrated by a gamma ray produces beryllium-8. What particle was released in the process?

20. By bombarding a boron-10 nucleus with an alpha particle, carbon-13 can be produced. What was the emitted particle?

21. When a deuterium nucleus (H^2) is bombarded by a tritium nucleus (H^3), a neutron is emitted. What is the resulting nucleus?

22. When a nucleus of arsenic-75 is penetrated by a deuteron, 9 protons and 12 neutrons are released. What is the remaining nucleus?

23. How can Geiger-Müller tubes be made to detect neutrons? What is the mechanism involved?

24. If in a certain nuclear reaction, mass is lost, what becomes of the mass? In other nuclear reactions mass is gained. Where did it come from?

25. What is meant by (a) *nuclear fission?* (b) *chain reaction?* (c) *critical mass?*

26. How much pure uranium-235 must be used to make a fission bomb which is equivalent to a 9×10^7 kg or a 100,000-ton TNT bomb, assuming the bomb is only 10% efficient (10% of the material experiences fission before it blows apart)?

27. In the nuclear reaction

$$_{92}U^{235} + {_0}n^1 \longrightarrow {_{57}}La^{140} + D^{80} + x({_0}n^1)$$

what is the element D, and what is the number (x) of neutrons released in the process?

28. What type of fuel is used in a nuclear reactor? What problem is involved in disposal of the waste material of a nuclear reactor?

29. What is nuclear fusion? What is the difference between nuclear fission and nuclear fusion?

30. Describe the evolution of a star. What will eventually happen to our Sun? How long before that will take place?

31. Why is hydrogen considered the fuel of the future? Why don't we use thermonuclear reactions to supply our energy needs?

32. What has been found in the nucleus besides protons and neutrons?

SUGGESTED REFERENCES

BAKER, ROBERT H., and LAURENCE W. FREDRICK, *An Introduction to Astronomy*, Chap. 16. D. Van Nostrand Co., Princeton, N. J., 1968.

FORD, KENNETH W., *Basic Physics*, Chaps. 25 and 26. Blaisdell Publishing Co., Waltham, Mass., 1968.

MEHLIN, THEODORE G., *Astronomy*, Chap. 2. John Wiley & Sons, New York, 1959 (on life story of a star).

MARION, JERRY B., *Physics and the Physical Universe*, Chap. 15. John Wiley & Sons, New York, 1971.

OSTRIKER, J., "The Nature of Pulsars," *Scientific American*, 224, no. 1 (January 1971), 48–60.

WHITE, HARVEY E., *Introduction to Atomic and Nuclear Physics*, Chaps. 28 and 29. D. Van Nostrand Co., Princeton, N. J., 1964.

19
Chemical Change

Change is a universal and inevitable characteristic of the physical world—nothing really endures. Living organisms grow, die, and decay. The steel hull of a sunken ship rusts away under the ceaseless action of salt water and air. Even the granite faces of mighty mountains are slowly worn down by the attack of wind and water coupled with heat and cold. Many seemingly desirable changes are creating problems of serious proportions. For example, the combustion of coal by the power industry in this country is now releasing approximately 8×10^6 tons of sulfur into the atmosphere each year in the form of sulfur dioxide, one of the most obnoxious air pollutants. The long-range effects of chemical changes are a major concern of chemistry today.

19-1
Pure Substances and Mixtures

Most of the vast number of materials that we see around us in the world are *mixtures*. Mixtures contain two or more pure substances which may be present in varying proportions. These pure substances present in mixtures retain their original characteristics and are not chemically combined. A given mixture may be *heterogeneous*, in which case a small sample taken from the mixture may be somewhat different in composition from another sample. A cocoanut cream pie is obviously such a mixture. Some mixtures, however, are *homogeneous*, with every part of the mixture having the same composition. A solution of sugar in water is an example of a homogeneous mixture.

Pure substances differ from mixtures in that all the molecules in a pure substance are exactly alike. When we say that molecules are exactly alike, we disregard any differences due to the presence of different isotopes of the elements in these molecules. We may also define a pure substance as one for which every sample of the material has identical properties. This definition provides us with an experimental criterion for distinguishing between pure substances and mixtures. For example, water is a colorless liquid with a density of 1 gram per cubic centimeter at 4° C, a freezing point of 0° C and a boiling point of 100° C. All samples of pure water display these properties, but the addition of some other substance results in a change in some or all of them. It should be noted that a pure substance may be either an element or a compound. A *compound* is formed when the atoms of two or more elements are united by chemical bonds. The properties of the elements are changed when they enter into chemical combination. The number of pure substances which we meet in our ordinary experience is small. Baking soda (sodium bicarbonate) and sugar (sucrose) are pure compounds with which we are familiar. The copper used in electrical wiring and the mercury in thermometers are examples of pure elements in common use.

19-2
Physical and Chemical Change

The changes in matter which we see all around us are of two types, physical and chemical. A substance undergoing a *physical change* retains its chemical identity while having some physical characteristic altered. Such changes as the freezing of water and the falling of a piledriver are physical changes.

Chemical changes are those changes which result in the formation of new and different substances. Many chemical changes may be observed in our ordinary experiences. The combustion of gasoline and the decay of wood are examples of chemical change. Every living organism carries out many complicated chemical changes. Green plants take raw materials, chiefly water and carbon dioxide, and convert them into complex compounds called carbohydrates. Each of our body processes, such as digestion and respiration, is dependent upon a series of complex chemical changes.

We are only beginning to realize the far-reaching effects of some chemical changes. Carbon dioxide (CO_2) gas is produced by the combustion of fossil fuels, the decay of organic matter, and respiration by living organisms. It is removed from the atmosphere by absorption in the oceans and in the photosynthetic processes of green plants. Carbon dioxide is important in the heat balance of the earth because it absorbs the infrared radiation from the earth and retards the cooling of the surface. It has been estimated that if all known reserves of fossil fuels were used in the next 500 years, the increase in atmospheric CO_2 would be sufficient to cause the average surface temperature of the earth to rise by about 10° C. Such a temperature increase would melt the polar icecaps, flooding densely populated coastal areas, as well as producing disastrous effects on the world's commercial fishing industry.

We saw in Chapter 16 that elements differ a great deal in the tendency to undergo chemical change by uniting with other elements. Some of them have no tendency to enter into such combination, while others are so active that they are kept in pure form only with great difficulty. An element is said to be *chemically active* when it enters into chemical combination readily.

The atoms of elements combine with one another in various ratios. The combining capacity of an element is known as the *valence* of the element. Atoms of hydrogen and chlorine combine with each other in the ratio of 1:1, and neither of these atoms ordinarily holds more than a single atom of any other element in chemical combination. Both hydrogen and chlorine are assigned a valence of 1. A single calcium atom will unite with two chlorine atoms, and one aluminum atom will combine with three chlorine atoms. Consequently, calcium and aluminum have valences of 2 and 3, respectively.

19-4
Chemical Bonds

Atoms which unite chemically are held together by forces which we call *chemical bonds*. These bonds vary in strength and mode of formation. The number of bonds which a given atom can form determines its valence, or combining capacity. Elements such as hydrogen and sodium are not capable of forming more than one chemical bond, so these elements have a valence of 1. Carbon usually forms four bonds, and so it has a valence of 4.

Chemically bonded atoms may be separated if sufficient energy is available to overcome the forces between them. In cases where the energy required to break the bonds is high, the substance is said to be *stable*. An *unstable* substance, on the other hand, is one in which the bond energy is low. Water molecules are quite stable, because the energy required to separate the hydrogen and oxygen atoms is very high. Sugar molecules are less stable, since the bonds between the carbon, hydrogen, and oxygen atoms may be broken with relatively low energy.

The tendency for the formation of chemical bonds by a given atom is related to the electronic structure of the atom, particularly to the outer-energy-level electrons, which are often called "valence electrons." The noble elements all have 8 outer-energy-level electrons, with the exception of helium which has 2 (see Chapter 16). Since these elements have little or no tendency to form chemical bonds, the arrangement of 8 electrons in the outer energy level must be a very stable one. All the other elements, which show more chemical activity than the inert group, have fewer than 8 valence electrons.

Thus we might reasonably expect to find that all atoms have a tendency to acquire the electronic structure of a noble gas as they enter into chemical combination.

19-5
Ionization Energy and Electronegativity

Valence electrons are held with varying forces by different atoms. The ionization energy, discussed in Chapter 16, is related to this force. Large atoms, in which the valence electrons are relatively far from the nucleus, would be expected to have low ionization energies. The alkali metals, which have the largest atoms of all the elements and only 1 valence electron, are found to have low ionization energies (see Fig. 16-2). The relatively small nonmetal atoms, having four or more valence electrons, have high ionization energies. In general, the ionization energies of the metals are lower than those of the nonmetals.

The tendency of an atom in a molecule to attract electrons to itself is known as *electronegativity*. An element with low electronegativity has little tendency to attract electrons, and one with high electronegativity has great attraction for electrons. Electronegativity is related to atomic size since the attractive force between the nucleus and electrons depends on the distance of separation. Large atoms with few valence electrons have relatively low electronegativity and small atoms with nearly complete valence shells have relatively high electronegativity. Thus metals have lower electronegativity than nonmetals. Those atoms having high electronegativity will also have high ionization energy. Ionization energy and electronegativity are useful concepts in understanding the formation of chemical bonds. The relative electronegativities of the elements are shown in Table 19-1.

19-6
Ionic Compounds

Ionic compuonds are formed when metal atoms give up electrons to nonmetallic atoms. The difference in electronegativity must be great enough to enable one atom to take an electron away from another. Consider the example of sodium, an active metal, and fluorine, an active nonmetal. Sodium atoms, with a single valence electron, have low ionization energy and low electronegativity. This valence electron can be removed with relatively little energy, forming a positively charged *sodium ion*. The sodium ions, with the same electronic structure as neon, have properties which are quite different from those of sodium atoms. Fluorine atoms, with high electronegativity, have great tendency to attract an extra electron, forming negative *fluoride ions*.

TABLE 19-1
Relative Electronegativities of the Elements*

H 2.1																	He –
Li 1.0	Be 1.5											B 2.0	C 2.5	N 3.0	O 3.5	F 4.0	Ne –
Na 0.9	Mg 1.2											Al 1.5	Si 1.8	P 2.1	S 2.5	Cl 3.0	Ar –
K 0.8	Ca 1.0	Sc 1.3	Ti 1.5	V 1.6	Cr 1.6	Mn 1.5	Fe 1.8	Co 1.8	Ni 1.8	Cu 1.8	Zn 1.6	Ga 1.6	Ge 1.8	As 2.0	Se 2.4	Br 2.8	Kr –
Rb 0.8	Sr 1.0	Y 1.2	Zr 1.4	Cb 1.6	Mo 1.8	Tc 1.9	Ru 2.2	Rh 2.2	Pd 2.2	Ag 1.9	Cd 1.7	In 1.7	Sn 1.8	Sb 1.9	Te 2.1	I 2.5	Xe –
Cs 0.7	Ba 0.9	57-71 1.1–1.2	Hf 1.3	Ta 1.5	W 1.7	Re 1.9	Os 2.2	Ir 2.2	Pt 2.2	Au 2.4	Hg 1.9	Tl 1.8	Pb 1.8	Bi 1.9	Po 2.0	At 2.2	Rn –
Fr 0.7	Ra 0.9																

*From J. V. Quagliano, *Chemistry*, Prentice-Hall, Inc., Englewood Cliffs, N.J., © 1969.

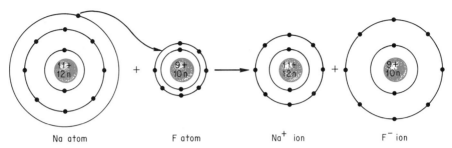

Na atom F atom Na⁺ ion F⁻ ion

FIG. 19-1 Formation of sodium fluoride.

These ions also have the same electronic structure as neon and are very stable. The formation of these ions by electron transfer is represented in Fig. 19-1. The electron energy levels are shown as circles for convenience, *but the electrons actually occupy three-dimensional orbitals.*

This combination of sodium with fluorine represents a chemical change in which the properties of the reacting substances are completely changed. Sodium is a soft, silvery metal so active that it cannot be exposed to air or water without chemical change. It reacts explosively with water. Fluorine is a pale yellow, poisonous gas which is very difficult to handle because it is so corrosive. These two elements react very rapidly to produce a stable, white crystalline solid.

The positive sodium ions and the negative fluoride ions are held together by electrostatic forces called *ionic bonds.* The sodium and fluoride ions, in a 1:1 ratio, arrange themselves in an orderly crystal structure, as shown in Fig. 19-2. The individual crystals of sodium fluoride, NaF, are found in the form of little cubes, very similar to the crystals of sodium chloride, familiar to us as table salt.

FIG. 19-2 Sodium fluoride crystal.

The combination of calcium with fluorine takes place in a similar fashion, but in a different ratio, as shown in Fig. 19-3. The calcium atoms have 2

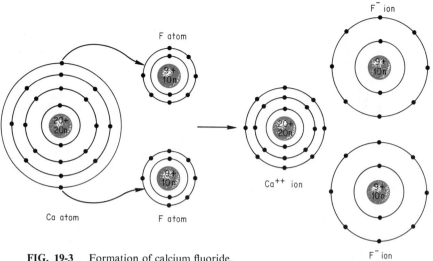

FIG. 19-3 Formation of calcium fluoride.

valence electrons which are relatively easily removed, forming *calcium ions* with a positive charge of 2 units. These two electrons are attracted by two fluorine atoms, forming two *fluoride ions*, each having a charge of negative one. The positive calcium ions attract the negative fluoride ions to form a crystal of calcium fluoride, which is represented by the formula CaF_2. The compound calcium fluoride has properties which are quite different from those of the elements calcium and fluorine. The ions are quire unlike the atoms from which they were formed.

Ionic bonds, due to attractive forces between ions of opposite charge, are quite strong. These bonding forces are nondirectional; that is, a given ion exerts attractive force in all directions. Ionic compounds are, therefore, generally hard, crystalline solids with relatively high melting points. Sodium chloride, for example, melts at a temperature of approximately 800° C. Ionic solids are not electrical conductors, but in the molten state they are excellent conductors of electricity. When an ionic crystal melts, the electrically charged ions are free to move and produce an electric current in the liquid. Water solutions of ionic compounds are also electrical conductors, since the ions are free to move in the solution.

19-7
Covalent Compounds

Covalent compounds are formed when atoms share electrons instead of transferring them, as was the case with ionic compounds. A *covalent bond* results when two atoms are held together by a pair of electrons occupying a *molecular orbital* and being attracted by the nuclei of both atoms. Consider the case of two hydrogen atoms, each of which has a single valence electron.

When the two hydrogen atoms come close together, the 2 electrons pair up and occupy a molecular orbital encompassing both nuclei. The mutual attraction between the electrons and the nuclei of both atoms constitutes the covalent bond. A hydrogen *molecule*, represented by the formula H_2, results when two hydrogen atoms are bonded together in this fashion.

Chlorine molecules are formed by a similar electron-sharing process. Each chlorine atom, having 7 electrons in the outer energy level, can acquire the inert gas structure by sharing an electron with another chlorine atom. This pair of electrons occupies a molecular orbital encompassing both nuclei.

Some cases of covalent bonding involve the sharing of more than one electron pair. The two carbon atoms in ethylene (C_2H_2) are united by two bonds resulting from the sharing of two electron pairs, and nitrogen molecules (N_2) are held together by three bonds, formed by sharing three pairs of electrons.

The formation of hydrogen and chlorine molecules is represented in Fig. 19-4. *The electron energy levels are represented as circles only for convenience.* We saw in Chapter 15 that electrons move in much more complicated ways. The electron pairs involved in covalent bonds are not actually stationary between the atoms, but move around both nuclei.

Atoms of different elements may be united by covalent bonds under certain circumstances. Such combinations usually involve nonmetals, although there are some cases of covalent bonding between metals, and between metals and nonmetals. Hydrogen and chlorine, for example, will combine to form molecules of hydrogen chloride. Hydrogen atoms have 1 valence electron and chlorine atoms have 7. When these two atoms come together they each contribute an electron to form a pair of electrons, which is shared by both atoms. Neither atom has sufficient electronegativity to pull the electron pair away from the other and form two ions. The hydrogen and chlorine atoms

FIG. 19-4 Formation of molecules.

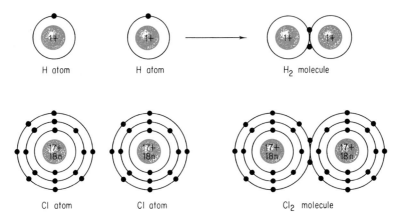

H atom   H atom H_2 molecule

Cl atom   Cl atom Cl_2 molecule

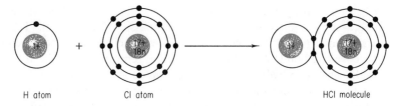

FIG. 19-5   Formation of hydrogen chloride molecules.

are bound together by a covalent bond to form a hydrogen chloride *molecule*. This situation is illustrated in Fig. 19-5.

Carbon forms more covalent compounds than any other element except hydrogen. The carbon atom has 4 valence electrons and usually forms four covalent bonds which are equally spaced around the central atom. Consider the combination of carbon, having 4 valence electrons, with chlorine, having 7. The carbon atom will acquire the noble gas structure by sharing an electron pair with each of four chlorine atoms. Each chlorine atom also acquires a noble gas structure in this process. The resulting molecule of carbon tetra-chloride has the formula CCl_4. This molecule is tetrahedral in shape. The four bonds are arranged symmetrically around the carbon atom with equal angles between them. This arrangement is shown in Fig. 19-6.

FIG. 19-6   (a) Tetrahedral molecule; (b) Model of CCl_4 molecule.

(a)   *(b)*

19-8
Polar and Nonpolar Molecules

Molecules such as H_2 and Cl_2 are formed from atoms having equal electro-negativity. Thus the shared electrons are not pulled closer to either atom, but may be thought of as spending equal time around both atoms. These molecules are not only electrically neutral, but are also completely symmetric; that is, the center of positive charge and the center of negative charge are, on the average, in the same place. Such a molecule acts like an uncharged particle and is called a *nonpolar molecule*.

This symmetric arrangement does not prevail with molecules such as hydrogen chloride. The two atoms in this molecule do not have equal electronegativity. The electronegativity of chlorine is considerably higher than that of hydrogen. As a result, the shared electrons are pulled closer to the chlorine, or they may be thought of as spending more time around the chlorine atom than around the hydrogen atom. This results in an asymmetric molecule, with the chlorine end slightly negative and the hydrogen end slightly positive. This situation is shown in Fig. 19-7, where the density of

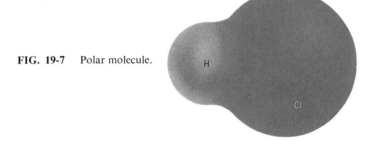

FIG. 19-7   Polar molecule.

the shading represents the electron density, or the probability of finding one of the valence electrons. The relatively high electron density around the chlorine gives it a partial negative charge, and the relatively low electron density around the hydrogen gives it a partial positive charge. Molecules such as hydrogen chloride are called *polar molecules*. The properties of such molecules are influenced by the attractive forces between the positive end of one molecule and the negative end of another. For example, hydrogen chloride, which is a gas at room temperature and pressure, is easily liquefied because of the intermolecular attraction resulting from the asymmetric distribution of the electrical charge in the molecules. Water, with very polar molecules, is very unusual in many of its properties because of this polarity. Such properties as boiling point and heat of vaporization are much higher than those of nonpolar substances of comparable molecular weight.

Differences in electronegativity between the atoms in a molecule do not always result in a polar molecule. The carbon tetrachloride molecule is nonpolar even though the carbon and chlorine differ in electronegativity. The shared electrons in the carbon-chlorine bonds are displaced toward the more electronegative chlorine. However, since the four bonds are arranged symmetrically around the carbon atom, the charge distribution in the molecule is uniform and it is nonpolar.

19-9
Chemical Bonds and Energy

Atoms go to a more stable state when they form chemical bonds. Thus, the two atoms held together in a chlorine molecule by a covalent bond are in a more stable state than they were as separate atoms. The potential energy decreases when any system goes to a more stable state, and this energy is given off in some form, such as heat or light. *Bond-formation processes release energy and bond-breaking processes require the input of energy.*

A chemical change in which energy is given off is called an *exothermic* process. The combination of hydrogen with oxygen to form water is such an exothermic process. When 2 grams of hydrogen react with 16 grams of oxygen to form 18 grams of water vapor, 58 kilocalories of heat are liberated. (A kilocalorie is 1,000 calories.) This process is exothermic because the energy liberated in the formation of bonds between hydrogen and oxygen in the water molecule is greater than the energy required to break the bonds in the oxygen and hydrogen molecules.

Most of the chemical changes we observe are exothermic. However, some chemical changes absorb energy and are called *endothermic* changes. Substances undergoing an endothermic change go to a state of higher potential energy. Heat is absorbed when nitrogen and oxygen molecules combine to form nitric oxide. When 14 grams of nitrogen combine with 16 grams of oxygen to form 30 grams of nitric oxide, 21.6 kilocalories of heat is absorbed. This is an endothermic process because the energy required to break the bonds in the nitrogen and oxygen molecules is greater than the energy released in forming bonds between nitrogen and oxygen atoms.

19-10
Molecules and Crystals

A *molecule* is the smallest particle of a pure substance that is capable of independent existence. Thus a molecule may be a fundamental unit of an element, or of a compound. The molecules of the noble gases are single atoms, since these atoms do not combine with each other. Elements such as oxygen, hydrogen, nitrogen, and chlorine form molecules consisting of two atoms each. Molecules of phosphorus contain four atoms arranged in a pyramid and sulfur molecules are rings with eight atoms in each. Models of chlorine, phosphorus, and sulfur molecules are shown in Fig. 19-8.

FIG. 19-8   Models of Cl_2, P_4, and S_8.

The simplest molecules of covalent compounds contain two atoms and the number ranges upward into the thousands for the most complex molecules, such as the proteins. A model of a very complex molecule is shown in Fig. 19-9. This is a Watson-Crick model of DNA (deoxyribonucleic acid), which plays an important role in the mechanism of heredity. The spheres in the model represent atoms of carbon, hydrogen, oxygen, nitrogen and phosphorus.

Ionic compounds do not exist as molecules in the solid state or in solution. An ionic substance, such as sodium fluoride, is *crystalline* in the solid state.

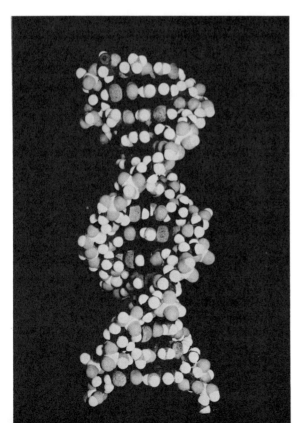

FIG. 19-9   Watson-Crick model of DNA molecule. (Courtesy Abbott Laboratories.)

The sodium fluoride *crystal* is made up of alternate positive sodium ions and negative fluoride ions arranged in cubic form. This arrangement is shown in Fig. 19-2.

The form of the crystal will vary for different ionic compounds, depending on such factors as ionic size and charge. A molecule of an ionic compound would exist only in the gaseous phase.

19-11
Chemical Changes in Compounds

Thus far we have discussed chemical changes involving the combination of atoms to form molecules or crystals. Chemical compounds also undergo chemical change. The most common chemical changes are those in which chemical compounds decompose or unite with other compounds or with elements. Unstable compounds may be decomposed quite easily. Common table sugar, a compound of carbon, hydrogen, and oxygen, may be destroyed by heating. When a sample of sugar is heated, water vapor is given off and a black residue of carbon remains.

Dichlorodiphenyltrichloroethane, better known as DDT, has been used as an effective control agent for insect pests. This stable compound has been accumulating in the environment because of its slow rate of decomposition. This has created a problem of serious proportions because of the potential danger of DDT to all animal life, including man.

Soap, the oldest detergent known to man, is decomposed relatively rapidly when released into the environment. A *biodegradable* substance is one which is decomposed rapidly by the action of living organisms, such as bacteria. Soaps are sodium salts of long-chain fatty acids, such as stearic acid. Soaps are made from animal fats, which are esters of fatty acids. There are several types of synthetic detergents. Sodium lauryl sulfate, made from a long-chain alcohol, is a common type (see Section 24-5). The synthetic detergents are more effective than soap in hard water. The metal ions in hard water react rapidly with soap to produce an insoluble precipitate, but do so less readily with synthetic detergents. Therefore, the synthetic detergents are in demand because of their greater cleaning effectiveness. The synthetic detergents made from branched-chain hydrocarbons have particularly effective detergent properties. These branched-chain detergents, which are not biodegradable, may produce problems because they persist in the environment for a long time. They are not removed in sewage disposal plants and may eventually get into the ground water and into municipal drinking-water supplies.

The manufacturers of detergents have devised many additives for detergents to enhance their appeal to the housewife. Detergents have a tendency to foam, although this action is not necessary for good detergent action. Foaming may interfere with the action of the washing machine, so chemicals have been added to minimize foaming. Certain compounds, known as builders, will tie up metal ions and prevent their interference with the action of the detergent. Phosphates have been used as builders, although this use has resulted in controversy over their possible contribution to the eutrophication of lakes (see Section 23-2). Suspending agents, such as carboxymethylcellulose, keep small particles in suspension almost indefinitely in a liquid medium. This will result in dirt and grease particles, suspended by the detergent, being washed away more completely. Additives are advertised for the purpose of making clothes "whiter and brighter." These are dyes which absorb ultraviolet light and emit this energy as visible light. Thus the washed article appears brighter, although it may not be cleaner. Bleaching agents are often added to oxidize stains to colorless products. This array of chemical additives contributes to the burden of pollutants which we add to the waters of our lakes and streams.

The rate of chemical change is sometimes influenced by substances called *catalysts*. A catalyst is a substance that will cause the rate of a reaction to be increased without undergoing any permanent change itself in the process Catalysts are important in many chemical changes. Green plants combine water and carbon dioxide to form simple sugars and give off oxygen as a by-product. This process is called *photosynthesis*, and the catalyst is a chlorophyll protein complex found in all green plants. The catalyst is not changed, but it increases the rate at which water and carbon dioxide combine to form sugars. The chemical changes in our bodies are under the control of catalysts which are called *enzymes*. You may demonstrate the action of a catalyst quite easily for yourself. A 3% solution of hydrogen peroxide, obtainable from any drugstore, decomposes slowly to oxygen and water. If you observe such a solution in a test tube, you will find that the decomposition is not rapid enough to enable you to see bubbles of oxygen form. However, if a small pinch of manganese dioxide is placed in the solution, the rate of decomposition is greatly increased and oxygen bubbles off rapidly. The manganese dioxide is a catalyst for this decomposition reaction. The only effect of the catalyst is to lower the energy which molecules must have to react, thus increasing the speed of the reaction.

The never-ending sequence of chemical changes is one of the permanent features of the physical world. Atoms combine to form molecules or crystals, molecules decompose or combine with other molecules or atoms, ad infinitum. Only the atoms are unchanging: Where were the atoms of your body 100 years ago?

The science of chemistry is primarily concerned with the understanding and control of chemical changes, and through chemical technology man has created many useful products which are not found in nature. The production of these new chemicals, or the release of these chemicals into the environ-ment, is producing problems, some of which may be very serious. We are just beginning to understand the fragile nature of our environment. Chemical balance is one of the vital factors in this environment. Our very survival depends upon the application of effective measures to preserve the delicate balance in the chemistry of the Earth.

We have looked at some general principles governing chemical change; we shall concern ourselves in the next chapter with the quantitative relation-ships that we find in chemical reactions. These relationships give us an increas-ing appreciation of the order we find in the world of atoms.

QUESTIONS AND PROBLEMS

1. What uncombined elements are found in the atmosphere?

2. The metals tend to form positive ions readily. What particular prop-erties of the metal atoms determine the ease with which such ions are formed?

3. Would you expect the hydrogen fluoride molecule to be polar? What general principles enable you to reach this conclusion?

4. Which of the following compounds would you expect to be predomi-nantly covalent and which would you expect to be predominantly ionic?
   (a) Hydrogen sulfide, H_2S.   (d) Sulfur dioxide, SO_2.
   (b) Potassium fluoride, KF.   (e) Sodium iodide, NaI.
   (c) Barium chloride, $BaCl_2$.

5. Rubidium chloride (RbCl) conducts an electric current when melted, but antimony trichloride ($SbCl_3$) is a nonconductor. What conclusions can you draw regarding these compounds and the elements in them?

6. What charge would you expect to find on the ions of the following elements: lithium (Li), magnesium (Mg), bromine (Br), aluminum (Al), sulfur (S), oxygen (O)?

7. In what ratio would you expect calcium (Ca) to combine with bromine (Br)? Calcium is a metal with low ionization energy and low electro-negativity. Bromine is a nonmetal with high ionization energy and electronegativity. In view of these facts, what type of compound would you expect from calcium and bromine?

8. Silicon dioxide (SiO_2) and calcium chloride ($CaCl_2$) are solids which may be melted. How would you expect the electrical conductivity of these two molten solids to compare?

9. Ammonia (NH_3) is very soluble in H_2O—approximately 1,200 volumes of gaseous NH_3 will dissolve in 1 volume of H_2O at room temperature. What does this suggest about the nature of NH_3 molecules? Explain.

10. How do you explain the fact that methane (CH_4) boils at $-161°C$

while water (H_2O), with molecules of about the same weight, boils at 100°C?

11. Nitrogen (N_2) and fluorine (F_2) differ greatly in chemical activity. Fluorine is very active and nitrogen has little chemical activity. What particular characteristic of the molecules of these two elements would account for this difference in activity?

12. The water molecule (H_2O) is a very polar molecule. What possible geometric structure for the molecule is excluded by this experimental fact?

13. The heat of formation of aluminum oxide, Al_2O_3, is 405 kilocalories per mole and the heat of formation of silver oxide, Ag_2O, is 7.7 kilocalories per mole. The heat of formation in each case is the heat liberated when a mole of the compound is formed from its elements. What difference would you predict in the properties of these compounds on the basis of their heats of formation?

14. Silicon combines with hydrogen to form a compound called silane (SiH_4). Considering relative electronegativities and the position of silicon in the periodic table, what properties would you predict for this compound?

15. Many chemical substances cause problems when released into the environment. Even biodegradable substances cause serious problems when released into streams in large quantities. How could a substance which is decomposed readily cause problems in water?

SUGGESTED REFERENCES

HORRIGAN, PHILIP A., *The Challenge of Chemistry*, Chaps. 4, 9, 13, 14, and 15. McGraw-Hill Book Co., New York, 1970.

KELLER, EUGENIA, "The DDT Story," *Chemistry*, 43, no. 2 (1970), 8.

MAXWELL, KENNETH E., *Chemicals and Life*, Chap. 9. Dickenson Publishing Co., Belmont, Calif. 1970.

WOOD, JESSE H., KEENAN, CHARLES W., and BULL, WILLIAM E., *Fundamentals of College Chemistry*, Chap. 5. Harper & Row, New York, 1968.

20

Chemical Bookkeeping

Chemical changes involve a rearrangement of atoms in the formation of new and different molecules. Atoms are neither created nor destroyed in chemical reactions, and atoms always combine in definite ratios to form compounds. Nature's books are always balanced. These and other general principles enable us to calculate weight relationships in chemical reactions and provide us with evidence of a fundamental order in the physical world.

20-1
Chemical Formulas

We have seen that most atoms tend to group themselves into stable aggregates called molecules, and that ions tend to arrange themselves in symmetric structures called crystals. Each of these aggregates is identified by a name and by a *chemical formula*. A formula is a group of symbols which tells us the composition of the group represented. Formulas represent molecules or crystals, whereas symbols represent atoms.

The formula for hydrogen gas is H_2, not H, since hydrogen atoms combine to form hydrogen molecules of two atoms each. The subscript 2 tells us that each hydrogen molecule contains two atoms. Likewise the formula for the oxygen molecule is O_2, for nitrogen N_2, and for sulfur S_8. The formula for neon is Ne, since neon atoms do not combine with each other and the molecule of neon is simply one atom.

The formula for a compound tells us what elements are present and the proportion in which they are combined. The formula for water is H_2O, telling us that a molecule of this compound is formed from hydrogen and oxygen in the ratio of two atoms of hydrogen to one of oxygen. The formula for cane sugar, or sucrose, is $C_{12}H_{22}O_{11}$, telling us that a molecule of this compound contains carbon, hydrogen, and oxygen atoms in the ratio of 12:22:11. Sodium chloride, an ionic compound, has the formula NaCl. There are no molecules of sodium chloride under ordinary conditions, but the formula tells us that a crystal of this compound contains sodium ions and chloride ions in a ratio of 1:1. The formula for a compound must be determined experimentally; the method by which this is done will be discussed in a later section.

It should be noted here that the formula for a compound tells us nothing about the structure of the molecules or crystals. Carbon dioxide, CO_2, and sulfur dioxide, SO_2, have formulas which look very similar. However, the shape of the CO_2 molecule is quite different from that of SO_2. The carbon dioxide molecule is linear and the sulfur dioxide molecule is bent, with an angle between the two oxygen-sulfur bonds of slightly more than 90 degrees.

We may even find important differences between molecules having the same formula. The same atoms may be arranged in different ways, giving compounds with quite different properties. Such compounds are called *isomers*. For example, there are two compounds that have the formula C_2H_6O. One of these is ethyl alcohol, C_2H_5OH, and the other is methyl ether, CH_3—O—CH_3. These compounds have the same number of carbon, hydrogen and oxygen atoms, but quite different properties due to the difference in arrangement of the atoms. These differences in arrangement are shown below. The atoms in these molecules are not all in the same plane as they are shown in this figure. The molecules are actually three-dimensional structures.

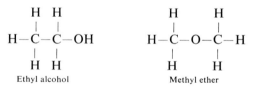

Ethyl alcohol   Methyl ether

20-2
Naming Compounds

A system of names for chemical compounds is important, just as names are important for distinguishing people. However, it is essential that no two compounds have the same name, as is sometimes the case with people, since no two compounds have the same properties. The naming of chemical compounds is somewhat complicated because of the very large number involved and because the older common names for compounds were not systematic names. Space will not allow a detailed discussion of chemical nomenclature here and we shall only attempt to describe the naming of a few compounds as examples.

Binary compounds are those formed from two different elements. The name for a binary compound is formed from the name of the more electropositive element, followed by the name of the more electronegative element with its ending by the suffix *-ide*. For example, consider the compound of lithium and bromine. Bromine is more electronegative than lithium, so we use the name *lithium bromide* for the compound having the formula LiBr. Examples of other binary compounds are:

KF, potassium fluoride	$CaBr_2$, calcium bromide
$BaCl_2$, barium chloride	Mg_3N_2, magnesium nitride
Na_2S, sodium sulfide	Al_2O_3, aluminum oxide

There are a few cases where compounds which contain more than two elements have names ending in *-ide*. For example, calcium hydroxide, $Ca(OH)_2$, is not a binary compound because it consists of three elements.

The compounds formed by elements of variable valence are named by two different systems. The Greek prefixes *mono-, di-, tri-, tetra-, and penta-* (meaning "one," "two," "three," "four," and "five," respectively) may precede the element to which they refer. The name *nitrogen dioxide* is given to the compound with the formula NO_2. Examples of other compounds named by this system are:

SO_2, sulfur dioxide	N_2O_3, dinitrogen trioxide
SO_3, sulfur trioxide	N_2O_5, dinitrogen pentoxide
CO, carbon monoxide	PCl_3, phosphorus trichloride
CO_2, carbon dioxide	PCl_5, phosphorus pentachloride

A Roman numeral may be used to indicate the valence of the more electropositive element in a binary compound. This method of naming is usually confined to compounds in which the more electropositive element is a metal. Several examples of this method are:

$SnCl_2$, tin (II) chloride	Cu_2O, copper (I) oxide
$SnCl_4$, tin (IV) chloride	CuO, copper (II) oxide

Compounds made up of more than two elements usually contain a group of elements that act as though they were one atom in chemical combinations. Such a group is known as a *radical* and has a definite charge and a definite combining capacity. Some of the more common radicals and their charges are given in Table 20-1.

Some representative names for compounds containing more than two elements are:

$Ba(NO_3)_2$, barium nitrate	Cu_2SO_4, copper (I) sulfate
Na_2CO_3, sodium carbonate	$CuSO_4$, copper (II) sulfate
$KMnO_4$, potassium permanganate	$Mg(NO_2)_2$, magnesium nitrite
Na_3PO_4, sodium phosphate	$KClO_3$, potassium chlorate

TABLE 20-1
Some Common Chemical Radicals

Radical	Name	Charge
NO_3^-	nitrate	-1
NO_2^-	nitrite	-1
$SO_4^=$	sulfate	-2
$SO_3^=$	sulfite	-2
$PO_4^{\equiv}$	phosphate	-3
$CO_3^=$	carbonate	-2
ClO_3^-	chlorate	-1
MnO_4^-	permanganate	-1

20-3
Formula Weight

As indicated in Chapter 9, we weigh objects by comparison with a standard mass. The formula weight for any compound is easily calculated if the formula for the compound is known. If the compound in question is molecular (covalent), the term *molecular weight* may be used instead of formula weight. For compounds of known formula, the formula weight or molecular weight may be obtained by adding the weights of the atoms making up the formula. The calculation of formula weights for two compounds is shown in Table 20-2.

TABLE 20-2
Calculation of Formula Weights

CARBON TETRACHLORIDE, CCl_4	
1 C atom $\times$ 12.011 amu/atom	12.011 amu
4 Cl atoms $\times$ 35.453 amu/atom	141.812
Molecular weight	153.823 amu
SUCROSE, $C_{12}H_{22}O_{11}$	
12 C atoms $\times$ 12.011 amu/atom	144.132 amu
22 H atoms $\times$ 1.008 amu/atom	22.176
11 O atoms $\times$ 15.999 amu/atom	175.989
Molecular weight	342.297 amu

The *gram formula weight*, or the *gram molecular weight*, is a convenient unit for chemical calculations. Expressed in grams, this is the weight of a substance that is numerically equal to the formula weight of the substance. Thus the gram molecular weight of CCl_4 is 153.823 *grams*. The gram molecular weight of any substance contains the same number of molecules as the gram molecular weight of any other substance.

The determination of formula weight for every compound was originally done by some experimental method. The formula weight or molecular weight must be known before the formula can be determined. There are several experimental methods for determining formula weights, one of which will be discussed here.

The method for determining the formula weight for a gas or vapor is based on a principle suggested by Amedeo Avogadro in 1811. This principle states that *equal volumes of pure gaseous elements or compounds contain equal numbers of molecules.* Therefore, equal volumes of any two pure gases would have weights proportional to the formula weights of the two gases. It has been found that the *gram molecular weight* of all gases and vapors occupy very nearly the same volume, 22.4 liters, at 0°C and 760 mm of mercury pressure. This volume is known as the *gram molecular volume.* Thus the gram molecular weight of any new substance that can be vaporized is obtained by determining the weight in grams of 22.4 liters of the vapor. This is known as the *vapor density method* for determining molecular weight. Consider the case of ammonia, which is found to have a density of 0.76 gram per liter at 0°C and 760 mm of mercury pressure. By multiplying the density by 22.4 liters, we obtain a value of 17.02 grams as the gram molecular weight of this compound.

20-4
The Mole

The *mole* is a unit that we shall find very convenient in dealing with quantitative relationships in chemical changes. The word *mole* comes from a Latin word meaning "pile" or "heap." The word *molecule* has the same origin, meaning "little pile." Before defining the mole, we must return to Avogadro's principle. This principle asserts that equal volumes of pure gaseous elements or compounds contain equal numbers of molecules. The number of molecules in a *gram molecular volume* of a gas is known as *Avogadro's number.* This number, 6.02×10^{23}, has been determined by several different experimental methods, all of which lead to approximately the same value. Avogadro's principle can be extended to substances other than gases. A gram molecular weight of a given compound contains exactly the same number of molecules as a gram molecular weight of any other compound. This number of molecules in a gram molecular weight is Avogadro's number. Likewise, a gram atomic weight of any element in the *atomic form* contains Avogadro's number of atoms.

A mole is defined as Avogadro's number of particles of whatever chemical species we are dealing with. It may be 6.02×10^{23} molecules, atoms, ions, or electrons. This specific number of particles will, of course, have a definite weight. For a molecular substance, it is a gram molecular weight. A mole of water is 6.02×10^{23} molecules, which weigh very close to 18 grams, and a mole of *atomic* oxygen is 6.02×10^{23} atoms, which weigh 15.999 grams. A mole of sodium chloride is 6.02×10^{23} sodium and chloride ion pairs, which weigh 58.44 grams.

20-5
Determination of a Chemical Formula

Chemical formulas are determined from experimental data. If the valences, or combining capacities, of the elements in the compound are known, the formula may be predicted. However, such a predicted formula must be verified by analysis of the compound before it can be established as correct.

The establishment of the formula for a given compound begins with the analysis of a pure sample of the compound; that is, the compound is decomposed and the percentage of each constituent element is determined. The compound *ethane*, a gas at room temperature, will be used to illustrate the steps in obtaining a chemical formula.

The analysis of ethane shows that this compound contains 20% hydrogen and 80% carbon. Let us assume that we decompose 100 grams of the compound, obtaining 20 grams of hydrogen and 80 grams of carbon. Since we know the weight of a mole of hydrogen atoms to be very close to 1 gram and that of a mole of carbon atoms to be 12 grams, we may calculate the number of moles of each element:

$$\frac{20 \text{ grams hydrogen}}{1 \text{ gram hydrogen/mole}} = 20 \text{ moles hydrogen}$$

$$\frac{80 \text{ grams carbon}}{12 \text{ grams carbon/mole}} = 6.67 \text{ moles carbon}$$

$$\frac{\text{moles hydrogen}}{\text{moles carbon}} = \frac{20}{6.67} = 3$$

Thus we see that 100 grams of the compound contain 3 times as many moles of hydrogen as carbon. Since a mole of hydrogen contains the same number of atoms as a mole of carbon, the number of hydrogen atoms in the 100-gram sample is 3 times that of the number of carbon atoms. Each molecule of ethane must also contain three times as many hydrogen as carbon atoms. Therefore, *the simplest formula for ethane is* CH_3. This is sometimes called an *empirical* formula.

The true formula for ethane may be the simplest formula, or it may be some multiple of the simplest formula. We see that the number of hydrogen atoms is 3 times the number of carbon atoms in C_2H_6 and C_3H_9, as well as in CH_3. We must have more experimental data to establish the true formula for ethane, and the molecular weight is what we need. This may be determined by the vapor density method (see page 352). By weighing a liter of ethane at $0°C$ and 760 mm of mercury pressure, we find the density to be 1.34 grams per liter. A gram molecular volume of the gas (22.4 liters) will weigh 30 grams, as shown in the following calculation:

$$22.4 \text{ liters} \times 1.34 \text{ grams/liter} = 30 \text{ grams}$$

Thus we know the molecular weight of ethane to be 30.

The formula weight for the simplest formula, CH_3, is 15, since the atomic weight of carbon is 12 and that of hydrogen is 1. The molecular weight is exactly 2 times the simplest formula weight. Therefore, the true formula must be $(CH_3)_2$, or C_2H_6.

Consider the case of ammonia, for which the experimentally determined gram molecular weight (see page 351) is 17.02 grams. A chemical analysis of ammonia shows a composition of 17.6% hydrogen and 82.4% nitrogen. Thus the gram molecular weight of 17.02 grams consists of 3.02 grams of hydrogen and 14 grams of nitrogen. Since the mole weight of hydrogen is very close to 1 gram and that of nitrogen is 14 grams, we have 3 moles of hydrogen and 1 mole of nitrogen in 1 mole of ammonia. The formula for ammonia, as determined from these data, is NH_3. Knowing a common valence of nitrogen to be 3 and that of hydrogen to be 1, we would predict the same formula, but the experimental verification is always necessary before any formula is accepted.

20-6
Chemical Equations

Chemical equations are descriptions of chemical changes which have taken place. They are based on experimental facts that must be known before an equation can be written with certainty.

It is an experimentally known fact that under certain conditions hydrogen will combine with oxygen to form water. We may describe this reaction by writing

hydrogen + oxygen $\longrightarrow$ water

The use of chemical formulas makes the writing of equations much simpler and we may state the same fact by writing

$$H_2 + O_2 \longrightarrow H_2O$$

Our equation now violates the fundamental principle of conservation of matter and must be modified. We have two atoms of oxygen on the left side of the equation and only one on the right side. We correct this situation by *balancing* the equation; that is, changing the number of molecules involved. This is accomplished by writing

$$2H_2 + O_2 \rightarrow 2H_2O$$

We now have equal numbers of atoms of both kinds on both sides of the equation and our equation is balanced. The molecules on the left side are called *reactants* and those on the right are called *products*.

This equation tells us what happens in the chemical change and it also tells us what quantitative relationships exist between the reactants and products:

$$2H_2 + O_2 \qquad \rightarrow 2H_2O$$

2 moles + 1 mole → 2 moles

4.032 grams + 31.998 grams → 36.03 grams

Our equation tells us that 2 moles of hydrogen react with 1 mole of oxygen to produce 2 moles of water.

It should be noted that this equation tells us nothing about the condition under which hydrogen and oxygen will combine or how fast they will combine once the reaction starts. When hydrogen and oxygen are mixed at room temperature, no chemical change takes place. The temperature must be raised to start the reaction, or the reaction may be started at room temperature with a suitable catalyst.

As another example of equation writing we shall consider the combustion of a compound of carbon and hydrogen, called a hydrocarbon. Propane (C_3H_8), which is an important constituent of "bottled gas," will burn to produce carbon dioxide and water vapor. Since burning is a chemical reaction with oxygen, the equation describing this change is

propane + oxygen → carbon dioxide + water

$$C_3H_8 + O_2 \qquad \rightarrow \qquad CO_2 + H_2O$$

Counting atoms, we find that our equation is not balanced and we make the necessary corrections by changing the number of molecules in the equation:

$$C_3H_8 + 5O_2 \qquad \rightarrow \qquad 3CO_2 + 4H_2O$$

1 mole + 5 moles → 3 moles + 4 moles

44.097 grams + 159.99 grams → 132.027 grams + 72.06 grams

Again, this equation tells us nothing about the conditions required for a reaction between oxygen and propane, or about the rate at which the reaction will occur. Experience has shown that this reaction will take place, and the equation tells us the quantitative relationship between the reactants and products of the reaction.

We have seen that definite quantitative relationships exist between the reactants and products of chemical reactions. These relationships enable us to use chemical equations to make calculations of the weights of various substances involved in reactions.

For example, suppose we wish to know what weight of calcium carbonate ($CaCO_3$) would be required to make 1 kilogram of calcium oxide (CaO). It is an experimentally known fact that calcium carbonate will decompose at a temperature sufficiently high to produce calcium oxide and carbon dioxide. We express this fact in the following equation, which is balanced:

$$CaCO_3 \xrightarrow{\text{heat}} CaO + CO_2$$

$$1 \text{ mole} \longrightarrow 1 \text{ mole} + 1 \text{ mole}$$

$$100 \text{ grams} \longrightarrow 56 \text{ grams} + 44 \text{ grams}$$

We see from this equation that 1 mole, or 100 grams, of calcium carbonate will produce 1 mole, or 56 grams of calcium oxide. Therefore, the weight of calcium carbonate required to produce 1 kilogram of calcium oxide would be in the same proportion. We may express this proportionality in the following form, remembering that 1 kilogram is 1,000 grams:

$$\underset{\text{100 grams}}{\overset{W}{CaCO_3}} \longrightarrow \underset{\text{56 grams}}{\overset{\text{1,000 grams}}{CaO}}$$

$$\frac{W}{100 \text{ grams}} = \frac{1,000 \text{ grams}}{56 \text{ grams}}$$

$$W \neq 1,785.7 \text{ grams}$$

As a final example of a calculation from a chemical equation, we shall consider the reaction of sulfuric acid with sodium chloride. Suppose we wish to know what weight of sulfuric acid will be required to produce 200 liters of HCl gas at 0°C and 760 mm of Hg pressure. Sulfuric acid reacts with sodium chloride to produce hydrogen chloride gas and sodium sulfate, according to the following equation:

$$H_2SO_4 + NaCl \longrightarrow HCl + Na_2SO_4$$

Balancing this equation, we obtain

$$H_2SO_4 + 2NaCl \longrightarrow 2HCl + Na_2SO_4$$

$$1 \text{ mole} + 2 \text{ moles} \longrightarrow 2 \text{ moles} + 1 \text{ mole}$$

$$98 \text{ grams} + 117 \text{ grams} \longrightarrow 73 \text{ grams} + 142 \text{ grams}$$

(44.8 l)

We see that 44.8 liters of HCl gas will be produced by reaction of 98 grams of H_2SO_4. A proportional weight of H_2SO_4 will be required to produce 200 liters of HCl:

$$\underset{\underset{98 \text{ grams}}{W}}{H_2SO_4} + 2NaCl \rightarrow \underset{\underset{44.8 \text{ liters}}{200 \text{ liters}}}{2HCl} + Na_2SO_4$$

$$\frac{W}{98 \text{ grams}} = \frac{200 \text{ liters}}{44.8 \text{ liters}}$$

$$W = 437.5 \text{ grams } H_2SO_4$$

Chemical symbols, formulas, and equations constitute the language of chemistry, which is very useful because it enables us to convey information in a concise, quantitative manner. These quantitative relationships in chemical changes are relatively easy to discover. It is much more difficult to find out exactly what takes place in every step of the chemical change. There are many important questions about chemical reactions that are not answered by equations.

QUESTIONS AND PROBLEMS

1. Write the chemical formula for each of the following compounds:
   (a) Calcium sulfide.   (d) Potassium carbonate.
   (b) Iron (II) chloride.   (e) Silicon dioxide.
   (c) Aluminum sulfate.

2. Name each of the following compounds:
   (a) $Zn(NO_3)_2$.   (d) $FeBr_3$.
   (b) Li_2SO_4.   (e) $Ca_3(PO_4)_2$.
   (c) $KMnO_4$.

3. Calculate the weight in grams of 10^{23} carbon dioxide (CO_2) molecules.

4. How many moles of water are contained in 1 liter of water at a temperature of 4°C?

5. How many molecules are present in 1 gram of oxygen?

6. What is the gram molecular weight of glycerine, $C_3H_5(OH)_3$? How many molecules are present in this quantity of glycerine?

7. How many chloride ions are present in 19.04 grams of magnesium chloride?

8. What is the formula weight for aluminum oxide?

9. A mixture of 8 grams of hydrogen and 32 grams of oxygen is placed in a strong steel cylinder and ignited. What substances are present in the cylinder after the reaction and what is the quantity of each?

10. How does the number of molecules in 64 grams of methyl alcohol (CH_3OH) compare with the number in 141 grams of phenol (C_6H_5OH)? Show how you arrive at your answer.

11. Ten liters of a certain gas at 0°C and 760 mm Hg pressure are found to weigh 7.14 grams. What is the molecular weight of this gas? What is the most reasonable formula for this compound if it contains only hydrogen and carbon?

12. Consider the following equation:

$$\text{carbon} + \text{water} \longrightarrow \text{glucose (sugar)}$$

$$6C + 6H_2O \longrightarrow C_6H_{12}O_6$$

All the substances mentioned in this equation are familiar to you. Charcoal is a form of carbon and glucose is a principal ingredient of corn syrup. What questions are immediately raised in your mind concerning this equation?

13. Ethane, C_2H_6, burns rapidly when mixed with oxygen and ignited. The process of burning is chemical combination with oxygen, and the products are carbon dioxide and water. How many moles of oxygen are required to burn 3 moles of ethane?

14. Zinc will combine with sulfuric acid, H_2SO_4, to produce zinc sulfate, $ZnSO_4$, and hydrogen. If 32.7 grams of zinc are added to a solution containing 50 grams of H_2SO_4, what will remain uncombined after the chemical action has ceased?

15. One hundred grams of a certain gaseous compound is found to be formed from 30.4 grams of nitrogen and 69.6 grams of oxygen. What is the simplest formula for this compound? One liter of this gas at 0°C and 760 mm of Hg pressure weighs 2.053 grams. What is the molecular formula for the compound?

SUGGESTED REFERENCES

KIEFFER, WILLIAM F., *The Mole Concept in Chemistry*. Reinhold Publishing Corp., New York, 1962.

SORUM, C. H., *How To Solve General Chemistry Problems*. Prentice-Hall, Englewood Cliffs, N.J., 1969.

WALKER, RUTH A., and HELEN JOHNSTON, *The Language of Chemistry*. Prentice-Hall, Englewood Cliffs, N.J., 1967.

21

Liquids and Solutions

The Koran proclaims, "Out of water all life is created." It may well be that life on this planet originated in the sea. Certainly water is vital to life as we know it. Most chemical reactions, whether they occur in nature, in a chemical laboratory, or in an industrial plant, occur in water solution. The body fluids of plants and animals are complex solutions, plants obtain their nutrients from solutions in the soil, and the air we breathe is a gaseous solution. The oceans are vast solutions containing many valuable minerals that man is now learning to recover. Solutions are so important that some knowledge of their properties is necessary for an understanding of the physical world. We shall confine our attention to water solutions, although there are many other kinds of solutions.

21-1
The Liquid State

Liquids, like gases and covalently bonded solids, are composed of molecules. Molecules exert attractive forces upon each other. These forces are quite large in solids, moderate in liquids, and very small in gases. The attractive forces between molecules in a liquid are sufficiently large to hold the liquid in a definite volume. These forces are small enough to allow the molecules to move past one another, resulting in the flow of liquids and the lack of a definite shape.

The attractive forces between the molecules of a liquid result in the formation of a surface film. The molecules at the surface are attracted by those in the interior, causing the liquid surface to act like a stretched membrane (see Fig. 21-1). The pull exerted by the liquid surface is called *surface tension*. It is expressed in terms of the force required to break a unit length of film:

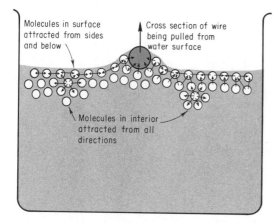

Molecules in surface attracted from sides and below

Cross section of wire being pulled from water surface

Molecules in interior attracted from all directions

FIG. 21-1. Molecular forces at liquid surface.

dynes per centimeter, or newtons per meter. The surface tension of water at 20°C is 73 dynes/cm, that of alcohol is 22 dynes/cm, and that of mercury is 480 dynes/cm.

The constant motion of molecules, as observed in Brownian movement, produces an effect known as *diffusion*. This is an intermingling of two substances as a result of the movement of individual molecules. Diffusion takes place most rapidly in gases because gas molecules are relatively far apart and move further between collisions than the molecules in liquids and solids. Diffusion in liquids may be demonstrated by carefully pouring some water over a concentrated solution of copper sulfate. At first, there will be a clear demarcation line between the blue copper sulfate solution and the water. The blue solution will slowly diffuse into the clear water; at the same time, the water will diffuse into the copper sulfate solution, but this cannot be readily observed.

21-2
Chemical Change in Solution

Substances in solution usually enter into chemical reactions very rapidly since they are highly subdivided. The molecules or ions of such a substance are relatively free to move and can undergo the collisions which are necessary for reaction. This idea can be demonstrated easily with ordinary baking soda (sodium bicarbonate) and a solid crystalline acid, such as citric acid. When these two compounds are mixed in the dry form, no chemical change takes place. When water is added, however, a very rapid reaction takes place, with the evolution of carbon dioxide. The ions of the solids were bound together by forces which prevented their free movement. When water was added, the ionic solids went into solution, the ions moved freely through the solution, and entered into new combinations.

The chemical reactions of the human body take place in solution. Protoplasm, contained in all cells, is 75 to 90% water. The various compounds in protoplasm may be in true solution or may be suspended as small particles. The solvent capacity of water brings about the intimate mixing of the many compounds in protoplasm and enhances their chemical reactivity.

21-3
Solubility

The distinction between the *solute* (the substance dissolved) and the *solvent* (the dissolving medium) is sometimes difficult to make. Ordinarily, the substance present in greatest amount is called the solvent. For solid-liquid solutions, the liquid is considered the solvent. The composition of a given solution, as we have already indicated, is not constant. Solution concentration, which is a measure of the amount of solute dissolved in a given quantity of solvent, may vary over a wide range. Dilute solutions contain relatively small amounts of solute and concentrated solutions contain large amounts. A solution is said to be *saturated* when the solvent contains all the solute it can hold at a given temperature.

The chemist may specify the concentration of a solution in terms of *molarity*. A *one-molar solution* contains 1 mole of solute in 1 liter of solution. For example, we could prepare a one-molar solution of methyl alcohol, CH_3OH, in water by dissolving 32 grams of the alcohol in sufficient water to make 1 liter of solution.

The amount of solute which can be dissolved in a given quantity of solvent varies over a wide range. This variation depends mainly on the nature of the solute, the nature of the solvent, and the temperature of the solution. The *solubility* of a solute is defined as the quantity of a solute which will saturate a definite quantity of a solvent at a given temperature. Solubilities may be expressed in grams of solute per 100 grams of solvent. For example, the solubility of sodium chloride in water is slightly over 39 grams at 100°C. This means that approximately 39 grams of sodium chloride will saturate 100 grams of water at 100°C.

An increase in temperature generally increases the solubility of solids in liquids. The solubility of potassium nitrate increases from 13.3 grams per 100 grams of water at 0°C to 249 grams per 100 grams of water at 100°C. The increase in solubility with an increase in temperature occurs when heat is absorbed in the solution process. Energy is required to disrupt the crystal structure of the solid, and an increase in temperature makes more energy available for this process. The exceptions occur when ions from the solute liberate a large amount of heat energy in the process of hydration (see page 365). Solubility decreases with an increase in temperature when heat is evolved in the solution process.

An increase in temperature decreases the solubility of a gas in a liquid. When the solution temperature is increased, the average kinetic energy of the dissolved gas molecules increases. As the dissolved gas molecules gain more kinetic energy, they have a greater tendency to leave the solution. When a pan of water is heated on a stove, bubbles of dissoved air escape long before the boiling point is reached. The water is able to hold less air in solution as the temperature increases.

21-4
Water

Water is an excellent solvent and most of the solutions that we meet in our everyday experience are water solutions, or aqueous solutions. Water is the only common liquid on Earth, and it has very unusual properties when compared with compounds having similar molecular weights. For example, water, with a molecular weight of 18, boils at 100°C, whereas methane, with a molecular weight of 16, boils at −161°C, and ammonia, with a molecular weight of 17, boils at −33°C. This relatively high boiling point of water indicates an unusually high attractive force between water molecules. Water is also unusual in its ability to dissolve certain types of chemical compounds. Sodium chloride crystals are held together by such strong electrostatic forces that a temperature of over 800°C is required to melt them. Water will dissolve these crystals, but will not dissolve butter to any appreciable extent, although butter softens and becomes liquid at a relatively low temperature. These and other unusual properties of water may be understood in terms of the structure of the water molecule.

Water molecules, as we have learned, are formed by the combination of two hydrogen atoms with one oxygen atom. The shape of the water molecule is the key to its properties. The oxygen atom has 6 outer-energy-level electrons, 2 in the 2s orbital, and 4 in the three 2p orbitals. One of the 2p orbitals has 2 electrons and the other two have 1 electron each which are capable of forming shared electron pairs with electrons from other atoms. This situation is shown in Fig. 21-2.

The lightly shaded orbitals in Fig. 21-2 contain only 1 electron each and the darkly shaded orbital is filled with 2 electrons. The 2s orbital is not shown in the diagram since it is not involved in the formation of chemical bonds. An atom such as hydrogen, having a single valence electron, can share this electron with the unfilled orbital of the oxygen atom and form a covalent bond. Thus the oxygen atom can form two covalent bonds with 2 hydrogen atoms. This situation is illustrated in Fig. 21-3.

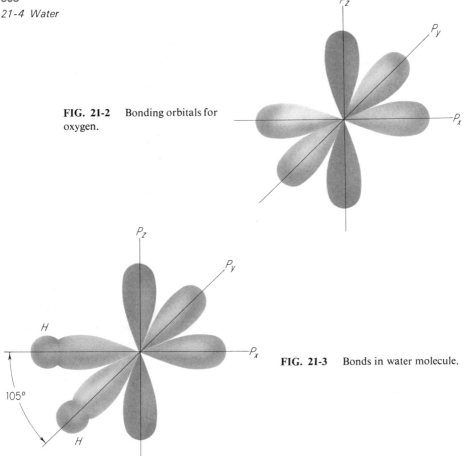

FIG. 21-2   Bonding orbitals for oxygen.

FIG. 21-3   Bonds in water molecule.

The *p* orbitals of oxygen forming the covalent bonds in water are at an angle of 90 degrees to each other. Thus we might expect the angle between the covalent bonds in water to be 90 degrees. However, actual measurements on the water molecule show this bond angle to be about 105 degrees. This increase in the bond angle may be explained in terms of the electrical charges in the molecule. The oxygen atom is more electronegative than the hydrogen atom, and the shared electrons spend more time around the oxygen than around the hydrogen. This leaves the hydrogens with a partial positive charge and the repulsive force between them increases the bond angle from 90 degrees to 105 degrees.

The water molecule, because of its geometry, is a polar molecule. The oxygen end of the molecule has a partial negative charge while the hydrogen end has a partial positive charge. This charge separation within the molecule is due to the difference in electronegativity between hydrogen and oxygen, and to the fact that the water molecule is a bent molecule. If the water

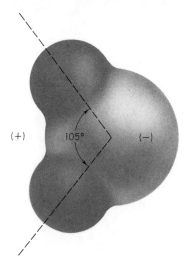

FIG. 21-4   Charge distribution in water molecule.

molecule were linear, the charge differences would cancel and the properties of water would be quite different. The diagram in Fig. 21-4 represents a model of the water molecule.

The polarity of the water molecule causes its abnormally high boiling point and certain other unusual properties. The partial charges on the molecules result in extra-attractive forces between molecules. The attractive force between the negative oxygen end of one molecule and the positive hydrogen end of another is called a *hydrogen bond*. The attractive forces of the two hydrogen bonds cause water molecules to cling together in groups, as shown in Fig. 21-5. The high boiling point of water is due to the energy required to separate the molecules, which are being held together by hydrogen bonds.

The peculiar behavior of water in expanding as it changes from a liquid to a solid is also due to hydrogen bonding. When the maximum number of hydrogen bonds form, each water molecule is surrounded by four others

FIG. 21-5   Hydrogen bonding in water.

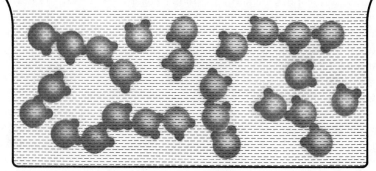

FIG. 21-6   Ice crystal model.

in a tetrahedral structure. This results in a very open crystal structure for ice, in which molecules actually occupy more space than in the liquid state. Thus water expands when it freezes into ice. A model of an ice crystal is shown in Fig. 21-6.

The ability of water to dissolve ionic solids, such as sodium chloride, is also due to the polarity of the water molecule. The attraction of the polar water molecules for the electrically charged ions helps to remove ions from the exposed surface of the crystal. The attractive forces between ions at the surface of the crystal are reduced because the polar water molecules partially neutralize the charge on the ions. The motion of the water molecules and the vibration of the ions in the crystal also aid in removal of the ions from the crystal structure. Water molecules colliding with the vibrating ions may cause them to break free from the weakened attractive forces in the crystal. Once the ions are free from the crystal they might be expected to regroup because of strong electrostatic attractive forces. However, the ions are surrounded by the polar water molecules, which they hold by electrostatic attraction. Ions in this condition are said to be *hydrated*. The shell of water molecules around the ions greatly reduces the electrostatic attraction between the ions and prevents them from reforming a crystal. Figure 21-7 illustrates the solution of an ionic solid in water.

A substance such as butter is made up of molecules which are not polar; that is, the electrical charges in the molecules are distributed symmetrically and there are no positive or negative ends in these molecules. Consequently, the water molecules attract each other more than they attract the butter molecules, and the butter molecules have no special attraction for water.

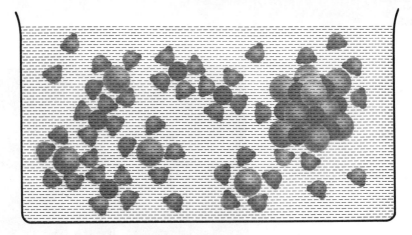

FIG. 21-7   Solution of ionic solid.

As a result of this situation, butter does not dissolve in water. Even if the butter is melted, the two liquids, having different densities, remain separated in two layers. However, butter is dissolved by a nonpolar liquid such as carbon tetrachloride. In general, we find that *like dissolves like;* that is, polar solvents will dissolve polar solutes and nonpolar solvents will dissolve nonpolar solutes. The methyl alcohol molecule, CH_3OH, is a polar molecule and is very much like water. Consequently, methyl alcohol is soluble in water in all proportions.

Since water does not dissolve fat molecules, the removal of grease from a surface by true solution will require a nonpolar liquid in which the grease is soluble. Grease may be removed with water if soap or some other detergent is used. The detergent molecules have very dissimilar ends, one end being polar and the other nonpolar. The polar end of the detergent molecule dissolves readily in water and the nonpolar end dissolves readily in a fat or grease. The detergent molecules surround small particles of grease with their nonpolar ends dissolved in the grease and their polar ends dissolved in the water, as represented in Fig. 21-8. This action prevents the grease particles

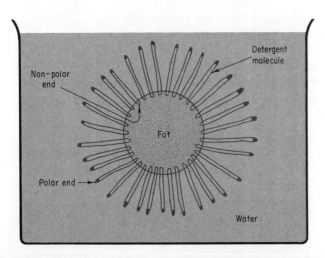

FIG. 21-8   Action of detergent molecules on fat.

from coming together and they are kept suspended in the water and washed away. The grease is said to be *emulsified* when held in suspension in water in this manner.

21-5
Properties and Uses of Solutions

The solvent in a solution always has a lower *vapor pressure* than the pure solvent at the same temperature. Vapor pressure is a measure of the tendency of a liquid to evaporate. The tendency of the solvent to evaporate is reduced by the addition of a solute. The solute molecules occupy part of the surface area of the solution; thus fewer solvent molecules escape from the surface. This situation is shown in Fig. 21-9. One container in this figure holds the solvent, water, and the other contains a solution of sugar in water. The sugar molecules, represented by black circles, take up part of the surface area in the solution and interfere with the escape of water molecules, resulting in a lower vapor pressure.

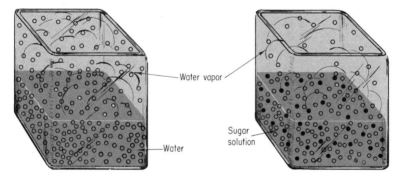

FIG. 21-9   Effect of solute on vapor pressure.

As a result of this situation, the boiling point of a solution is higher and the freezing point is lower than that of the pure solvent. The boiling point of a liquid is the temperature at which its vapor pressure becomes as high as the surrounding atmospheric pressure. In a similar way, the freezing point is the temperature at which the vapor pressure of the solid form is equal to that of the liquid. Pure water boils at 100°C and freezes at 0°C when the atmospheric pressure is 760 mm of mercury. A solution of salt in water will boil at a temperature above 100°C and freeze at a temperature below 0°C. The extent of change in these temperatures depends on the concentration of the solution. As more solute is added to a solution, the boiling point increases and the freezing point decreases.

We make practical use of this principle, particularly in winter. Water is circulated through the engines of most automobiles to remove heat and prevent overheating. Since water expands upon freezing, the engine would be damaged if precautions were not taken to prevent the freezing of the water in winter. A noncorrosive substance can be dissolved in the water to lower the freezing point and prevent damage to the engine in winter. Methyl alcohol, CH_3OH, and ethylene glycol, $C_2H_4(OH)_2$, are the compounds most often used for this purpose. Ethylene glycol, having a relatively high boiling point, is the principal ingredient of the "permanent" type of antifreeze. These liquids also counteract the expansion effect of water on freezing because they contract when freezing.

One of the methods for determining molecular weights is based on the reduction in freezing point by a dissolved solute. A solution containing 1 mole of solute in 1,000 grams of solvent is known as a *one-molal solution*. When 1 mole of any nonionized solute is dissolved in 1,000 grams of water, the freezing point is reduced by a constant amount, $1.87°C$. Thus, if a known weight of solute is dissolved in a known weight of water, the freezing point depression is proportional to the number of moles contained in the known weight of solute. For example, suppose we dissolve 1 gram of a given nonionized solute in 20 grams of water and find the freezing point of the solution to be $-0.935°C$. One gram of solute in 20 grams of water is equivalent to 50 grams of solute in 1,000 grams of water. Since the freezing point is reduced by one-half of the standard $1.87°$, we know that the 50 grams of solute is $\frac{1}{2}$ mole. Thus the weight of 1 mole is 100 grams, and the molecular weight is 100.

Salts such as sodium chloride and calcium chloride are used on sidewalks and roads to aid in the removal of ice and snow in winter. These compounds form water solutions with freezing points below zero and if the temperature is not too extreme they will allow snow and ice to melt. A mixture of ice and pure water will have a minimum temperature of $0°C$. However, we may obtain a lower temperature by using ice in a salt solution.

The blood in our bodies is a complex solution. Many body functions are controlled by the concentration of various components in the blood. For example, the rate of breathing is determined by the concentration of carbon dioxide in the blood. The respiratory center, located in the brain, is the source of nerve impulses which control the rate of breathing. An increase in the carbon dioxide content of the blood stimulates the respiratory center and results in an increase in both rate and depth of breathing. The oxygen content of the blood has little or no effect upon the respiratory center. Thus the breathing rate is increased by an increase in carbon dioxide concentration in the blood, not by a lack of oxygen.

Another property of a solution which is related to concentration is known as *osmotic pressure*. This property may be illustrated by considering a cellophane bag half-filled with a concentrated sugar solution and immersed in a container of pure water. Water molecules can go through the cellophane, but sugar molecules cannot. The water molecules go through the cellophane into the sugar solution at a greater rate than in the opposite direction. Every molecule striking the cellophane on the water side is a water molecule, and each one has a chance to get through. However, the rate at which water molecules strike the cellophane on the solution side is lower because some of the molecules are sugar molecules. Thus there are fewer chances for water molecules to penetrate the cellophane from the solution side. This situation is shown in Fig. 21-10, where water molecules are represented by open circles and sugar molecules by black circles. Thus the volume of the solution in the cellophane bag will increase, since water will enter faster than it will leave.

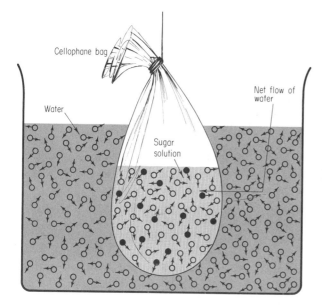

FIG. 21-10   Relative concentration of water and osmosis.

The pressure causing the flow of water into the cellophane bag is known as *osmotic pressure*. If the bag were surrounded by a solution of the same concentration as that inside, there would be no osmotic pressure and no net flow of water. On the other hand, if the bag were surrounded by a solution at a higher concentration of solute than that inside, there would be a net loss of water from the bag.

The red blood cells behave in a manner similar to the cellophane bag described above. Under normal conditions the osmotic pressure within the cells is the same as that of the blood plasma. If blood cells are placed in distilled water, they gain water, swell, and rupture. If they are placed in a concentrated salt solution, they lose water and shrink. Therefore, the addition of fluids to the blood must be made with care. Any solution injected into the blood, such as glucose in intravenous feeding, should have the same osmotic pressure as the solution within the blood cells. Failure to observe this precaution may lead to extensive damage to red blood cells, with serious consequences for the individual.

QUESTIONS AND PROBLEMS

1. Milk is more than 90% water. Butterfat, which is insoluble in water, is present in milk to the extent of about 3 to 4%. How do you account for these facts?

2. Mercury forms almost spherical droplets on a clean glass surface, but water spreads out on the glass. How do you explain this difference?

3. Predict the relative solubility of iodine in water. Consider the nature of water and iodine molecules.

4. Benzene is much less polar than water. How would you expect the solubility of iodine in benzene to compare with that in water?

5. Ammonia is a gas made up of polar molecules. How do you account for the fact that ammonia can be converted to the liquid form by pressure and applied directly in the soil as a fertilizer without significant loss?

6. Glycerine has a molecular weight of 92 and is quite soluble in water. What freezing-point temperature would you expect for a solution made by dissolving 110.4 grams of glycerine in 400 grams of water?

7. Dried whole fruit, such as prunes, are shrunken and wrinkled in appearance. A dried prune placed in water soon swells and acquires a smooth, plump appearance. How do you explain this behavior?

8. Many of the foods we eat contain starch which is insoluble in water. What change takes place in digestion to enable us to assimilate this food?

9. Nitrates from agricultural fertilizers and animal wastes are one of the principal contaminants involved in the water pollution problem. What physical property of nitrates is responsible for this situation? (*Hint:* Check the properties of nitrates in a chemistry text.)

10. Magnesium is present in the oceans in the form of soluble compounds. Sea water is 0.13% magnesium by weight. A commercial process has been developed to extract magnesium metal from sea water. Assuming that all of the dissolved magnesium could be recovered, how many cubic feet of water (density = 64 lb/ft^3) must be processed to obtain 1 pound of metal?

11. What practical problem is produced by the orderly arrangement of water molecules in the crystal structure of ice?

12. Suppose you wanted to experimentally determine the solubility of a certain compound in water at 25°C. How would you proceed?

13. A solution containing 250 grams of compound *X* dissovled in 1,000 grams of water freezes at −4.67°C. What is the molecular weight of compound *X*?

14. What reason could you suggest for the fact that some ionic compounds, such as barium sulfate, have very low solubility in water?

15. What simple experimental test could be used to determine whether or not a given solution of sodium chloride in water is saturated?

SUGGESTED REFERENCES

CHOPPIN, G. R., "Water—H_2O or $H_{180}O_{90}$?" *Chemistry*, 38, no. 3 (1965), 6.

DAVIS, KENNETH, and JOHN A. DAY, *Water: The Mirror of Science*. Anchor Books, Garden City, N.Y., 1961.

OTHMER, D. F., "Water and Life," *Chemistry*, 43, no. 10 (1970), 12.

REVELLE, R., "Water," *Scientific American*, 209, no. 3 (1963), 93.

22

Acids, Bases, and Salts

As knowledge accumulates in any field, systems of classification become necessary for efficient use of this knowledge. Chemists classify compounds for convenience of nomenclature and study. All the members of a given class of compounds have similar chemical properties. We shall consider three of the many known classes of compounds. Acids, bases, and salts are important classes of compounds that we frequently encounter in our everday experience.

22-1
Acids

Many natural substances are characterized by a sharp, sour taste. Lemons, rhubarb, and sour milk all have a taste which would suggest the presence of similar substances. The compounds responsible for the sour taste have been isolated and given the name *acids* from the Latin word *acidus*, meaning "sharp" or "biting" to the taste. The sour taste in lemons is due to *citric acid*, in rhubarb to *oxalic acid*, and in sour milk to *lactic acid*.

Acids have common properties other than sour taste. They react with metals to liberate hydrogen gas, and they also react very readily with the compounds called *bases*. Acids produce color changes in certain dyes called "indicators." Litmus, a plant product, is such an indicator: it changes from a blue color to red in the presence of an acid. Phenolphthalein, another indicator, is pink in base solutions and colorless in acid solutions. Many other compounds also serve as indicators and are commonly used in chemical laboratories to test for the presence of acids.

Acids exhibit their characteristic properties only when they are in solution. Water is the most common solvent and we shall consider only aqueous acid solutions. Pure acids in liquid form are not electrical conductors, indicating that they are not ionic compounds. The electrical conductivity of aqueous acid solutions suggests that acid molecules react with water to form ions. Pure water contains a few ions, even though water is a molecular substance. The ions in water result from a reaction between water molecules:

$$H_2O + H_2O \longrightarrow H_3O^+ + OH^-$$

The H_3O^+ and OH^- ions, produced in equal numbers in pure water, are present at a concentration of about 10^{-7} mole per liter. Thus, since there are about 55 moles of water per liter, only about 1 water molecule in every 550 million enters into this reaction to produce ions. The H_3O^+ ion is really a hydrogen ion, or proton, H^+, attached to a water molecule. This ion is called the *hydroniun ion*, but we shall refer to it as a hydrogen ion, although we know it is always attached to a water molecule.

The reaction of acid solutions with metals to liberate hydrogen suggests the presence of hydrogen ions in these solutions. If a hydrogen ion should gain an electron from a metal atom, the ion would become an uncharged hydrogen atom and the metal atom would become a positive ion. This reaction is shown in Fig. 22-1. The hydrogen atoms immediately combine to form hydrogen molecules. The properties of acid solutions are due to the presence of hydrogen ions, so we may define an acid as a substance which will increase the hydrogen ion concentration in a water solution. We may express this same idea by saying that an acid is a *proton donor*.

Acids are molecular compounds which do not contain hydrogen ions in the pure form, but which react with water to form these ions. For example, hydrogen chloride reacts with water according to the following equation:

$$HCl + H_2O \longrightarrow H_3O^+ + Cl^-$$

The hydrogen chloride molecules give up protons to water molecules, forming hydronium ions and chloride ions. The solution of hydrogen chloride in water is known as *hydrochloric acid*.

When we examine the chemical composition of acids we find them to be composed of nonmetals. Such elements as chlorine, bromine, nitrogen, phosphorus, and sulfur are acid-forming elements. These nonmetals have

FIG. 22-1 Action of hydrogen ions on a metal.

relatively high electronegativity, and certain compounds of these elements with hydrogen give up hydrogen ions easily because the electron pair holding the hydrogen is shifted toward the more electronegative part of the molecule. Many, but not all, acids contain oxygen. In fact, oxygen was at one time thought to be responsible for acidic properties, but we now recognize hydrogen as the common constituent of acids. There are more general definitions for acids, in which other elements are responsible for acidic properties, but we shall limit our consideration of acids to those substances which are proton donors.

Acids do not all react with water to the same extent. Hydrogen chloride, mentioned above, reacts so completely with water that solutions of this compound are practically 100% in ionic form. An acid which reacts very extensively with water is known as a *strong acid*. Acetic acid, present in vinegar, is a *weak acid* since it reacts with water only to the extent of about 2%; that is, about 98% of the acid is present in molecular form and about 2% in ionic form. The reaction of acetic acid with water is shown in the following equation:

$$HC_2H_3O_2 + H_2O \rightarrow H_3O^+ + C_2H_3O_2^-$$

Acids such as hydrochloric (HCl), nitric (HNO_3), and sulfuric (H_2SO_4) are strong acids, and they react almost completely with water to form ions. Acids such as acetic ($HC_2H_3O_2$) and oxalic ($H_2C_2O_4$) are weak acids, and react only to a slight extent with water to form ions. Thus the strength of an acid depends on the extent to which the compound gives up hydrogen ions to a solvent such as water. Acid strength and concentration are different concepts, as explained in Section 22-4.

22-2
Bases

Bases are characterized by a bitter taste, a slick, soapy texture, and corrosive action on protein material. They also produce color changes in indicators. Litmus turns blue in the presence of a base, and phenolphthalein turns pink. Bases combine chemically with acids in a reaction which results in a drastic change in the properties of both compounds.

Most pure bases in liquid form are electrical conductors. Therefore, they are ionic compounds and reaction with a solvent is not necessary for the formation of ions. Sodium hydroxide, a base with the formula NaOH, is a crystalline solid. When dissolved in water, the positive sodium ions and the negative hydroxide ions (OH^-) are released from the crystal structure and diffuse throughout the solution. Such a solution is sometimes called an *alkaline* solution. The hydroxide ions are responsible for the basic properties of the solution. Therefore, we may define a *base* as a substance which, when dissolved in water, will increase the concentration of OH^- ions. A base may also be defined as a *proton acceptor*. The OH^- ions will combine readily with protons, or hydrogen ions, so that the OH^- ion is a proton acceptor.

The sulfide ion, $S^=$, is a base in the sense of being a proton acceptor. Sulfide ions in water solution take protons from water molecules, forming hydrogen sulfide (H_2S) and OH^- ions:

$$S^= + 2H_2O \longrightarrow H_2S + 2OH^-$$

Therefore, the sulfide ion is also a substance which increases the OH^- ion concentration in a water solution. Baking soda, which is sodium bicarbonate ($NaHCO_3$), is a base. The bicarbonate ion, HCO_3^-, can take protons from water and increase the OH^- ion concentration as shown in the following equation:

$$HCO_3^- + H_2O \longrightarrow OH^- + H_2CO_3$$
$$\hookrightarrow H_2O + CO_2$$

The strength of a base, like that of an acid, depends on the extent to which it produces ions in solution. Bases such as sodium hydroxide ($NaOH$) and potassium hydroxide (KOH) are strong because they are ionic in the solid form, and are completely ionized in solution because they are very soluble in water. Magnesium hydroxide, $Mg(OH)_2$, is a weak base since it is only slightly soluble in water and, therefore, will not produce a very large increase in the OH^- concentration. This weak base is used in the form of "milk of magnesia" to counteract excess stomach acidity.

Our most common bases are compounds of metals (in contrast with the acids, which are compounds of nonmetals). Metallic oxides, if they are soluble, react with water to produce the corresponding ionic hydroxide and the OH^- ion concentration in the solution increases. The oxide of sodium is very soluble and will react with water to increase the hydroxide ion concentration. The oxide of iron, on the other hand, is quite insoluble in water and will not produce any appreciable increase in the hydroxide ion concentration. The hydroxides of the very active metals are strong bases. The metals in group IA of the periodic table (see Table 16-3) are called "alkali metals" because of their strong base-forming property. The metals in group IIA form somewhat weaker bases and are called "alkaline earth metals."

It is important to note that the presence of an OH group in a compound does not necessarily mean that the compound is a base. For example, all alcohols contain at least one OH group, but these compounds are not bases. They do not increase the OH^- ion concentration when dissolved in water because the OH groups are tightly bound and remain attached to the alcohol molecules. The sulfuric acid molecule, usually indicated by the formula H_2SO_4, contains OH groups as shown in the formula below:

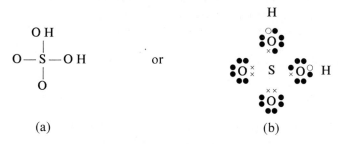

(a)   or   (b)

Each dash in formula (a) represents a shared pair of electrons. Formula (b) shows the valence electrons of each atom in the molecule. The electrons indicated by × originally belonged to the sulfur atom, those indicated by solid circles belonged to oxygen atoms, and those indicated by open circles belonged to hydrogen atoms. This molecule gives up hydrogen ions, not OH^- ions, in water solution. The electron pairs holding the two hydrogens are pulled away from the hydrogens by the highly electronegative sulfur and oxygen atoms. This displacement of the electrons weakens the bonds holding the hydrogen so they are given up easily, and the compound acts as an acid. Compounds such as potassium hydroxide, KOH, release OH^- ions readily because metals such as potassium have low electronegativity and do not attract an electron pair as strongly as does oxygen. The metallic elements in general have low electronegativity and are base-forming elements.

22-3
pH Scale For Acidity

We indicated on page 373 that pure water contains a low concentration of H_3O^+ and OH^- ions, 10^{-7} mole per liter of each. The H_3O^+ ion concentration is increased in acid solutions and decreased in alkaline solutions. The product of H_3O^+ concentration and OH^- concentration in aqueous solutions is always constant at 10^{-14}. A strongly acidic solution might have a H_3O^+ ion concentration of 10^{-1} mole per liter and an OH^- ion concentration of 10^{-13} mole per liter.

The acidity of solutions is most conveniently expressed on a logarithmic scale known as the pH *scale*. The pH is defined as the negative logarithm of the H_3O^+ concentration. For a neutral solution, $pH = -\log 10^{-7} = 7$. The pH for acidic solutions is less than 7 and that for basic solutions is greater than 7. For example, a solution with an H_3O^+ ion concentration of 10^{-2} has a pH of 2 and one with an H_3O^+ ion concentration of 10^{-10} has a pH of 10 (see Fig. 22-2).

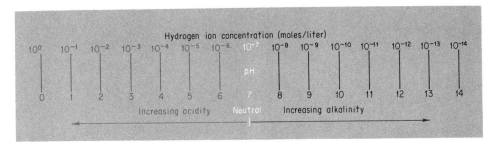

FIG. 22-2   The pH scale.

22-4
Neutralization

Positive hydrogen ions and negative hydroxide ions have a great tendency to combine when they approach each other. Thus an acid solution would be expected to react rapidly with a basic, or alkaline, solution. This chemical reaction is called *neutralization* because both the acidic and basic properties disappear in the reaction. The completion of the neutralization reaction may be detected with an indicator.

Consider the addition of a 500-ml solution containing 0.1 mole of sodium hydroxide to a 500-ml solution containing 0.1 mole of hydrochloric acid. The hydroxide ions in the basic solution combine very rapidly with the hydrogen ions in the acid solution to form water. This reaction may be represented by the equation:

$$Na^+ + OH^- + H^+ + Cl^- \longrightarrow H_2O + Na^+ + Cl^-$$

Or we may simply write:

$$H^+ + OH^- \longrightarrow H_2O$$

The positive sodium ions from the basic solution and the negative chloride ions from the acid solution do not undergo any change. We could, if we wished, evaporate the water from the solution and obtain 0.1 mole of sodium chloride. The solution resulting from this reaction is the same as that which we would have obtained by adding 0.1 mole of sodium chloride to enough pure water to make 1 liter of solution. Thus we see that neutralization is essentially a reaction between hydrogen ions and hydroxide ions to form water

We saw in the example above that 1 mole of sodium hydroxide reacts with 1 mole of hydrochloric acid. This is true because 1 mole of sodium hydroxide will furnish 1 mole of hydroxide ions and 1 mole of hydrochloric acid will furnish 1 mole of hydrogen ions. Acids and bases do not all react in this 1 : 1 ratio. Consider the reaction of potassium hydroxide, KOH, and sulfuric acid, H_2SO_4. Each mole of potassium hydroxide will furnish 1 mole of hydroxide ions and each mole of sulfuric acid will furnish 2 moles of hydrogen ions. The equation representing this reaction may be written as:

$$2KOH + H_2SO_4 \rightarrow 2H_2O + K_2SO_4$$

The ionic form of the equation is written:

$$2(K^+ + OH^-) + 2H^+ + SO_4^= \rightarrow 2H_2O + 2K^+ + SO_4^=$$

Thus we see that 2 moles of potassium hydroxide are required to react completely with 1 mole of sulfuric acid. The ratio of acid to base in a neutralization reaction is determined by the number of moles of hydroxide ion provided by a mole of base and the number of moles of hydrogen ion provided by a mole of acid.

We should differentiate clearly between the strength and the neutralizing capacity of an acid or a base. If we dissolve 1 mole of hydrogen chloride, HCl, in a liter of water, and 1 mole of acetic acid, $HC_2H_3O_2$, in a liter of water, we shall find that these solutions differ greatly in acid strength. The hydrogen ion concentration in the HCl solution is quite high, whereas that in the $HC_2H_3O_2$ solution is quite low. The HCl is a strong acid and the HC_2-H_3O_2 is a weak acid. However, both the hydrochloric acid solution and the acetic acid solution will neutralize the same quantity of any base. The neutralizing capacity of these two acids is the same, but their strengths as acids are quite different.

The term *neutralization* would suggest that the solution resulting from the complete reaction between an acid and a base would be neutral; that is, it would be expected to have neither acidic nor basic properties. Such a neutral solution is produced in the reaction of strong acids, such as hydrochloric acid, with strong bases, such as sodium hydroxide. However, a reaction between a weak acid and a strong base, or between a strong acid and a weak base, will result in a solution which is not neutral. In general, the reaction between a strong base and a weak acid will produce a basic solution, and the reaction between a weak base and a strong acid will produce an acidic solution.

Consider the reaction between 0.1 mole of acetic acid, a weak acid, and 0.1 mole of potassium hydroxide, a strong base. The acetic acid, $HC_2H_3O_2$, can furnish 1 mole of hydrogen ions for each mole of acid since only one of the hydrogens in the molecule will be given up in the neutralization reaction. The potassium hydroxide, KOH, will provide 1 mole of hydroxide ions for each mole of base. Thus the reaction may be represented by the equation:

$$HC_2H_3O_2 + K^+ + OH^- \rightarrow H_2O + K^+ + C_2H_3O_2^-$$

The formula for acetic acid is written in the molecular, rather than the ionic, form on the left side of the equation because it is a very weak acid and is only ionized to the extent of approximately 2 % in water solution. The acetate ions, $C_2H_3O_2^-$, produced in the reaction have a very strong attraction for hydrogen ions. This is shown by the fact that acetic acid is a weak acid—the acetate ions tend to hold the hydrogen ions. The acetate ions take hydrogen ions, or protons, from some of the water molecules in the solution:

$$H_2O + C_2H_3O_2^- \rightarrow HC_2H_3O_2 + OH^-$$

Thus the solution resulting from the reaction between acetic acid and potassium hydroxide is not neutral, but slightly basic, because of the excess of OH^- ions produced by the reaction of acetate ions and water.

The same result would be obtained by dissolving potassium acetate in water. The resulting solution would not be neutral, but slightly basic due to the reaction between acetate ions and water:

$$K^+ + C_2H_3O_2^- + H_2O \rightarrow HC_2H_3O_2 + OH^- + K^+$$

The potassium ions are not changed in this process. Such a reaction between an ion and water is known as *hydrolysis*.

22-5
Salts

The neutralization reaction, as we have seen, is essentially that of hydrogen ions combining with hydroxide ions to produce water. The resulting solution contains positive ions from the base and negative ions from the acid. If this solution is evaporated, a crystalline solid known as a *salt* is obtained. Thus, in the reaction between sodium hydroxide, NaOH, and hydrochloric acid, HCl, the salt obtained is sodium chloride, NaCl, and in the reaction between potassium hydroxide, KOH, and acetic acid, $HC_2H_3O_2$, the resulting salt is potassium acetate, $KC_2H_3O_2$. It should be evident from these examples that salts are named on the basis of the positive ion that comes from the base and the acid that contributes the negative ion. A *salt* is defined as an ionic compound containing a positive ion other than the hydrogen ion and a negative ion other than the hydroxide or oxide ion. The positive ion of a salt is usually a metallic ion.

The ions of a salt are held in a crystal structure by strong electrostatic forces. Because of these strong bonding forces, salts are generally quite hard and have relatively high melting points. The melting point of sodium chloride is 801°C, and that of sodium fluoride is 990°C. Solids with covalent bonding are generally not so hard and have lower melting points, although there are some exceptions.

Salts are more soluble in polar liquids than in nonpolar liquids. All salts are soluble to some extent in water, although some, such as calcium carbonate, are only slightly soluble. Water solutions of salts are electrical conductors, due to the presence of free ions in such solutions.

These compounds have many practical uses which affect us directly or indirectly every day. They are not only important because of industrial uses, but also play an important part in the functioning of the human body.

Salts have many uses, but space limitations will allow the mention of only a few of them. Most of us think of sodium chloride when the word "salt" is mentioned. This compound is essential in our diet and also has many industrial uses. The importance of sodium chloride in the ancient world is indicated by the fact that it was used as a medium of exchange in many lands. This salt occurs in large natural deposits and is the basic raw material in the manufacture of other sodium compounds and free chlorine. Every time we take a picture we are using a salt, usually silver bromide, which is the light-sensitive substance on the photographic film. Ordinary limestone is almost pure calcium carbonate, $CaCO_3$. This salt is widely used as a construction material and in the preparation of other chemical compounds, such as calcium hydroxide, an important base. Many salts are common household items. Among these are baking soda, which is sodium bicarbonate, $NaHCO_3$; cream of tartar, which is potassium hydrogen tartrate, $KHC_4H_4O_6$; alum, or potassium aluminum sulfate, $KAl(SO_4)_2$; and washing soda, or sodium carbonate, Na_2CO_3.

Serious water pollution problems are presented by cyanides and salts of mercury. These very poisonous compounds may usually be traced to industries using electrolytic processes.

Large quantities of bases are used in the manufacture of soap, rayon, paper pulp, and household cleansers. Bases are also quite important in petroleum refining. Sodium hydroxide, calcium hydroxide, and aqueous ammonia (ammonium hydroxide) are important bases which are used on a large scale.

The proper functioning of the human body depends on the proper acid or base concentration at many points. The digestive *enzymes* are substances which bring about chemical changes in the foods we eat. These enzymes function properly only in the presence of the acid or base concentration proper for each. The enzyme in saliva functions properly in a near-neutral medium. The gastric juice of the stomach contains enzymes which function only in an acid medium, so hydrochloric acid is secreted along with the gastric juice. The enzymes of the small intestine require a basic medium for proper functioning. Bicarbonate ions, normally present in the body fluids, are important in maintaining the basic condition in the small intestine.

The ratio of hydrogen and hydroxide ions in the blood and other body fluids is quite critical. This ratio, known as the "acid-base balance," must be maintained with a slight excess of hydroxide ions. That is, the blood and body fluids have a pH above 7. The proper acid-base balance in the body is maintained in part by compounds known as buffers. These buffers consist of mixtures of weak acids and their salts which are normally present in the body. Proteins dissolved in the blood also serve as buffers. A pronounced change in the acid-base balance would have very serious consequences, and could result in death. This balance is a matter of body metabolism and is not appreciably altered by drinking acidic or alkaline solutions.

The liquid effluents dumped into streams by many industries often contain strong acids or bases. Paper mill wastes may be either an acidic sulfite or a calcium hydroxide solution, depending upon the specific process used to separate lignin from cellulose in the wood pulp. Most coal mine runoff water is acidic because of the presence of oxides of sulfur. Steel mill effluents contain strong acids used in steel processing. These acidic or alkaline wastes kill plant and animal life in water and consequently produce an excessive oxygen demand upon the water.

Acids are manufactured on a large scale for industrial purposes. The production of sulfuric acid in this country is about 18 million tons per year; that of nitric acid is about 3 million tons. These and other acids are used for such purposes as cleaning metals and masonry, neutralizing bases, refining petroleum, and manufacturing fertilizers, explosives, and other chemicals. Nitric acid, a compound of nitrogen, is very important in the fertilizer industry. Nitrogen compounds, particularly nitric acid and nitrates, have had great influence on the course of history and we shall briefly examine some aspects of this influence.

22-7
Nitric Acid and Nitrates

Nitrogen is an abundant element on the Earth; the atmosphere consists of almost 80% of this gaseous element by volume. Despite the abundance of the element, nitrogen compounds are difficult to form. For centuries, man was dependent upon a few natural nitrate deposits, animal wastes, and certain species of bacteria growing on the roots of legumes for combined nitrogen. All proteins contain nitrogen, and since nitrogen compounds are removed from the soil by growing plants, it is a key element in the maintenance of soil fertility. The primitive practice of burying fish in the soil when planting corn was a means of replenishing nitrogen compounds in the soil.

Since nitrogen is reluctant to enter into chemical combination, it is not surprising to find that some nitrogen compounds decompose rapidly and are used as explosives. Potassium nitrate, known as "saltpeter," was an essential ingredient of black gunpowder, along with sulfur and powdered charcoal. During the Civil War, Union and Confederate troops fought for control of caves containing deposits of saltpeter in the Appalachian Mountains. Dynamite, a more modern explosive, is made from a nitrogen compound, nitroglycerine.

Men have long sought natural deposits of nitrates, but only a few significant deposits have been found on the Earth. The solubility of these compounds in water greatly restricts the areas were they might accumulate. The largest nitrate deposit, rich in sodium nitrate, is located in an arid region of western Chile. This deposit gave Chile a world monopoly on sodium nitrate for many years. This was a monopoly with tremendous economic and political significance in the early years of this century, since natural sodium nitrate was the principal source of nitrogen fertilizers and of nitric acid for the manufacture of explosives. No nation could play at the game of power politics without a dependable food supply and a munitions industry. Germany, faced with the prospect of being denied access to this nitrate supply by the British navy during the years prior to World War I, set her chemical industry to the task of developing synthetic sources of combined nitrogen.

Fritz Haber, a German chemist, developed a successful method for combining the nitrogen of the air with hydrogen from water to form ammonia. This chemical change is represented by the equation

$$N_2 + 3H_2 \longrightarrow 2NH_3 + \text{Heat}$$

This equation looks simple, but the reaction yields very little ammonia under ordinary conditions because of the tendency of ammonia to decompose almost as fast as it forms. Remember that equations tell us nothing about the conditions required for reaction, how far the reaction goes, or the rate of the reaction. Haber's success lay in finding the optimum conditions of temperature and pressure and a suitable catalyst for this reaction. The nitrogen and hydrogen are reacted at a temperature of about 500°C and a pressure of 500 to 1,000 atmospheres. The catalyst is usually a mixture of iron and potassium aluminate. The Haber process made it possible to convert about 50% of the nitrogen and hydrogen to ammonia and opened the door to an unlimited supply of combined nitrogen.

Wilhelm Ostwald, another German chemist, developed a method for making nitric acid from ammonia. The ammonia is first oxidized to nitric oxide, using platinum as a catalyst:

$$4NH_3 + 5O_2 \longrightarrow 4NO + 6H_2O$$

The nitric oxide is then converted to nitrogen dioxide by reaction with oxygen:

$$2NO + O_2 \longrightarrow 2NO_2$$

The nitrogen dioxide is reacted with warm water to produce nitric acid, which can be used to make nitrates or other nitrogen compounds:

$$3NO_2 + H_2O \longrightarrow 2HNO_3 + NO$$

Fortunately, the world is no longer dependent upon the nitrates of Chile. These deposits are still being worked, but could not begin to meet the present demand. We live in an age in which military power is dominated by nuclear explosives rather than nitrogen-based explosives. However, the importance of nitrogen for fertizilers is greater than ever. Liquid ammonia and other nitrogen fertilizers are being used on a very large scale in modern agriculture. The demand for food, particularly proteins, to meet the world's population explosion will make it imperative that every acre of land produce to capacity. Fritz Haber's discovery did not bring success to his nation in World War I, but it has been the means of feeding millions through increased soil productivity, and it may be one of the major instruments of peace in the future. It serves to remind us that the applications of science may be for good or for evil—the choice rests with man.

Nitrates from animal wastes and agricultural fertilizers constitute a health hazard in drinking water. Nitrates are converted to nitrites by bacterial action in the intestine and the nitrites react with hemoglobin in the blood, resulting in a loss of its oxygen transporting ability. Therefore, high nitrate levels in drinking water may cause methemoglobinema (the cause of "blue babies") in infants. The public health limit for drinking water is 10 parts per million nitrogen as nitrate.

QUESTIONS AND PROBLEMS

1. A nitric acid solution is an excellent electrical conductor, while an acetic acid solution of the same concentration is a very poor conductor. What does this experimental evidence tell us about the relative strength of these acids? Explain.

2. Pure sulfuric acid (H_2SO_4) is a nonconductor of electricity. What chemical characteristic of H_2SO_4 is suggested by this evidence?

3. Methyl alcohol (CH_3OH) is not a base, even though this molecule contains the OH group. How do you explain this fact?

4. HCN is a very weak acid and KOH is a very strong base. In view of these facts, would you expect a water solution of the salt KCN to be acidic or basic? Explain.

5. How many moles of calcium hydroxide, $Ca(OH)_2$, can be neutralized by 146 grams of hydrochloric acid, HCl?

6. Hydrochloric acid, HCl, is a strong acid and is 100% ionized in solution. What is the pH of a 0.001-molar solution of HCl?

7. A solution of hydrogen chloride, HCl, in benzene, C_6H_6, is not a good conductor of electricity. However, a solution of hydrogen chloride in water, known as hydrochloric acid, is an excellent electrical conductor. How do you explain these facts?

8. Write the name and formula for the salt produced by the neutralization reaction of the following acids and bases:
   (a) Aluminum hydroxide and nitric acid.
   (b) Potassium hydroxide and hydrochloric acid.
   (c) Lithium hydroxide and phosphoric acid.
   (d) Sodium hydroxide and sulfuric acid.
   (e) Barium hydroxide and acetic acid.

9. Ammonium chloride will react with calcium hydroxide as described by the following equation, which is not balanced:

$$NH_4Cl + Ca(OH)_2 \longrightarrow CaCl_2 + NH_3 + H_2O$$

How many moles of calcium hydroxide will be required to produce 68 grams of ammonia (NH_3)?

10. The oxide ion, $O^=$, is a very strong base. What happens to oxide ions when they are dissolved in water, as in the case of dissolving calcium oxide?

11. Ammonium nitrate, NH_4NO_3, is sometimes mixed with fuel oil, a mixture of hydrocarbon compounds, to make an explosive. Explain the action of this mixture as an explosive.

12. Five hundred milliliters of 0.3-molar HCl solution are mixed with 500 ml of 0.2-molar NaOH solution. Calculate the pH of the resulting mixture.

13. Liquid ammonia, with a boiling point of approximately $-33°C$ at 1 atmosphere of pressure, is used extensively as an agricultural fertilizer. What property of this compound makes this possible without significant loss of the ammonia as a vapor? How does the use of this fertilizer contribute to our pollution problem?

14. The negative ion of every acid, being a proton acceptor, is a base. For example, a chloride ion (Cl^-) can accept a proton to form HCl, an acid. Therefore, Cl^- is a base. Perchloric acid ($HClO_4$) is a very strong acid. What can you say about the strength of the perchlorate ion (ClO_4^-) as a base? Explain.

15. One liter of a solution containing 0.3 mole of HCl is mixed with 7.4 grams of $Ca(OH)_2$. Will the resulting solution be acidic, basic, or neutral? Calculate the pH of this solution.

SUGGESTED REFERENCES

Morris, D. L., "Bronsted-Lowry Acid-Base Theory—A Brief Survey," *Chemistry*, 43, no. 3 (1970), 18.

Vanderwerf, Calvin A., *Acids, Bases and the Chemistry of the Covalent Bond*, Chaps. 1, 2, 3, and 4. Reinhold Publishing Corp. New York, 1961.

23

Chemical Reactions

All life is based on chemical reactions. At the same time, certain chemical reactions threaten to upset the delicate chemical balance of the earth and destroy our life support systems. An increased understanding of the chemical effects of the world population explosion and the growth of modern technology is an absolute necessity for solution of the environmental problems facing us. The number of chemical reactions is extremely large and we shall attempt to describe only a few examples to illustrate some important types.

The chemical reactions taking place all around us may involve the combination of elements to form compounds, the decomposition of compounds, the combination of elements with compounds, or the combination of compounds. The substances entering into the chemical reactions are known as *reactants* and the substances produced in the reactions are *products*.

23-1
Combustion—a Rapid Reaction

Combustion is one of the most familiar phenomena in our experiences, and as children we all learned that such things as paper, gasoline, and dry wood shavings are very combustible materials. Fire, as you will remember, was considered one of the four elements by the ancients. Although man worshipped fire in his early history and used it for protection against predatory animals as well as to cook his food and warm himself in the cold of winter, he did not come to any understanding of the process of burning until the eighteenth century. It was an inquiry into the nature of combustion which led to one of the great scientific advances and established chemistry as a quantitative science.

An elaborate theory for the explanation of combustion was developed late in the seventeenth and early in the eighteenth centuries. This theory, known as the *phlogiston theory*, was founded by Georg Ernst Stahl and Johann Joachim Becher. All combustible substances were considered to have one component in common which escaped during the process of burning. This component, called *phlogiston*, was considered to be a very "subtle fluid"; that is, it was considered to be an invisible fluid, and one quite difficult actually to detect. The fact that no one had ever seen phlogiston, or could identify a single property of this mysterious fluid, did not seem to be a serious obstacle to the acceptance of the idea. You will recall that the early theories of heat and electricity considered these forms of energy to be "fluid." According to the phlogiston theory, wood, a combustible substance, contains phlogiston, which escapes into the air in the process of burning. Something obviously escapes when wood burns and ashes are left. Thus the idea appealed to common sense based on simple observations. Water, which is not combustible, contains no phlogiston, according to this theory.

The phlogiston theory also provided a convenient explanation for the metallurgical process of smelting. When a metallic ore, which was called a *calyx*, is heated with charcoal, a metal is obtained. Charcoal is supposedly rich in phlogiston and gives its phlogiston to the ore, producing the metal. According to this view the metal is more complex than its ore.

There were serious difficulties associated with the phlogiston theory, even though it did explain many experimental facts. The greatest difficulty with this theory, and the one which eventually led to its overthrow, was the discovery that metals gain weight when burned. Quantitative experiments were not very common until the time of Lavoisier, late in the eighteenth century. Thus this disturbing experimental fact was ignored for a long time.

A further difficulty with the phlogiston theory is the fact that air is required for combustion. The proponents of the theory explained this by asserting that phlogiston must not only escape from a burning material, but must combine with the air. This assumption provided a reasonable explanation for an experiment such as the following. Suppose we light two identical candles standing on a table and invert a large beaker over one and a small beaker over the other. We observe that the candle under the smaller beaker goes out first. The phlogiston theory explained this by saying that the smaller beaker contains less air than the larger one and this smaller volume of air can combine with less phlogiston. Therefore, it will sustain combustion for a shorter period of time.

The phlogiston theory, in spite of its faults (which seem obvious to us), was quite successful in explaining the experimental observations of the time. It was eventually abandoned because it was unable to account for facts learned from careful experimentation. This example should warn us again that an accepted scientific theory is not necessarily true, or final, simply because it provides an explanation for many experimental facts.

The overthrow of the phlogiston theory was brought about late in the eighteenth century by the discovery of oxygen and the recognition of this element as a constituent of the atmosphere. The weight gain in combustion was also an important factor. It is interesting to note that Joseph Priestley, who discovered oxygen in 1775, never gave up his adherence to the phlogiston theory. The notion of something escaping in the process of combustion had apparently become so ingrained in Priestley's mind that he was unable to consider seriously the idea that combustion might be a combination process. The reluctance to change our ideas and established ways of thinking is one of the greatest impediments in the search for knowledge. The inability to look at the facts with an open mind, unprejudiced by prior opinions, is present to some extent in all men. This difficulty in judging the evidence impartially has, contrary to popular opinion, caused many scientists to go up blind alleys of fruitless investigation.

Antoine Lavoisier was the principal figure in the overthrow of the phlogiston theory and its replacement by a scheme based on combination with oxygen. Even though Priestley did not give up the phlogiston theory, his experiments helped to prepare the foundation upon which Lavoisier constructed his theory of oxidation. Lavoisier's experiments on the combustion of sulfur and tin led him to propose the theory of oxidation. He was able to show that these elements gained weight when burned; that is, the product of the combustion weighed more than the original sample of the element. He was also able to show, by rather ingenious experiments in closed vessels, that a part of the air is used in these combustion processes. This part of the air consumed in combustion proved to be oxygen, or in the words of Priestley, "dephlogisticated air." The gain in weight of the substance burned was shown to be equal to the loss of weight in the air. Lavoisier later burned hydrogen in oxygen and measured all the quantities involved in the synthesis of water. He concluded from these experiments that combustion is a process of chemical union with oxygen, and a combustible substance is one which will combine rapidly with oxygen. Lavoisier demonstrated the law of conservation of mass experimetally and introduced the idea of the chemical equation. The ideas of Lavoisier produced a chemical revolution and led to rapid progress in the understanding of chemistry.

The proponents of the phlogiston theory made determined efforts to hold on to the concept of phlogiston. They tried to explain away the weight gain in combustion by assuming a negative weight for phlogiston; that is, they said that the Earth repels, rather than attracts, phlogiston. A further attempt to defend the phlogiston theory was based on the assumption that a metal oxide absorbed water from the atmosphere as it was formed from the metal. Thus the loss in weight by the removal of phlogiston was more than compensated for by the weight gain due to the absorbed water. This effort to hold on to a familiar concept provides still another example of the human tendency to resist new ideas.

23-2
Oxidation

The chemical combination of oxygen with another substance is called *oxidation*. This reaction may take place quite slowly, as is the case in the rusting of iron to form iron oxide. The oxidation process is known as "combustion" when it takes place rapidly, giving off heat and light. Hydrogen, when mixed with oxygen in the proper proportion, will undergo very rapid combustion, forming water vapor. This oxidation is so rapid that it is called an "explosion." Much heat is given off in a very short time, resulting in rapid expansion of the reaction products and the surrounding atmosphere. These oxidation reactions may be described by the following equations:

$$4Fe + 3O_2 \longrightarrow 2Fe_2O_3$$

$$2H_2 + O_2 \longrightarrow 2H_2O$$

Many chemical compounds may also be oxidized under appropriate conditions. Compounds of carbon and hydrogen, known as *hydrocarbons*, are oxidized readily and give off large quantities of heat in the process. The products of the oxidation of hydrocarbons are carbon dioxide and water, as shown in the following equation for the oxidation of propane (C_3H_8):

$$C_3H_8 + 5O_2 \longrightarrow 3CO_2 + 4H_2O$$

Fuel oil, gasoline, and natural gas are mixtures of hydrocarbons which produce carbon dioxide and water when they are burned with sufficient oxygen.

The combustion of hydrocarbon fuels is usually an incomplete process, particularly in automobile engines. This process results in an exhaust containing oxides of nitrogen, sulfur dioxide, unburned hydrocarbons, and carbon monoxide. Automobiles alone add approximately 100 million tons of these dangerous gases to the atmosphere each year in the United States. Power plants, home furnaces, industrial processes, and garbage incineration combine to add more than 100 million tons of pollutants to our air each year. Pollution in some areas has reached levels sufficiently high to produce serious effects on vegetation and to become a health hazard for humans (see Fig. 23-1). Engines designed for more complete combustion and other effective measures will be required to reduce air pollution to tolerable levels.

Oxidation may take place without free oxygen if some compound is present to supply oxygen. Compounds such as potassium chlorate ($KClO_3$) and hydrogen peroxide (H_2O_2), which decompose easily to provide oxygen, are known as *oxidizing agents*. Rocket engines use oxidizing agents and are not dependent upon an oxygen-containing atmosphere. The solid-fuel engine

FIG. 23-1   Gateway to the West arch in St. Louis, half hidden by smog. (Courtesy St. Louis Post-Dispatch.)

has the fuel and oxidizing agent in a solid mixture which will burn without contact with air.

Oxidation has important consequences for the condition of our lakes and streams. When organic matter is added to these bodies of water, it is oxidized by bacterial action. This process consumes the oxygen dissolved in the water. When the oxygen content drops below a certain level, the water will no longer sustain life. The dumping of sewage, containing much organic matter, into a lake or stream will certainly contribute to the depletion of dissolved oxygen in the water.

High levels of nutrients, such as phosphates and nitrates, entering lake water from agricultural fertilizers and detergents in sewage will contribute to the rapid growth of algae in the water (see Fig. 23-2). The decay of excessive quantities of algae depletes the oxygen in the lake water and leads to a condition known as *eutrophication*. The water is fouled by decay, the oxygen level is lowered, and aquatic life can no longer be supported at the normal level.

The contribution of phosphates from detergents to the problem of eutrophication has been the subject of considerable controversy. There is some evidence to suggest that excessive carbon dioxide from the decay of sewage is the major contributor to excessive algal growth. The replacement of phosphates as builders in detergents is complicated by the difficulty in finding a safe and efficient substitute (see Section 19-11). Nitrilotriacetic acid (NTA),

FIG. 23-2 Detergents in surface water.

a promising substitute for phosphate builders in detergents, was withdrawn from use because of evidence suggesting that it produced cancer in test animals. The solutions to technology problems often create new and more serious problems!

The release of energy in the animal body is brought about by oxidation reactions. Compounds such as carbohydrates and fats are oxidized in the cells to liberate energy. These oxidations in living cells are very closely regulated by enzymes or organic catalysts. These reactions are quite complex and take place in a step-by-step process which ends in the formation of carbon dioxide and water as reaction products.

23-3
Reduction

Reduction is a process in which oxygen is removed from a compound. This reaction, which is the reverse of oxidation, is brought about by means of a *reducing agent*, a substance having a strong affinity for oxygen. When lead oxide is heated with carbon, the oxygen is removed from the oxide and metallic lead is produced:

$$2PbO + C \rightarrow CO_2 + 2Pb$$

The carbon is the reducing agent in this case and lead oxide is the oxidizing agent. The lead oxide is reduced and carbon is oxidized. In such processes, oxidation and reduction always take place simultaneously, the oxidizing agent being reduced and the reducing agent being oxidized.

Metals act as reducing agents for oxides of less active metals. For example, iron oxide may be reduced by aluminum:

$$Fe_2O_3 + 2Al \longrightarrow Al_2O_3 + 2Fe$$

This reaction produces so much heat that the iron is liberated in the molten form. The alkali metals are strong reducing agents since they have a very great affinity for oxygen.

23-4
Oxidation-Reduction as Electron Changes

It can be shown that certain elements other than oxygen will support combustion. For example, kerosene will burn in an atmosphere of chlorine, and a mixture of zinc and sulfur will burn rapidly without the presence of air. The behavior of the chlorine and sulfur, which is quite similar to that of oxygen in supporting combustion, suggests a broader definition for oxidation and reduction. Consider the reaction of zinc and sulfur and compare it with the reaction between zinc and oxygen:

$$Zn + S \longrightarrow ZnS$$
$$2Zn + O_2 \longrightarrow 2ZnO$$

In terms of electron changes, the sulfur and oxygen have experienced the same change; that is, they have gained electrons to become negative ions. The zinc gives up electrons in both reactions to become a positive ion. Zinc is oxidized in both reactions, and both sulfur and oxygen are oxidizing agents.

We may define oxidation as a process in which electrons are given up, and reduction as a process in which electrons are gained. Sulfur and oxygen both gain electrons in the reactions described above. Thus they are oxidizing agents and are reduced. Zinc gives up electrons as it is oxidized and is, therefore, a reducing agent. The nonmetals tend to gain electrons in chemical changes and are, therefore, oxidizing agents. The metals are reducing agents since they tend to give up electrons and are easily oxidized.

23-5
Displacement Reactions

A copper wire placed in a solution of silver nitrate will soon be covered with needle-like crystals of metallic silver, and the original clear solution will gradually acquire a blue color characteristic of copper ions in water solution. These changes are the result of a chemical reaction in which copper is oxidized to copper ions and silver ions are reduced to metallic silver. This reaction may be represented by the equation:

$$Cu + 2Ag^+ \longrightarrow Cu^{++} + 2Ag$$

Reactions of this kind are sometimes called *displacement* reactions.

Metals differ in the ease with which they give up electrons and enter into chemical combination. The most active metals are those which give up valence electrons most easily. In the foregoing example, copper atoms give up electrons to silver ions, and the silver is displaced from chemical combination. The more active metals will always give up electrons to the ions of less active metals.

A list of metals arranged in order of decreasing activity is known as the *activity series*, or the *electrochemical series*. Any element in such a series will displace any element below it when that element is in an ionic solution. An activity series is shown in Table 23-1. The elements high in the series are strong reducing agents and give up their valence electrons easily to the ions of elements below them in the series. For example, magnesium will displace zinc from a solution of zinc nitrate. Hydrogen is included in the series and the elements above it will liberate hydrogen gas from acid solutions. Such an activity series is of value in predicting the possibility of certain chemical reactions.

TABLE 23-1
Activity Series of Some Metals

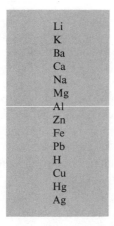

Li
K
Ba
Ca
Na
Mg
Al
Zn
Fe
Pb
H
Cu
Hg
Ag

23-6
Electrolytic Oxidation-Reduction

A cell whose two electrodes are connected to a source of direct current provides an effective means of chemical oxidation and reduction. The positive electrode will gain electrons and bring about oxidation. Reduction will take place at the negative electrode, since it will give up electrons. Consider such

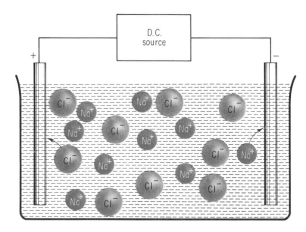

FIG. 23-3   Electrolysis of sodium chloride.

a cell, into which molten sodium chloride is placed. A diagram of such an arrangement is shown in Fig. 23-3.

Since sodium chloride is ionic, the molten material contains ions that are free to move. When the negative chloride ions drift to the positive electrode, or *anode*, they give up electrons and are *oxidized* to chlorine atoms. These atoms combine to form molecules of chlorine gas:

$$2Cl^- \longrightarrow Cl_2 + 2 \text{ electrons}$$

The positive sodium ions drift to the negative electrode, or *cathode*, where they gain electrons to become sodium atoms. This process of reduction produces metallic sodium. Two atoms of sodium are formed at the cathode for each molecule of chlorine at the anode. The total number of electrons given up in oxidation must equal the total number gained in reduction:

$$2Na^+ + 2 \text{ electrons} \longrightarrow 2Na$$

This process is used for the industrial production of sodium, since sodium ions are very difficult to reduce. The chlorine is a valuable by-product. The electrolytic cell is used in many industrial processes because it provides a powerful means of oxidation and reduction.

Most elements are found in the form of chemical compounds and oxidation or reduction is therefore required for the production of pure elements. The metals are found in oxidized form and must be reduced to the metallic form. This reduction process may be accomplished by means of a chemical reducing agent, as in the case of iron oxide reduced by carbon in a blast furnace. This reaction is described by the equation

$$2Fe_2O_3 + 3C \longrightarrow 4Fe + 3CO_2$$

Sodium and potassium ions are quite difficult to reduce, and these metals are produced in an electrolytic cell.

Nonmetals often occur in the reduced state, and the process of oxidation is required to produce the free elements. Chlorine ions, for example, occur in sodium chloride or in hydrochloric acid solution. These ions may be oxidized electrically, as described in the previous section, or by a chemical oxidizing agent, such as manganese dioxide:

$$4HCl + MnO_2 \rightarrow MnCl_2 + Cl_2 + 2H_2O$$

No chemical oxidizing agent will oxidize fluoride ions and, consequently, the element fluorine can be produced only by electrolytic oxidation.

23-7
Reaction Rate

Some chemical reactions are inherently rapid and others are quite slow. The term *rate of reaction* means the quantity of reactants converted to products in a unit of time. The rate of a given reaction may vary over a wide range, depending on the conditions under which the reaction takes place. We shall briefly consider the factors which control reaction rates.

Nature of Reactants

Substances differ greatly in their tendency to undergo chemical change. Sodium is an active element and will react quite rapidly with water or oxygen at room temperature. This metal is so active that it must be submerged in a liquid such as kerosene in order to keep it in the metallic form. Carbon, on the other hand, is a much less active element. It has no tendency to react with water or oxygen at room temperature, but must be heated to react with these substances.

Compounds, as well as elements, show differences in the tendency to enter into chemical changes. For example, aluminum oxide is a very stable compound; that is, it may come into contact with a great variety of chemical reagents without experiencing any change. Hydrogen peroxide, on the other hand, is an active compound. It will react with many substances and is difficult to keep because of its tendency to decompose.

Chemical reactions involve the breaking of certain chemical bonds and the formation of other bonds. The nature of these bonds is a major factor in determining reaction rate. In cases where little energy is required for the breaking of bonds and much energy is released in the formation of other bonds, the reaction rate is likely to be high. Substances which are in ionic form in solution will react very rapidly, since the ions are ready to react and no bond breaking is necessary. A solution of sodium chloride reacts almost instantaneously with one of silver nitrate to form a precipitate of silver chloride:

$$Na^+Cl^- + Ag^+NO_3^- \rightarrow AgCl + Na^+NO_3^-$$

Reactions between substances in molecular form are generally slower than ionic reactions. Ethyl alcohol will react with acetic acid to produce ethyl acetate and water:

$$C_2H_5OH + CH_3COOH \rightarrow CH_3COOC_2H_5 + H_2O$$

This reaction is quite slow since both reactants are in molecular form and bonds must be broken before new bonds can be formed.

Temperature

The rate of all chemical reactions increases with temperature. However, the increase in rate for a given temperature increase is not the same for all reactions. If iron in the form of "steel wool" is exposed to pure oxygen, it will oxidize slowly. However, if the steel wool is heated to red heat and exposed to pure oxygen, it will oxidize so rapidly that it burns with a brilliant light.

The increase in reaction rate with temperature can be explained in terms of the kinetic molecular theory. As the temperature is increased, the molecules or ions move faster. This increased rate of motion gives more molecules or ions energy sufficient to break chemical bonds and also increases the rate of collision. When more molecules have enough energy to react and when they collide more frequently, the rate of reaction increases.

Concentration

The *concentration* of a substance is a measure of the amount of that material per unit volume. An increase in the concentration of one or more reactants will increase the rate of reaction. When a wood splint is ignited in the air, it burns at a moderate rate. However, if this burning splint is placed in pure oxygen, it burns much more rapidly. The increase in the reaction rate is brought about by the increase in the concentration of oxygen. As another example, consider the action of hydrochloric acid on zinc. If a few pieces of zinc are covered with very dilute hydrochloric acid, a slow evolution of hydrogen gas takes place. However, if concentrated acid is used, the rate of evolution of hydrogen is greatly increased. The effect of an increase in concentration can also be understood in terms of the kinetic molecular theory. As the concentration is increased, the collisions between molecules or ions become more frequent, leading to an increase in reaction rate.

State of Subdivision

A piece of coal is not immediately ignited by the application of a burning match. However, if this same piece of coal is crushed to a fine powder and mixed with air, it may be ignited with a spark and burned so rapidly that a violent explosion is produced. Such coal dust explosions are a hazard in coal mines. Any combustible material that can be made into a dust will behave in a similar manner. When a material such as coal is crushed into small particles, the surface area is greatly increased. This increased surface area allows more contact with oxygen and results in a higher rate of reaction.

Catalysts

Potassium chlorate, $KClO_3$, will decompose when heated to produce oxygen and potassium chloride:

$$2KClO_3 \rightarrow 2KCl + 3O_2$$

When pure potassium chlorate is used, this reaction is not very rapid, even when the potassium chlorate is melted and the resulting liquid is boiled. However, if a small amount of manganese dioxide, MnO_2, or iron oxide, Fe_2O_3, is added to the potassium chlorate, the reaction goes much faster. The oxide is not permanently changed in the reaction and may be completely recovered at the end of the reaction. A substance which will change the rate of reaction without any change in its own composition is called a *catalyst*.

The presence of a catalyst will not change the amount of product that is obtained in a reaction, but will decrease the time required to obtain the product. For example, 10 grams of potassium chlorate will produce 3.9 grams of oxygen when completely decomposed by heating. If a catalyst is added to the 10 grams of potassium chlorate, the oxygen will be evolved more rapidly, but the quantity obtained is still 3.9 grams.

The action of catalysts is not completely understood. In some cases, the catalyst enters into the reaction to form some intermediate product which decomposes to liberate the catalyst again. In other cases, one of the reactants may be adsorbed by the catalyst. Adsorption is a process in which the particles of one substance adhere to the surface of another substance. The adsorbed molecules become more reactive because the bonds in these molecules are weakened by the attractive forces involved in the process of adsorption. In any case, the catalyst lowers the energy that molecules must have to react, and this increases the reaction rate.

Catalysts are necessary in industrial processes where reaction rates are very important. The petroleum industry uses large quantities of platinum as a catalyst in the production of gasoline, and a single oil refinery will have invested many thousands of dollars in this metal. Catalysts are also important in the chemistry of living organisms. Enzymes are organic catalysts which control the rate of many physiological reactions, such as those of digestion and cellular oxidation.

The digestion of starch is an example of a physiological reaction which is under the control of enzymes. This process involves reaction with water and the breakdown of the giant starch molecules to the small, water-soluble molecules of glucose. Although this reaction takes place in several stages, we may represent it by the equation

$$\underset{\text{starch}}{(C_6H_{10}O_5)_xH_2O} + (x - 1)H_2O \rightarrow \underset{\text{glucose}}{xC_6H_{12}O_6}$$

This reaction will not take place when starch is simply mixed with water. However, it proceeds rapidly in the digestive system where the starch-digesting enzymes catalyze the reaction. The process starts in the mouth, where the enzyme ptyalin is present in the saliva, and is completed in the small intestine where several carbohydrate-digesting enzymes are secreted.

23-8
Reversible Reactions

Most chemical reactions are reversible; that is, the product or products will react to produce the original reactants. The reaction between hydrogen and nitrogen to produce ammonia is a reversible reaction. We indicate reversibility by using a double arrow between the reactants and products:

$$N_2 + 3H_2 \rightleftarrows 2NH_3$$

When nitrogen and hydrogen are brought together at a favorable temperature and pressure, the molecules of these gases react to produce ammonia. As the number of ammonia molecules increases, some of them begin to decompose to produce nitrogen and hydrogen. As the nitrogen and hydrogen are consumed, the rate at which they react decreases. As the amount of ammonia increases, the rate of its decomposition increases. Eventually, the forward reaction and the reverse reaction are taking place at the same rate and no further change in concentration will occur as long as the temperature and pressure remain unchanged. This situation of a forward and a reverse reaction taking place at the same rate is known as *chemical equilibrium*. A state of chemical equilibrium will be reached by any chemical reaction that occurs under conditions such that the reverse reaction can also occur.

23-9
Irreversible Reactions

Many chemical reactions are reversible, but some reactions are irreversible or are reversible only to a slight extent. Methane combines with oxygen in combustion to form carbon dioxide and water:

$$CH_4 + 2O_2 \rightarrow CO_2 + 2H_2O$$

This reaction is not reversible, since the carbon dioxide and water will not react to form methane and oxygen.

Reactions which are irreversible, or are reversible to a very slight extent, are said to "go to completion." Reactions between ions in solution go to completion when some of the ions are effectively removed from the reaction process by being tied up in nonionized substances or forming a gas that escapes. Neutralization reactions go practically to completion, since the water which is formed ionizes to a very slight extent and does not react appreciably with the ions of the salt to form the original acid and base. Some neutralization reactions are reversible to a slight extent because of the tendency of the ions produced in the reaction to react with water.

Reactions in which a precipitate is formed also go essentially to completion. The formation of a precipitate removes ions from solution and makes them unavailable for reaction. The reaction between sodium chloride and silver nitrate in solution is essentially irreversible because of the formation of a silver chloride precipitate.

A reaction in which one or more of the products is a gas will go to completion, particularly if the gas is allowed to escape as it is formed. The reaction between sodium bicarbonate and hydrochloric acid goes to completion with the escape of carbon dioxide gas.

23-10
"Driving Force" of Chemical Reactions

There are two universal tendencies which govern the direction of natural processes, including chemical reactions. The first of these is the tendency to reach the state of minimum energy. We see this general tendency in operation when we observe water running downhill, but never uphill. The second universal tendency is that of a large number of objects or particles to go to the most random possible distribution. If 100 pennies are shaken in a closed box, we would not expect them to come to rest with all the "heads" up. Likewise, if we could place 1 liter of oxygen gas in one end of a closed cylinder and 1 liter of nitrogen gas in the other end of the same cylinder, we would not expect these gases to remain separated. We would find them completely mixed in the most random possible distribution after a very short time. The measure of randomness in a system is called the *entropy* of the system, and there is a universal tendency for entropy to increase. When ice melts to water, the entropy increases; that is, there is a more random distribution of water molecules in the liquid state. Carbon in the form of graphite will react with water vapor at temperatures above 1,000°C to form carbon monoxide (CO) and hydrogen (H_2). The entropy, or disorder, will increase as a result of this reaction, since a crystalline solid is reacting with a gas to form two gaseous products. The molecules are in a less orderly arrangement after the reaction than before.

The net driving force for any change resulting from the tendency toward minimum energy and maximum entropy is called the *free energy change*. This is the difference between the change in energy or heat content and the change in randomness or entropy. All spontaneous changes are accompanied by a *decrease in free energy*. A system is in equilibrium when a change in any direction would result in an increase in free energy.

23-11
Energy from Chemical Reactions

Most chemical reactions that take place spontaneously are exothermic reactions; that is, most spontaneous reactions go in such a direction as to give up energy, and this energy is usually in the form of heat. In such reactions the decrease in heat content may be accompanied by an increase in entropy or, if the entropy decreases in the change, the effect of the decrease in heat content is greater than the effect of the decrease in entropy. The combustion of carbon is an exothermic reaction in which 94.4 kilocalories of heat are liberated in the formation of each mole of carbon dioxide:

$$C + O_2 \longrightarrow CO_2 + 94.4 \text{ kcal}$$

There are exceptions, in which reactions take place spontaneously with the absorption of energy. Such a spontaneous reaction is possible only if the tendency toward maxium entropy or randomness is *greater* than the tendency toward minimum energy, or heat content. The reaction between carbon and water vapor mentioned above is a spontaneous endothermic reaction at a reaction temperature of 1200° C:

$$\underset{\text{solid}}{C} + \underset{\text{gas}}{H_2O} \longrightarrow \underset{\text{gas}}{CO} + \underset{\text{gas}}{H_2} - 15.7 \text{ kcal}$$

This reaction absorbs heat, but it is spontaneous because of the increase in entropy, or randomness, resulting from the reaction.

Reactions that liberate energy are very useful to us, and man has been transforming chemical energy into other useful forms of energy since the discovery of fire. The first such transformation was simply the liberation of heat and light by burning a substance such as wood or coal. A more useful transformation was achieved when man learned to transform the heat resulting from chemical changes into mechanical energy in the steam engine and internal-combustion engine. The transformation of chemical energy into electrical energy is now widely used in various types of electric batteries. All such batteries have the disadvantage of relatively short life. More recently, man has learned to convert the energy of oxidation directly into electrical energy in a device known as a *fuel cell*. For example, hydrogen can be oxidized to produce electrical energy rather than heat. Fuel cells are not yet commercially practical, but may be developed for the future.

The energy involved in a chemical reaction may be expressed as the *heat of reaction*. This is the quantity of heat liberated or absorbed for each mole of the substance reacting. For example, 1 mole (27 grams) of aluminum liberates 390 kilocalories of heat when it reacts with oxygen to form aluminum oxide, Al_2O_3. The heats of oxidation for several substances are given in Table 23-2. These heat values are measured by burning the substance in a calorimeter filled with pure oxygen (see Chapter 11).

A substance having a high heat of oxidation may be used as a fuel if it is readily available. Natural gas is largely methane, CH_4, which delivers 210.8 kilocalories per mole (16 grams) when burned. Cane sugar, or sucrose $(C_{12}H_{22}O_{11})$, with a heat of oxidation of 1,349.6 kilocalories per mole is a high-energy food. Celery, on the other hand, produces only 85 kilocalories per pound when burned.

TABLE 23-2
Heats of Oxidation

Substance	Heat of Oxidation, kcal/mole	Product(s)
H_2	68.4	H_2O
C	94.4	CO_2
Ca	152.0	CaO
CH_4	210.8	CO_2 & H_2O
C_3H_8	526.3	CO_2 & H_2O
$C_{12}H_{22}O_{11}$	1,349.6	CO_2 & H_2O

The stability of a chemical compound is related to the amount of heat evolved or absorbed in the formation of the compound. A stable compound results when a large quantity of heat is liberated in the reaction that forms the compound. The formation of 1 mole of aluminum oxide from aluminum and oxygen is accompanied by the liberation of 390 kilocalories of heat, whereas the formation of 1 mole of water from hydrogen and oxygen liberates 68.4 kilocalories. Aluminum oxide is a more stable compound than water since more energy would be required to decompose it. Compounds formed in reactions that absorb heat are relatively unstable and energy is liberated in the decomposition of such compounds. Hydrogen iodide, formed from hydrogen and iodine with the absorption of 5.9 kilocalories per mole, is an unstable compound.

Chemistry is primarily concerned with increasing the understanding of chemical reactions and in the solution of problems involving chemical reactions. The chemist is interested in discovering general principles that will enable him to predict the outcome of any particular reaction—the conditions necessary for reaction, the rate of the reaction, and the reaction products. He is also interested in more knowledge of *reaction mechanisms*; that is, he would like to understand the step-by-step processes which take place in a chemical reaction. Equations may be written for a large number of chemical reactions, but the mechanism by which the reaction proceeds is known for very few reactions. The important reaction of photosynthesis may be used as an illustration of this idea. We may describe this reaction by the equation

$$6CO_2 + 6H_2O \rightarrow C_6H_{12}O_6 + 6O_2$$

As was pointed out in Chapter 20, this equation tells us nothing about the reaction except the relative quantities of reactants and products. It tells us that 6 moles of carbon dioxide react with 6 moles of water to produce 1 mole of a simple sugar and 6 moles of oxygen. We know that this reaction does not take place in one step with the collision of six carbon dioxide molecules with six water molecules. The reaction mechanism involves many intermediate steps, some of which are known. However, this reaction mechanism is not completely understood and much research is being conducted in an attempt to work out all the details. Many reactions that may be described by simple equations really proceed by very complicated mechanisms. Someone has said, "The only simple chemical reactions are the ones we do not understand."

The study of chemical reactions is important not only to obtain a more satisfying picture of nature, but also because the understanding of reactions has practical value. As we have seen, certain chemical reactions provide us with sources of energy. New high-energy reactions are constantly being sought as man turns his attention to space travel. The ability to understand and control chemical reactions has brought us a multitude of new products in the fields of plastics, synthetic fibers, building materials, and drugs. More knowledge of reactions will undoubtedly make available in the future products that are beyond our imagination today. One of the major goals of the study of chemical reactions is an increased understanding of those reactions taking place in biological systems. Man is just beginning to learn something about the chemistry of life, and it is evident that a better understanding of such phenomena as aging, disease, and the transmission of hereditary characteristics may be achieved by further study of the chemistry of living cells.

Applications of chemistry to technology have produced serious environmental problems along with the many benefits which most of us now take for granted. Many of these problems have resulted from unanticipated effects of chemical compounds released into the environment. Air pollution has reached dangerous levels in some areas because of fumes produced by automobiles, power plants, garbage incinerators, and various industrial plants. Water pollution is present in varying degrees in most of our streams and lakes, and now threatens the oceans. Sewage, pesticides and herbicides, plant nutrients, and organic chemical wastes from industrial plants are the major contributors to water pollution. It is now painfully clear that we must give more attention to the effects of chemical reactions upon our environment, particularly the long-range effects of small amounts of very toxic chemicals.

The toxicity of certain chlorine-containing organic compounds is illustrated by dioxin (2,3,7,8-tetrachlorodibenzodioxine), which is found as a contaminant in the herbicide 2,4,5-T. An oral dose of 10^{-6} gm of dioxin per kg of body weight will kill 50% of a large population of guinea pigs. Neurological disturbances and birth defects are also produced by very small doses of this compound. The effects of this and other highly toxic compounds on humans are not well understood. The advantages gained by the use of chemical compounds in the future must be balanced against the possible dangers of these compounds. This will require very extensive testing prior to actual introduction of a new product.

QUESTIONS AND PROBLEMS

1. In what way was the phlogiston theory of combustion similar to the caloric theory of heat? What experimental evidence cast doubt on both theories?

2. How did the work of Joseph Priestly contribute to the chemical revolution initiated by Antoine Lavoisier?

3. Sulfur dioxide (SO_2) is produced in the combustion of fuels and in the metallurgy of sulfide ores of metals. What valuable chemical might be made by the recovery and use of SO_2?

4. Why should eutrophication be a less significant problem in rapidly flowing streams than in large shallow lakes?

5. When a copper wire is placed in a solution of silver nitrate, crystals of metallic silver appear on the wire in a short time. Write the equation for the chemical reaction which takes place. What is the reducing agent in this solution? What is the oxidizing agent?

6. Proteins are converted to simpler substances called amino acids in the digestive process. Pepsin is an important enzyme for protein digestion in the stomach. What is the function of pepsin in the chemical reaction of protein digestion?

7. How do you account for the fact that metals such as sodium and potassium are very powerful reducing agents?

8. How much could the temperature of 1 kg of water be increased by the heat released in the combustion of 10 grams of cane sugar?

9. Why isn't aluminum used as a fuel, since it has a very high heat of oxidation?

10. Which of the following elements are likely to be good oxidizing agents? (a) zinc, (b) chlorine, (c) sulfur, (d) lithium, (e) copper, (f) carbon.

11. Why is the reaction described by the following equation not an oxidation-reduction reaction?

$$Na_2SO_4 + BaCl_2 \rightarrow \underline{BaSO_4} + 2NaCl$$

(The $BaSO_4$ precipitates from solution due to very low solubility.)

12. Which of the following elements would be displaced from their ionic solutions by zinc? (a) silver, (b) magnesium, (c) potassium, (d) copper.

13. The reaction between hydrogen and oxygen to produce water is very slow at room temperature. Suggest some possible ways of increasing the rate of this reaction.

14. How would you suggest that metallic cesium could be obtained from cesium chloride, assuming that this compound might be found on the Earth? Explain in some detail.

15. What weight of silver could be displaced from a solution of silver nitrate by the complete reaction of 6.537 gm of zinc? (Assume a quantity of silver nitrate sufficient to react with all the zinc.)

16. Manganese will displace silver, copper, and zinc from their ionic solutions, but will not displace potassium, sodium, or aluminum. Where would you place manganese in the activity series of Table 23-1?

17. Which of the following elements would be expected to liberate hydrogen from a solution of hydrochloric acid? (a) mercury, (b) silver, (c) magnesium, (d) aluminum.

18. If the electricity required to produce 1 pound of aluminum by electrolytic reduction costs 10 cents, what would be the cost of the electricity needed to produce 1 pound of potassium by the same process? (*Suggestion:* Consider the atomic weights and the charges on the ions.)

19. When iron oxide reacts with aluminum to produce aluminum oxide and iron, the quantity of heat released is so large that a temperature of about 3,000°C is reached. What do these facts tell us about the relative strength of the chemical bonds in aluminum oxide and iron oxide?

20. Assuming that we shall continue to use internal-combustion engines in automobiles, what changes in the operation of these engines will be necessary to accomplish a major reduction in their contribution to air pollution? Explain in some detail.

SUGGESTED REFERENCES

GALE, GEORGE, "Phlogiston Revisited—Explanatory Models and Conceptual Change," *Chemistry*, 41, no. 4 (1968), 16.

HORRIGAN, PHILIP A., *The Challenge of Chemistry*, Chaps. 13 and 14. McGraw-Hill Book Co., New York, 1970.

KIEFFER, WILLIAM F., *Chemistry: A Cultural Approach*, Chaps. 3 and 16. Harper & Row, New York, 1971.

24
Carbon Compounds

Life depends upon the element carbon in many ways. Fossil fuels, living tissues, detergents, flavors, perfumes, and fibers, both natural and synthetic, are composed of molecules built upon chains or rings of carbon atoms.

The diamond, a crystalline form of carbon, is the hardest known natural substance, with a melting point above 3,500° C. Each carbon atom in a diamond crystal is covalently bonded to four other carbon atoms in a tetrahedral structure, as shown in Fig. 24-1. The electrical conductivity is very low, since all the valence electrons are involved in strong covalent bonds.

Graphite is a soft, black, crystalline form of carbon. The layers in this crystal contain hexagonal rings of carbon atoms, with each carbon atom bonded to three other atoms in the same plane. These layers are held together

FIG. 24-1 Diamond crystal model.

FIG. 24-2   Graphite crystal model.

by relatively weak bonding forces, as shown in Fig. 24-2. Molecules of water, oxygen, and nitrogen, when absorbed between the layers of carbon atoms, will weaken the bonding forces between the layers. This weakening allows the graphite crystal layers to slide over one another easily. Thus graphite is a good lubricant in the atmosphere, but not in a vacuum or in outer space.

The formation of compounds containing carbon and hydrogen was originally thought to require special conditions found only in living organisms, and these compounds came to be known as "organic" compounds because they originated in plants and animals. However, it has been recognized for more than 100 years that the organic chemist can synthesize compounds of carbon, hydrogen, and other elements without the aid of a living organism. Over 90% of the organic compounds known today are synthetic compounds. The remaining known organic compounds have been found in animals, plants, coal, and petroleum.

The number of known carbon compounds is in excess of 1 million and the number continues to grow as new organic compounds are synthesized. This large number of compounds is possible because the carbon atom is able to combine with four other atoms or groups of atoms, and carbon atoms are able to combine with each other indefinitely to produce stable molecules in the form of rings or long chains. The elements that combine with carbon in organic compounds are generally confined to hydrogen, oxygen, nitrogen, sulfur, phosphorus, and the halogens.

24-1
Bonding in Carbon Compounds

The carbon atom is capable of forming four covalent bonds, arranged symmetrically in space with an angle of slightly more than 109 degrees between any two bonds. The ability of the carbon atom to form four covalent bonds is not obvious from the electronic structure of the atom. There are 2 electrons in the $2s$ orbital and 2 unpaired electrons in the three $2p$ orbitals of the carbon atom. Thus it would appear that carbon should form two covalent bonds by sharing the $2p$ electrons with other atoms having unpaired electrons. The carbon atom is able to form four covalent bonds because one of the paired $2s$ electrons is shifted to the vacant $2p$ orbital. This results in an atom with 4 unpaired electrons and the formation of four bonds. The energy released in the formation of two extra bonds is more than sufficient to shift the $2s$ electron to the higher-energy $2p$ orbital.

The four bonding orbitals of the carbon atom are all exactly alike. They are called sp^3 hybrid orbitals since they were formed from one s orbital and three p orbitals. The sp^3 orbitals are directed tetrahedrally in space as shown in Fig. 24-3. We might think of these bond angles as resulting from the mutual repulsion of electrons. The four bonding electron pairs would be located as far apart as possible on the spherical surface of the carbon atom. The tetrahedral arrangement is the one giving the maximum separation of the four electron pairs.

FIG. 24-3   *sp^3 orbitals of carbon.*

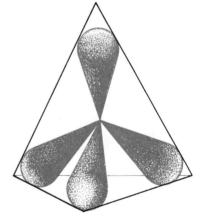

A methane molecule, CH_4, has the shape of a tetrahedron, as shown in Fig. 24-4(a). One or more of the hydrogens in methane may be replaced by atoms of other elements to form different compounds, as shown in Fig. 24-4(b) and (c), where chlorine atoms have been substituted for hydrogen. The three molecules shown in Fig. 24-4 are quite different in properties. Methane, CH_4, an important constituent of natural gas, has a boiling point of $-161°$ C. Methyl chloride, CH_3Cl, with a boiling point of $-24°$ C, is used by physicians as a local anesthetic. When the liquid is sprayed on the skin, rapid evaporation causes freezing of the area. Methylene chloride,

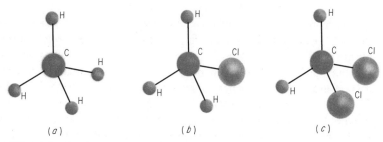

FIG. 24-4   Methane and related molecules.

CH_2Cl_2, with a boiling point of 40° C, is used as a refrigerant in air-conditioning systems.

Covalent bonds may form between carbon atoms, in which case the molecules are chain or ring structures. The chains may be either continuous or branched, as shown in Fig. 24-5. These molecules, each containing five carbon atoms, are: (a) normal pentane, (b) isopentane, and (c) cyclopentane. Each dash connected to the carbon atom represents a pair of electrons forming a covalent bond. The carbon atom has a covalence of 4 and is usually bonded to four other atoms or groups of atoms. In some cases two pairs, or even three pairs, of electrons are shared between 2 carbon atoms or between a carbon atom and an atom of some other element. Such bonds are called double or triple bonds and are symbolized by two or three dashes, as in $H_2C = CH_2$ and $H\text{-}C \equiv C\text{-}H$, the formulas for ethylene and acetylene. Formulas showing the manner in which the atoms are arranged in a molecule are called *structural formulas*. They give much more information about a molecule than molecular formulas, which tell us only the total number of atoms of each element in the molecule. The bonding of carbon atoms into rings and chains makes possible the formation of a great many different molecules, particularly when different atoms or groups of atoms may be bonded to the carbons in the chain or ring.

FIG. 24-5   Carbon chains and rings.

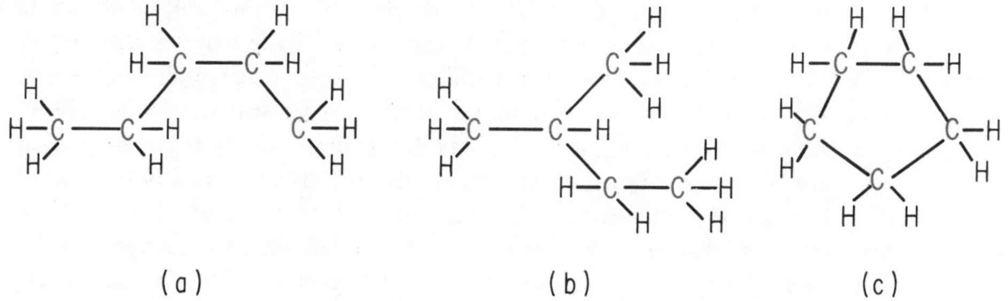

(a)   (b)   (c)

Hydrocarbons are organic compounds containing only carbon and hydrogen. *Saturated hydrocarbons* contain only single bonds and have the maximum possible hydrogen content, while *unsaturated hydrocarbons* contain double or triple bonds and do not have the maximum hydrogen content. *Aliphatic compounds* include open-chain carbon structures and certain types of ring structures.

Benzene is an unsaturated cyclic hydrocarbon with the molecular formula C_6H_6. The structure of the benzene molecule is represented by the following formula:

Benzene and analogous compounds and their substitution products are known as *aromatic compounds*. Aromatic compounds are obtained from coal and may also be synthesized from aliphatic hydrocarbons. Atoms of other elements or other hydrocarbon groups may be substituted for the hydrogen atoms on the benzene ring to form a very large number of benzene derivatives.

24-3
Classes of Organic Compounds

The very large number of carbon compounds complicates the study of organic chemistry. The task of studying over 1 million compounds individually would be hopeless. We see here the importance of some system of classification to simplify the study of these compounds. The vast number of carbon compounds can be divided into a relatively small number of families of compounds, or classes of compounds. The compounds within a family contain a characteristic group of atoms, called a *functional group*, and exhibit similar chemical properties. Thus, if we know the chemical behavior of a particular functional group, we will be able to predict the general characteristics of any member of the family characterized by that functional group. We shall briefly examine a few of the important families of organic compounds. Space will not permit the consideration of all of them or a detailed discussion of any one family. We shall direct our attention primarily to those compounds related to the chemistry of living organisms.

Alkanes

Alkane molecules contain only single bonds and the number of carbon atoms ranges from 1 to more than 30. Some of the simpler members of the family are listed in Table 24-1. The most important source of the alkanes is natural gas and petroleum. Natural gas may contain up to 97% methane. Petroleum is a very complex mixture of organic compounds, mainly hydrocarbons. In addition to alkanes, petroleum also contains hydrocarbons with double and triple bonds (unsaturated hydrocarbons) and cyclic hydrocarbons. The process of fractional distillation is used to separate petroleum into various fractions in the production of gasoline, lubricating oil, and other prod-

TABLE 24-1
Alkanes

Name	Formula
Methane	CH_4
Ethane	C_2H_6
Propane	C_3H_8
Butane	C_4H_{10}
Pentane	C_5H_{12}

ucts. The alkanes are very combustible and have relatively high heats of oxidation (see Chapter 23). They are used on a large scale as fuels in the form of natural gas, gasoline, and fuel oil. They are also used in large quantities as starting materials in the synthesis of other chemical compounds. Among the important products made from the chemical compounds in petroleum are detergents, insecticides, paints, cosmetics, drugs, plastics, and synthetic rubber.

Alcohols

The removal of a hydrogen atom from any of the alkanes produces an *alkyl group*. These alkyl groups are named on the basis of the alkane from which they are derived. The methyl group, CH_3—, is derived from methane, the ethyl group, C_2H_5—, from ethane, and the propyl group, C_3H_7—, from propane. The alkyl groups are not compounds and have no independent existence for any appreciable time, but they occur in molecules, where they are bonded to some other atoms or group of atoms.

An *alcohol* is produced when an OH group is combined with an alkyl group. The hydroxyl group,—OH, is the functional group common to all alcohols. For example, methyl alcohol, CH_3OH, contains a methyl group, CH_3—, bonded to an OH group. The OH is bonded to the carbon, as indicated when the formula is written

$$H-\overset{\displaystyle H}{\underset{\displaystyle H}{C}}-OH$$

This molecule is not planar, but is a three-dimensional structure with the bonds on the carbon approximately tetrahedral. Even though the alcohol molecule contains an OH group, it does not have the properties of an inorganic base. The hydroxide-ion concentration is not increased when methyl alcohol is dissolved in water. Methyl alcohol is sometimes called "wood alcohol," since it was at one time obtained by the destructive distillation of wood. It is now made on a very large scale from carbon monoxide and hydrogen. The ethyl alcohol molecule, C_2H_5OH, contains an ethyl group, C_2H_5—, bonded to an OH group. This alcohol, known as "grain alcohol," has been produced since ancient times by the fermentation of carbohydrates. It is now produced in large quantities from petroleum. These alcohols, and similar ones formed from other alkyl groups, have many important industrial uses as solvents and in the production of useful chemicals.

Some alcohols contain more than one OH group in each molecule. Glycerine, or glycerol, is an important alcohol that has three OH groups in each molecule. This alcohol has the formula $C_3H_5(OH)_3$. In contrast to the alcohols previously mentioned, glycerol has a sweet taste and is an essential component of a class of foods known as fats.

Organic Acids

The carboxyl group, COOH or $-\overset{\displaystyle O}{\overset{\displaystyle \|}{C}}-OH$, is the functional group found in all *organic acids*. The hydrogen in the carboxyl group is given up in acid-base reactions. These acids may be represented by the general formula RCOOH, where R is a hydrogen atom (in the simplest acid) or an alkyl group (in the others). The organic acids are relatively weak acids, some of them being so weak that they do not have a noticeably sour taste.

Formic acid, HCOOH, the strongest acid of this group, is present in the fluid injected by the sting of insects such as ants and bees. One of the early methods of preparation for this acid was by the distillation of red ants. The second member of the group, acetic acid, is the most widely known, as the acidic constituent of vinegar. Acetic acid has the formula CH_3COOH, sometimes written $HC_2H_3O_2$. In this case, as in all organic acids, only the hydrogen in the COOH group is given up in the formation of hydrogen ions in solution. The organic acids may be formed by the oxidation of alcohols. The bacterial oxidation of ethyl alcohol (C_2H_5OH) in apple cider is an old method for making vinegar. The higher molecular weight acids of this group are involved in the formation of fats and are consequently sometimes called *fatty acids*. Stearic acid, $C_{17}H_{35}COOH$, is an important fatty acid which we shall consider later in our discussion of fats.

Amino Acids

An *amino acid* contains an NH_2 group in addition to a carboxyl group. If one of the hydrogens in the methyl group of acetic acid is replaced by an NH_2 group, we have a molecule of aminoacetic acid, or glycine, the simplest amino acid:

$$
\begin{array}{cc}
\text{H} \quad \text{O} & \text{NH}_2 \; \text{O} \\
| \quad \parallel & | \quad \parallel \\
\text{H}-\text{C}-\text{C}-\text{OH} & \text{H}-\text{C}-\text{C}-\text{OH} \\
| & | \\
\text{H} & \text{H}
\end{array}
$$

Acetic acid   Aminoacetic acid (glycine)

Amino acids are the building blocks of proteins, and all of these acids related to proteins have the amino group, NH_2, bonded to the carbon atom adjacent to the carboxyl group, as in aminopropionic acid, or alanine:

$$
\begin{array}{c}
\text{H} \;\; \text{NH}_2 \; \text{O} \\
| \quad | \quad \parallel \\
\text{H}-\text{C}-\text{C}-\text{C}-\text{OH} \\
| \quad | \\
\text{H} \;\; \text{H}
\end{array}
$$

Aminopropionic acid (alanine)

The general formula for an amino acid may be written as

$$
\begin{array}{c}
\text{NH}_2 \; \text{O} \\
| \quad \parallel \\
\text{R}-\text{C}-\text{C}-\text{OH} \\
| \\
\text{H}
\end{array}
$$

where R is a radical, usually an alkyl radical. Approximately 20 different amino acids have been obtained by the decomposition of proteins.

Esters

Organic acids react with alcohols to form a class of compounds called *esters*. For example, acetic acid reacts with methyl alcohol to form methyl acetate. Hydrogen ions from a strong acid will catalyze this reaction:

$$\underset{\text{acetic acid}}{CH_3\overset{\displaystyle O}{\overset{\|}{C}}-OH} + \underset{\text{methyl alcohol}}{HO-CH_3} \xrightarrow{H+} \underset{\text{methyl acetate}}{CH_3\overset{\displaystyle O}{\overset{\|}{C}}-O-CH_3} + H_2O$$

When ethyl alcohol reacts with acetic acid, the ester formed is ethyl acetate:

$$CH_3-\overset{\displaystyle O}{\overset{\|}{C}}-O-C_2H_5$$

There are many possibilities for the formation of esters, since each organic acid could react with each one of the alcohols.

Esters are very pleasant compounds, since most of them have fragrant odors. The fragrance of flowers and fruits is due to the presence of esters, and many esters are now synthesized for use as artificial flavors and perfumes. For example, the odor of oranges is due to octyl acetate and that of pineapple results from ethyl butyrate. Esters are also important as industrial solvents and are used in making lacquers. Fats, as we shall see later, are esters formed from fatty acids and glycerol.

24-4
Carbon Compounds in Living Organisms

The importance of carbon compounds in living organisms has long been recognized, but only in recent years has man begun to understand the complex chemical reactions that occur in plants and animals. The science of *biochemistry* is concerned with the composition and structure of living organisms, and with the chemical reactions which are involved in the life processes of these organisms. Proteins, carbohydrates, fats, vitamins, hormones, and nucleic acids are among the carbon compounds found in complex organisms. The first three are present in greatest abundance, and we shall consider their structures and properties.

Proteins

Proteins are the most complex substances found in living organisms, and the greatest proportion of protoplasm is protein. They are giant molecules whose molecular weights range from several thousand to many millions. Most of these molecules are so complex that their detailed structures have not been worked out, but the general nature of the structures is known.

Amino acids are the building blocks of the proteins. A protein molecule is formed by the union of many hundreds or thousands of amino acid molecules. The carboxyl group of each molecule combines with the amino group of another as many molecules join together to form long chains. A complex molecule built up by the combination of many simple molecules is known as a *polymer*, and the process is known as *polymerization*.

The combination of amino acids is illustrated below in the combination of glycine and alanine, two simple amino acids:

$$
\underset{\text{alanine}}{
\text{H}-\overset{\displaystyle\overset{\text{H}}{|}}{\underset{\displaystyle\underset{\text{H}}{|}}{\text{C}}}-\overset{\displaystyle\overset{\text{NH}_2}{|}}{\underset{\displaystyle\underset{\text{H}}{|}}{\text{C}}}-\overset{\displaystyle\overset{\text{O}}{\|}}{\text{C}}-\text{OH}
}
\ + \
\underset{\text{glycine}}{
\text{H}-\overset{\displaystyle\overset{\text{H}}{|}}{\underset{\displaystyle\underset{\text{H}}{|}}{\text{N}}}-\overset{\displaystyle\overset{\text{H}}{|}}{\text{C}}-\overset{\displaystyle\overset{\text{O}}{\|}}{\text{C}}-\text{OH} \ \rightarrow
$$

$$
\underset{\text{alanylglycine}}{
\text{H}-\overset{\text{H}}{\underset{\text{H}}{\text{C}}}-\overset{\text{NH}_2}{\underset{\text{H}}{\text{C}}}-\overset{\text{O}}{\text{C}}-\overset{}{\underset{\text{H}}{\text{N}}}-\overset{\text{H}}{\underset{\text{H}}{\text{C}}}-\overset{\text{O}}{\text{C}}-\text{OH}
}
\ + \ \text{H}_2\text{O}
$$

The $-\overset{\displaystyle\overset{\text{O}}{\|}}{\text{C}}-\overset{\displaystyle\overset{\text{H}}{|}}{\text{N}}-$ group, known as *peptide link*, is the connecting link between amino acid groups in all proteins. The alanylglycine molecule contains a carboxyl group and an amino group, and could form peptide links with other amino acids. Thus the polymer could continue to increase in size as more amino acid units join the chain.

The combination of different amino acids in different arrangements makes possible many different protein molecules. There are 6 different ways to arrange 3 different amino acid molecules, and nearly 4 million ways to arrange 10 different amino acids. A relatively simple protein molecule containing 100 amino acid units could, therefore, be arranged in a very large number of ways. One of the most amazing characteristics of the living cell is its ability to control the order in which the amino acids are joined in order to produce a specific protein. Specific proteins are made by each cell type, and these vary in all species of plants and animals.

The synthesis of protein by body cells is controlled by a constituent of the chromosomes known as deoxyribonucleic acid (DNA). A model of this molecule is shown in Fig. 19-9. The DNA molecules are similar to the proteins in that they are long chains formed by the combination of simpler units. The "backbone" of the molecule consists of alternate phosphate groups and 5-carbon sugar molecules known as deoxyribose. The four constituent units attached to the DNA chain that allow for variation in the molecule are known as adenine, thymine, guanine, and cytosine. The schematic arrangement of the molecule is shown in Fig. 24-6. The DNA molecules in a cell nucleus may contain as many as 100 million of these attached units, and the order of arrangement constitutes a code, carrying all the hereditary infor-

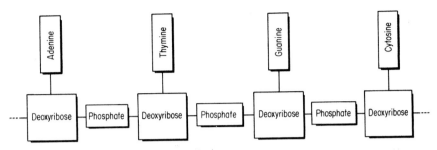

FIG. 24-6   Schematic representation of a small section of DNA molecule.

mation for the individual. The DNA molecules serve as "templates" and control the synthesis of proteins by the body cells.

Most of the common water-soluble proteins of the body have compact, spheroidal molecules and are called globular proteins. Myoglobin, a globular protein, is a relatively simple protein with a molecular weight of about 17,000. Myoglobin is quite similar to the hemoglobin of the red blood cells, and also has a great affinity for oxygen. The muscles of dolphins and seals have a high myoglobin content, contributing to the ability of these animals to remain under water for long periods.

Proteins are important as the principal structural material in animals and in the control of life processes. The enzymes, or organic catalysts which control chemical reaction rates in living organisms, are proteins. It has been estimated that approximately 30,000 enzymes are involved in the control of chemical reactions in the human body. Certain hormones, such as insulin, are also proteins.

Carbohydrates

The *carbohydrates* are built from carbon, hydrogen, and oxygen. The hydrogen and oxygen are usually present in the same ratio as in water. Carbohydrates are synthesized by plants in a process called photosynthesis. The energy of sunlight is utilized to convert carbon dioxide and water to a carbohydrate. The overall reaction is usually represented by the equation

$$6CO_2 + 6H_2O \rightarrow C_6H_{12}O_6 + 6O_2$$

where the formula $C_6H_{12}O_6$ represents glucose, a carbohydrate. This is an extremely important chemical reaction, since it is the ultimate source of most of the energy available for our use. It is far more complicated than the simple equation written above would indicate. This process is known to involve a series of reactions, but the detailed steps are not completely understood. The carbohydrates may be separated into three classes: sugars, starch, and cellulose.

The *sugars* are the simplest of the carbohydrates and are sweet-tasting, water-soluble compounds. Glucose and fructose, found in fruits, flowers, and honey, are simple sugars with the molecular formula $C_6H_{12}O_6$. These two sugars are isomers, having different structural arrangements of the atoms within the molecule. Glucose is made in large quantities from corn starch, and much of it is sold as corn syrup. This sugar is unusual among the foods in that it requires no digestion and can be absorbed directly into the blood.

Sucrose, $C_{12}H_{22}O_{11}$, is the common household sugar, obtained from cane or sugar beets. Maltose and lactose are isomers of sucrose. In the digestion process, one molecule of sucrose reacts with one molecule of water to form two molecules of simple sugar.

Although sweetness is commonly associated with sugars, it is not unique to this class of compounds. Glycerol, an alcohol, has a sweet taste and several synthetic organic compounds are far sweeter than sugar. Sucaryl sodium and sucaryl calcium, known collectively as cyclamates, are about 50 times as sweet as sucrose and have been used as sweeteners in food products. The structure of sucaryl sodium is shown below:

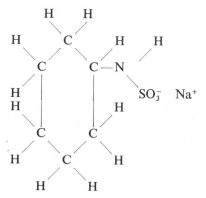

Cancer has been induced in rat bladders by very large doses of cyclamates (50 times the daily maximum recommended for human consumption). resulting in a ban on the use of cyclamates in food products. It should be noted that this ban was based on the effects produced by massive overdosage.

Starch is a more complex compound than the sugars. It is insoluble in water and is stored as a reserve food in many plant seeds and tubers. The chemical formula for starch is indefinite and is usually written as $(C_6H_{10}O_5)_x$ H_2O, where x is a very large number. This substance belongs to the class of compounds known as polymers and is made up of a large number of glucose units with a molecule of water removed from each. Certain digestive enzymes will catalyze the reaction of complex starch molecules with water to form simple sugars. This reaction is also catalyzed by acids and is used in the production of glucose from corn starch. The following equation describes this reaction:

$$(C_6H_{10}O_5)_xH_2O + (x - 1)H_2O \rightarrow xC_6H_{12}O_6$$

Starch serves as the major source of food for humans in such plant products as corn, rice, and potatoes. Glycogen is a starch that is stored in the animal body as a reserve energy supply.

Cellulose is a complex carbohydrate found in plants, where it is the major structural material, and it is extracted from wood and made into paper on a very large scale. Cellulose is similar to starch in structure, but, unlike starch, it cannot be digested by humans. It is also used to make a synthetic fiber, cellulose acetate, and rayon.

Fats

Fats belong to the class of organic compounds known as esters. They are formed from glycerol, an alcohol, and organic acids known as fatty acids. A glycerol molecule has three OH groups and reacts with three fatty acid molecules to form a molecule of fat. The relationship between the alcohol, the acid, and a fat may be seen from this equation:

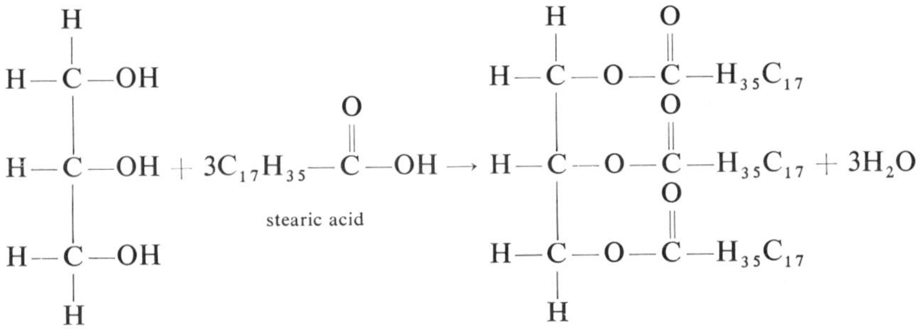

The combination of different fatty acids with glycerol will produce fats with different characteristics. For example, fatty acids in which some of the carbon atoms are connected by double bonds will produce liquid fats, or oils. These compounds are called *unsaturated fats.*

Fats are sources of highly concentrated energy and are also important because other essential constituents of body tissues are manufactured from them. Fats also serve as heat insulators and protect the body from mechanical injury. The fats of plants are found mainly in the seeds where they serve as a food reserve for the plant embryo.

The digestion of fats involves reaction with water and the splitting of the fat molecule into glycerol and fatty acid molecules. This reaction, known as a *hydrolysis* reaction, occurs primarily in the small intestine, where it is promoted by specific digestive enzymes. Fats may develop a rancid odor and taste if allowed to remain in contact with air at room temperature. This change results from hydrolysis or oxidation of the fat molecules. Certain fatty acids resulting from hydrolysis, along with other compounds produced by oxidation, are the cause of the unpleasant odor and taste.

It is a strange fact that man now has a better understanding of the non-living aspects of the world than of the living. The study of chemical reactions in living organisms is difficult, and effective techniques have only recently been developed. Intensive research in biochemistry will eventually lead to greater knowledge of the chemical processes in living systems and to the possible control of such diseases as cancer and such abnormalities as mental retardation.

The key to a greater knowledge of the chemistry of life lies in a more detailed understanding of carbon compounds, particularly those consisting of giant molecules such as the proteins and DNA. The study of such molecules and their relationship to living systems constitutes one of the most active research areas in science today.

24-5
Soaps and Synthetic Detergents

As indicated in Section 21-4, a detergent molecule has two dissimilar ends—one end is attracted to polar water molecules, and the other end is attracted to nonpolar substances, such as grease. Soap, the oldest detergent known, is made by reacting sodium hydroxide with a fat:

$$C_3H_5(O-\overset{\overset{O}{\|}}{C}-C_{17}H_{35})_3 + 3NaOH \longrightarrow 3C_{17}H_{35}-\overset{\overset{O}{\|}}{C}-O^-Na^+ + C_3H_5(OH)_3$$

glyceryl stearate (a fat)   sodium stearate (a soap)   glycerol

Synthetic detergents may be represented by such general formulas as $R-O-SO_3Na$ and $R-C_6H_4-SO_3Na$, where R is an alkyl group. These compounds will function in hard water because their calcium, magnesium, or iron salts are soluble in water. Sodium lauryl sulfate, an $R-O-SO_3Na$ type, is made by the following reactions:

$$CH_3(CH_2)_{11}OH \xrightarrow{H_2SO_4} CH_3(CH_2)_{11}OSO_3H \xrightarrow{NaOH} CH_3(CH_2)_{11}OSO_3^-Na^+$$

lauryl alcohol   lauryl hydrogen sulfate   sodium lauryl sulfate

An example of an $R-C_6H_4-SO_3Na$ detergent is found in sodium n-dodecyl-benzenesulfonate:

$$CH_3(CH_2)_{11}-C \begin{array}{c} H \\ | \\ C \\ \diagup \diagdown \\ C \\ | \\ H \end{array} \begin{array}{c} H \\ \diagup \\ C \\ \diagdown \\ C \\ \diagup \\ C \\ | \\ H \end{array} \begin{array}{c} O \\ || \\ S-O^-Na^+ \\ || \\ O \end{array}$$

The great demand for synthetic detergents led to large-scale production by polymerization of unsaturated hydrocarbons from petroleum. This process produced branched-chain detergent molecules, which are not biodegradable. Most detergent manufacturers have gone back to the use of straight-chain detergent molecules, even though the production of these detergents is more expensive.

24-6
Pollution by Carbon Compounds

Many carbon compounds are contributing to our air pollution problems, along with oxides of nitrogen, sulfur dioxide, and particulate matter in smoke. Unsaturated hydrocarbons and aromatic compounds from automobile exhausts and industrial plants react with oxides of nitrogen under the influence of sunlight to produce smog. Such smog has been shown to reduce crop yields, particularly in fruits. The effects of smog on humans, while not fully understood, is certainly unfavorable.

Certain organic compounds are serious water pollutants, particularly where industrial plant effluents are dumped into streams without proper treatment and in streams draining agricultural areas where pesticides and herbicides are heavily used. Streams in heavily industrialized areas have actually caught fire because of combustible organic compounds floating on the water surface.

Most chemical control agents now being used in agriculture are chlorinated hydrocarbons. One of the earliest and most effective insecticides was dichloro-diphenyltrichloroethane, commonly known as DDT. Lindane, Chlorodane, Parathion, and Dieldrin are trade names for other chlorinated hydrocarbons used as insecticides. Dichlorophenoxyacetic acid, known as 2,4-D, is an example of a herbicide which kills broad-leaved weeds, but does not affect cereal plants, such as corn or wheat. These chlorinated hydrocarbons are highly poisonous and most of them are chemically stable and not readily subject to breakdown. While they are not applied in high concentration, they tend to accumulate in animals. They are concentrated in animal predators by the natural operation of the food chain. Chlorinated hydrocarbons are fat-soluble and are recoverable in minute amounts from the fat of humans in most areas of the world.

It is estimated that we have in the United States 10,000 species of insects, 600 weed species, 1,500 plant diseases, and 1,500 species of nematodes (microscopic worms) that are capable of causing serious economic loss to crops. Untold thousands of humans starve to death every year and the human population is increasing at a rate of somewhat more than 100 every minute. The continued use of chemical control agents, along with increased use of fertilizers and improved plant hybrids, will be necessary to cope with the world food problem. However, we definitely need more care in the use of chemicals of all kinds, as well as research into alternative methods of control for insect pests. We cannot afford the risk of long-range cumulative effects which could affect human health on a broad scale and even endanger the whole life-support system of the Earth.

QUESTIONS AND PROBLEMS

1. Write the molecular formulas and give the names of two compounds having the empirical formula CH.

2. What alkyl radical is formed from propane? What alcohol contains this alkyl radical?

3. In what way is the bonding in propane (C_3H_6) different from that in ethylene (C_2H_4)?

4. How would you name the ester produced by the reaction of acetic acid and butyl alcohol?

5. What functional group, or radical, is common to all organic acids? Write the formula for the acid resulting from the oxidation of butyl alcohol (C_4H_9OH).

6. Write the structural formulas for the isomers of C_4H_{10}. Remember that each carbon must have four single bonds and each hydrogen one single bond.

7. How would the number of moles of sodium hydroxide that could be neutralized by 1 mole of acetic acid compare with the number of moles of sodium hydroxide that could be neutralized by 1 mole of hydrochloric acid? Explain.

8. What is the relationship of DNA to the proteins produced in the body?

9. Glucose may be formed as a result of a chemical reaction between starch and water. Why is glucose not produced by simply mixing starch with water? Explain in some detail.

10. Why do you think the Food and Drug Administration might be reluctant to allow the sale of a new "artifical sweetener" which is not a carbohydrate but is intensely sweet, even though this compound produces no immediately observable ill effects upon humans consuming it?

11. The odor of rancid butter is due in part to the odor of butyric acid. How do you account for the presence of this acid in rancid butter?

12. Protein is a crucial component in the world food supply, and the diet of millions of people is deficient in protein. How is this problem related to the synthetic production of ammonia?

13. The digestion of fat involves the reaction of water molecules with fat molecules. Why does this reaction not take place when a fat is mixed with water in a test tube?

14. A corn plant has a leaf surface area of 4×10^3 cm^2. The sun provides about 2 calories per minute on each square centimeter of surface, and the plant is able to utilize about 10% of this energy in photosynthesis. The heat of oxidation for glucose is 673 kcal per mole. Calculate the actual photosynthesis time required for this plant to produce 10 grams of glucose.

15. Show that there are six different possible combinations for three different amino acid molecules. Since there are twenty naturally occurring amino acids, what might you conclude about the possible variety of protein structures?

SUGGESTED REFERENCES

BENFEY, O. THEODOR, *From Vital Force To Structural Formulas.* Houghton Mifflin Co., Boston, 1964.

CHELDELIN, V. H., and R. W. NEWBURGH, *The Chemistry of Some Life Processes.* Chaps. 1 and 2. Reinhold Publishing Corp., New York, 1964.

FINLEY, K. THOMAS, and JAMES WILSON, JR., *Fundamentals of Organic Chemistry*, Chaps. 1, 2, 10, and 11. Prentice-Hall, Englewood Cliffs, N.J., 1970.

HERZ, WERNER, *The Shape of Carbon Compounds.* W. A. Benjamin, New York, 1963.

KELLER, EUGENIA, "The DDT Story," *Chemistry*, 43, no. 2 (1970), 8.

25
Science,Technology, and Man

Science remains the endless frontier. It will, by its very nature, always remain unfinished. The concepts which provide answers to old questions raise more new questions, so the realm of the unknown continues to widen. The theories and conceptual schemes, and even the "facts" of today, will be modified in the light of new knowledge which is continuously being accumulated. James B. Conant, an eminent organic chemist, has suggested that "science is not a quest for certainty; it is rather a quest which is successful only to the degree that it is continuous." The "facts" of 1900 are, in many instances, not considered facts now. It was a "fact" of science in 1960 that the element xenon would not unite with any other element to form a chemical compound. However, in 1962, a compound of xenon and fluorine was made. There is little reason to doubt that many of the "facts" of today will suffer the same fate.

25-1
Growth of Scientific Knowledge

The rate at which man was able to acquire new knowledge in science was relatively constant throughout his history until the seventeenth century. A dramatic change occurred at this point in history, when the rate of acquisition of scientific knowledge began to accelerate. This accelerating growth of knowledge has now reached a point where the number of published scientific papers is doubling every twelve years. This rate of increase obviously cannot be maintained indefinitely. The mass of scientific information in print is now so great that the retrieval of information is a problem of major proportions.

The goals of science have not changed since the beginning of the scientific revolution in the seventeenth century. Science is still concerned with the realm of ideas—it seeks a rational interpretation of natural phenomena. The theories and conceptual schemes of science are the principal tools for this interpretation. However, it is becoming increasingly evident that science must be concerned with the social consequences of scientific knowledge. The direct effects of the applications of science to technology and the awesome possibilities which can be seen for future uses of scientific knowledge demand serious consideration. Individual scientists, as well as scientific societies such as the American Association for the Advancement of Science, the American Physical Society, and the American Chemical Society, are directing increasing attention to the interactions of science and society.

The means of scientific investigation have undergone great changes in the last 300 years. The scientists of the seventeenth, eighteenth, and early nineteenth centuries were individual investigators, usually amateurs, working with limited facilities. Michael Faraday, for example, discovered the principles of electromagnetic induction with equipment no more elaborate than that found today in an ordinary high school physics laboratory. Antoine Lavoisier laid the foundation of modern chemistry with equipment no more complicated than a balance that would be considered inadequate for a modern analytical laboratory. The accomplishments of such men, without elaborate equipment and facilities, are a tribute to their intellectual abilities and scientific imagination. Scientific investigation is no longer conducted by amateurs, but by highly specialized scientists, often working as teams in large laboratories with highly sophisticated instruments.

Despite these great differences in the methods of scientific investigation, there is still a common ingredient, which has always been the most important element in the advancement of knowledge. The imagination of man remains the most essential factor in the advancement of science. Every scientific instrument is a product of the mind of man. These instruments cannot interpret the measurements which are made by them and they are unable to weave a mass of data into a useful theory or to construct a new conceptual scheme. The imagination of the scientist is still as important as in the days of Galileo and Newton and will remain the *sine qua non* of scientific advancement. Science appeals to the inquiring mind because it offers opportunity for the use of creative imagination.

Although the past achievements of science are very impressive, many important and exciting problems remain to be solved. Problems such as protein synthesis, the structure of the atomic nucleus, the mechanisms of chemical reactions, and the pathways and physiological effects of certain elements and compounds in the food chain challenge the ingenuity and imagination of scientists.

Technology is the activity by which man devises and creates material objects of practical value. Automobiles, television sets, synthetic detergents, spacecraft, and synthetic fibers are products of technology. Science and technology are often confused, particularly by our mass communication media seeking to sell certain products by associating them with the "miracles of modern science." Although science deals with ideas, and technology with material products, these two activities are closely related. Our space exploration program has demonstrated a particularly close relationship between science and technology. Scientific knowledge is the basis for technological progress, and research aimed at developing a particular product may lead to the discovery of scientific principles. The ability of man to leave the Earth and to walk on the Moon represents the ultimate in the application of scientific principles to the solution of practical problems. This technological triumph has, in turn, advanced scientific knowledge in many areas.

It is not possible to predict the "usefulness" of the results of scientific research, or even what results might come out of a particular investigation. Hahn and Strassman were experimenting in 1938 with the possibility of producing new elements by bombarding uranium with neutrons. They discovered nuclear fission, and the results—scientific, political, and sociological—were certainly beyond their imagination at that time. Who would have predicted the consequences of Faraday's studies on electromagnetic induction or of Davy's investigations on the electrolysis of chemical compounds? We need only to read the history of science to be convinced that the great advances in science have come in very unpredictable ways.

While science helps to satisfy our intellectual curiosity by a rational interpretation of natural phenomena, technology serves our physical needs by providing us with the means for a more comfortable life. Millions of people living today have no access to the products of modern technology, and the explosive growth of the world's population multiplies the need for material goods.

25-3
Technology and Human Need

Adequate energy sources will be one of the crucial factors in satisfying the material needs of all men. Our supplies of fossil fuels are limited, and while the estimates of our reserves vary, there is no doubt that our dependence on these energy sources will eventually end. The energy demands of the industrial nations of the world are increasing, and the underdeveloped nations seek to enter the machine age and to free their people from hard physical labor. Some of the future energy needs may be met by methods of using solar energy, such as solar batteries. However, these devices are not very efficient at present, and their future uses will depend on further development. Nuclear reactors that use uranium or plutonium hold promise as a major energy source of the future. The fissioning of 1 pound of uranium-235 will liberate approximately the same amount of heat as the combustion of 1,550 tons of coal. Several nuclear reactors are now in operation, producing electricity from steam generated by the heat of the fission reaction. Much work remains to be done in solving such problems as the direct conversion of fission energy to electricity, the safe handling of radioactive fission waste products from reactors, and the heat dissipation from the reactor.

The thermonuclear reaction, or fusion reaction, in which heavy hydrogen isotopes combine to form helium, will provide a tremendous new energy source if man can learn to control this reaction. An uncontrolled thermonuclear reaction takes place in the explosion of a hydrogen bomb, and in contrast to the fission process, this fusion reaction produces very little by-product radioactivity. Every gallon of water on earth contains sufficient heavy hydrogen to produce as much energy as 300 gallons of gasoline—if man can learn to control the thermonuclear reaction. Thus the oceans contain enough energy to supply the world's needs for the foreseeable future.

Two-thirds of the world's people are undernourished, with an estimated food intake of approximately 2,000 calories per day. A diet supplying 2,500 calories per day is considered minimum for adequate nutrition. The technological know-how is now available to eliminate much of this hunger, but there are many barriers to the application of this knowledge. As the world population grows, the food problem will become more acute. The elimination of hunger will require population control, new developments in food technology and agriculture, and further application of present knowledge. The process of photosynthesis, the primary source of all our food, converts the energy of sunlight into chemical energy of carbohydrates. In using 0.1% of the energy received by the Earth from the Sun each year, the plants on Earth store about 100 times the energy used by man with all his machines. A complete understanding of this complex process may enable man to increase his food and energy supply to levels beyond our present imagination.

Energy and food are only two of the areas in which technology must provide for the increasing material needs of mankind. A similar situation exists with respect to clothing, shelter, transportation, and medical supplies. There is no hope of relief from want for the underdeveloped nations of the world except through an increased application of appropriately regulated modern technology. However, the application of scientific knowledge is not enough. Science and technology will not abolish ignorance nor assure an equitable distribution of the world's material goods. The application of technology will do nothing to guarantee equal justice to all men. There are other realms of knowledge which must be developed and applied if we are to achieve the "good life" which man has sought throughout history.

25-4
Technology and the Environment

The world population increased from 1 billion in 1830 to 2 billion in 1930. The next 1-billion increase, to 3 billion, required only 30 years. The 4-billion mark will be reached by 1975. This increase in population, made possible in part by the rise of technology, has been accompanied by an alarming increase in the pollution and deterioration of the environment. Much of the world population growth is taking place in underdeveloped countries. However, the United States, with only 6% of the world population, consumes almost 50% of the world's goods and produces about half of the world's pollution.

We are pouring great quantities of dangerous chemical substances into our air and water. Estimates of the total emission of atomspheric pollutants in the U.S. range from 125 to 300 million tons per year. Dust, hydrocarbons, carbon monoxide, sulfur dioxide, and the oxides of nitrogen seriously threaten our life-support system. Our water supplies are endangered by oxygen-demanding wastes, plant nutrients, organic chemicals, sediment from land erosion, radioactive wastes, infectious agents, and heat from industrial plants.

Our pollution problems of the future will be intensified by population growth, urbanization, and technological growth. By the end of this century 95% of an estimated 280 million Americans will be concentrated in urban areas.

The idea of a return to a pristine condition of the environment is unrealistic. Technology is necessary to sustain the present level of population and there can be no technology without some pollution. The real problem is to reduce pollution of both air and water to minimum levels with appropriate controls on all technological processes, agricultural practices, and waste disposal methods. Reducing levels of pollution and maintaining them at tolerable levels is going to be expensive, and this expense must be reckoned as a part of the cost of the products of our technological society. Governmental regulation and individual cooperation will be necessary if we are to keep the pollution problem under control. We really have no choice—no organism can survive in its own waste products!

25-5
Public Understanding and Support of Science

Science has become one of the major intellectual forces in society, and technology has become the predominant factor in meeting the material needs of men. Science affects our lives whether we like it or not, and will affect us increasingly in the future. The electromagnetic wave theory, developed by James Clerk Maxwell in the 1860's and demonstrated experimentally in 1881 by Heinrich Hertz, has influenced all those alive today. Events from around the world are now brought almost instantaneously to the eyes and ears of millions of people by communications devices based on this theory. Louis Pasteur's investigations in microbiology of 100 years ago and Fritz Haber's more recent studies of nitrogen fixation have produced great changes in the health and nutrition of the world population.

The time lag between the discovery of scientific knowledge and the application of that knowledge in ways that touch our lives has been continually decreasing. Sir Humphry Davy first used the electric current to isolate active metals, such as sodium and potassium, from their compounds in 1807. This principle was first applied to the production of aluminum in 1886 by Charles Martin Hall, but it was not used on a large scale until about 1920. The principle of nuclear fission, discovered in 1938, was being used to generate electricity on a commercial scale and to propel ships and submarines in 1960. The studies of polymers by J.A. Nieuwland and W. A. Carothers in the 1930's resulted in the production of the first synthetic rubber some 10 years later.

A vigorous scientific enterprise demands an ever-increasing public understanding of science, particularly in a democratic society such as ours. It is especially important that the public understand the folly of restricting research to the solution of immediate practical problems. William Perkin's amateurish attempt to synthesize quinine in 1856 led to an accidental discovery that initiated that great synthetic dye industry and stimulated the development of synthetic organic chemistry. The unrestricted pursuit of scientific knowledge will provide the foundations for technological advances of the future. A generation ago scientific research was primarily centered in college and university research laboratories. It is there, and in our national laboratories, that scientists must continue to find freedom of investigation without any thought of the "usefulness" of the knowledge which will be gained.

The industrial applications of science and technology have grown to such an extent that most major industrial firms now maintain research divisions. There are approximately 30,000 industrial research laboratories in the United States today. The total national expenditure for research and development increased from approximately $6 billion in 1955 to more than $20 billion in 1965, according to figures compiled by the National Science Foundation. Science has also become a major concern of government as the political implications of scientific developments become more apparent. Our government is spending billions of dollars each year on scientific research and development, and the returns on this investment have been immense. It is unfortunate that much of this effort is necessarily directed toward defense. Intelligent decisions regarding such governmental agencies as the Atomic Energy Commission, the National Aeronautics and Space Administration, the National Science Foundation, and the National Institutes of Health require an informed electorate, as well as a Congress with a considerable understanding of science.

Science can feed the spirit of man as well as provide the fundamental knowledge for technological advances. The subtle and elegant beauty in science, beyond that which we obtain through the sense perception of form and color, is visible only to those willing to devote the time and effort required for understanding. A deeper appreciation for the beauty of the starlit sky follows from an understanding of the laws which precisely describe the planetary motions, the vastness of interstellar space, and the thermonuclear reactions providing the energy of the stars. A colorful bright-line spectrum has more aesthetic appeal to the mind prepared to relate the pattern of colors to the structure of the atoms from which they come. The miracle of man himself becomes more magnificant with some understanding of the biochemistry of his life processes.

We have seen that the technology developed from science is not always a beneficent genii—it is sometimes a Pandora's box. The genetic dangers from radioactive fallout, the health hazards and ecological consequences of pesticides and herbicides, the detrimental effects of inadequately tested drugs, and even the undesirable ecological effects of hard detergents have shown us that the application of scientific knowledge requires careful consideration of long-range effects as well as of immediate advantages. The application of scientific knowledge may lead to evil as well as to good. A broad public understanding of science is essential for the development and application of scientific knowledge for the benefit of all men. It is our hope that this book has given you some understanding of the nature of science and that you will continue to broaden your knowledge. It is only by such continuous education that you will find life intellectually satisfying and be able to exercise your citizenship responsibilities intelligently.

GLOSSARY

Aberration of Starlight An apparent displacement of a star in the direction an observer is moving.

Absolute Magnitude The magnitude a star would have if viewed from a distance of 32.6 light-years.

Absolute Zero The temperature at which the molecules of a substance would have no linear kinetic energy.

Acceleration The rate of change of velocity.

Acceleration Due to Gravity The acceleration of a freely falling object; 980 cm/sec^2, or 9.8 m/sec^2.

Acid A substance which acts as a proton donor in a solution.

Aliphatic Compound A compound containing carbon atoms arranged in a straight or branched chain.

Alpha Particle A positively charged particle emitted by the nuclei of certain radioactive elements. It consists of 2 protons and 2 neutrons tightly bonded together.

Ampere One coulomb of charge passing by a point in a conductor in 1 second.

Angstrom A distance unit equal to 10^{-10} meter.

Anode The electrode in an electrolytic cell where oxidation takes place.

Apogee The point in the orbit of a satellite that is farthest from the Earth.

Aromatic Compound A compound containing carbon atoms connected by alternate single and double bonds in a ring structure.

Asteroid One of thousands of small planetoids revolving around the Sun between Mars and Jupiter.

Astronomical Unit A unit of distance used in astronomy. It is the average distance between the Sun and the Earth, equal to 9.3×10^7 miles.

Atom The smallest particle of an element that retains the chemical properties of the element.

Atomic Number The number of positive charges in the atomic nucleus.

Atomic Weight (mass) A number representing the weight (mass) of an atom relative to the most common isotope of carbon at 12.0000 atomic mass units.

Avogadro's Number The number of atoms (6.02×10^{23}) in 1 gram atomic weight of an element, or the number of molecules in 1 gram molecular weight of a compound.

Base A substance which acts as a proton acceptor in a solution.

Beta Particle A particle emitted from certain radioactive nuclei; identical to an electron if negatively charged and to a positron if positively charged.

Biodegradable Substance A substance which is decomposed readily by the action of living organisms.

Brownian Movement The random motion of colloidal particles suspended in a fluid. The motion is caused by impacts of continuously moving molecules in the fluid.

429

Bubble Chamber A chamber used to observe the tracks produced by bubble formation on ions produced by high-speed ionizing particles.

Buffer A substance which resists a change in the pH of a solution.

Calorie The amount of heat needed to raise the temperature of 1 gram of water 1 degree Celsius.

Catalyst A substance which will influence the rate of a chemical reaction without undergoing any permanent change in the process.

Cathode The electrode in an electrolytic cell where reduction takes place.

Cathode Rays A stream of electrons radiated from the cathode, or negative terminal, of a discharge tube.

Celestial Equator The equator of the Earth extended to the sky or celestial sphere.

Celsius Scale A temperature scale developed by Celsius using the melting point of ice as 0° and the boiling point of water under standard conditions as 100°. It is sometimes called the centigrade scale.

Centrifugal Force The force on the constraining object that keeps a moving body in a circular path.

Centripetal Force The central force needed to keep a moving object in a circular path.

Chain Reaction A self-sustaining nuclear fission reaction.

Chemical Bond The attractive force holding atoms together in molecules and crystals.

Chemical Equilibrium A condition under which a reaction proceeds in both the forward and reverse directions at the same rate.

Chromosphere The layer of the Sun's atmosphere above the photosphere. It is scarlet during an eclipse because of an abundance of hydrogen and is the region of prominences.

Coefficient of Linear Expansion The amount a unit length of a solid expands or contracts with a temperature change of 1 degree.

Coefficient of Volume Expansion The amount a unit volume of a substance changes with a temperature change of 1 degree.

Comet A celestial object orbiting the Sun. When visible, it usually has a long, spectacular tail.

Conduction of Heat Transfer of heat energy from molecule to molecule.

Convection of Heat The transfer of heat energy by the circulation of molecules or convection currents in a fluid.

Copernican System A planetary system which assumes the Sun is the central figure.

Corona The outermost atmosphere of the Sun.

Coronograph A special type of telescope for viewing the corona at any time the Sun is visible.

Coulomb A unit of charge equal to 3×10^9 statcoulombs, or 6.25×10^{18} electrons.

Covalent Compound A compound made up of molecules in which atoms are bonded by shared electron pairs.

Critical Mass The smallest amount of material needed to guarantee a continuous nuclear fission reaction.

Curie A unit for measuring the rate at which a radioactive material disintegrates: 3.7×10^{10} disintegrations per second.

Cyclotron A device that can accelerate charged particles to very high energies.

Deferent A circle around the Earth along which the center of a planet's epicycle was thought to move, according to the Ptolemaic theory.

Diffusion The intermingling of two substances as a result of the movement of individual molecules.

Direct Proportion A relationship between two variables in which an increase or decrease in one results in a proportionate increase or decrease in the other.

Dyne A unit of force in the metric system. That force necessary to give a 1-gram mass an acceleration of 1 cm/sec^2.

Ecliptic The apparent path of the Sun among the stars.

Efficiency of Machines The fractional part of the energy received by a machine that is finally delivered from it in the form of useful work.

Electrical Current An electrical charge in motion.

Electrical Potential The amount of work required to move a positive charge from infinity to the point in question.

Electrical Power The rate at which electrical energy is dissipated, expressed in watts.

Electrical Resistance An opposition to the flow of electrical charges, expressed in ohms.

Electric Field Field of influence around an electrical charge.

Electromotive Force (emf) The maximum potential difference produced by an electrical source.

Electron A fundamental unit of negative charge equal to 1.6×10^{-19} coulomb.

Electron Volt The energy given 1 electron by a potential difference of 1 volt. It is equivalent to 1.6×10^{-19} joule.

Electronegativity The relative attraction of an atom for a pair of electrons being shared with another atom.

Element A fundamental substance in which all atoms have the same atomic number.

Endothermic Process A process in which energy is absorbed.

Energy The ability to perform work.

Entropy A measure of the randomness in a system.

Enzyme An organic catalyst which controls a reaction rate in a living organism.

Epicycle A concept of the Ptolemaic theory; the circular path of a planet about a center moving along another circle with the Earth at its center.

Equinox The point where the celestial equator crosses the ecliptic.

Erg The amount of work done by a force of 1 dyne acting through a distance of 1 centimeter.

Eutrophication A condition in a body of water under which aquatic life can no longer be supported at the normal level.

Exothermic Process A process in which heat energy is liberated.

Fahrenheit Scale A temperature scale developed by Fahrenheit using the melting point of ice as 32° and the boiling point of water under standard conditions as 212°.

Fission The splitting of a heavy nucleus into two lighter nuclei.

Free Energy The component of the total energy which determines the capacity of a given substance to enter into a chemical reaction.

Functional Group A group of atoms producing a characteristic set of chemical properties common to a large number of related compounds.

Fusion A nuclear reaction in which lighter elements are combined to form a heavier element.

Galaxy A group of billions of stars, nebulae, clusters, and celestial matter.

Gamma Ray An electromagnetic wave emitted by the nuclei of certain radioactive elements. It is identical to an X ray, but is in general more energetic.

Geiger Counter A device used to detect and count ionizing particles and rays.

Gibbous The phase of the moon or a planet between quarter and full.

Gram Molecular Volume The volume occupied by 1 gram molecular weight of a gas at standard temperature and pressure.

Gravitational Constant The proportionality factor in Newton's gravitational law. It is numerically equal to 6.67×10^{-11} nt-m^2/kg^2 or 6.67×10^{-8} dyne-cm^2/gm^2.

Greenwich Meridian A great circle through the North and South poles and Greenwich, England.

Half-Life The interval of time required for half of the remaining quantity of a radioactive material to disintegrate.

Heat of Reaction The quantity of heat liberated or absorbed for each mole of the substance reacting.

Hertzsprung-Russell (H-R) Diagram A chart that relates the absolute magnitude of stars to their spectral type.

Hydrogen Bond The attractive force between an electronegative atom, such as oxygen or nitrogen, in one molecule and a hydrogen atom in an adjacent polar molecule.

Hydrolysis A reaction between water and some ion or molecule.

Hydronium Ion A proton combined with a water molecule (H_3O^+).

Hypothesis An intelligent guess as to *why* a thing behaves as it does.

Inertia The property of matter to resist any change in its motion.

Inverse Proportion A relationship between two quantities such that when one increases the other decreases proportionately.

Ion A charged particle formed from an atom or a chemically combined group of atoms.

Ionic Compound A compound made up of positive and negative ions forming a crystalline structure in the solid state.

Isomers Compounds with the same formula, but different geometric arrangements of the atoms.

Isotopes Atoms that have the same atomic number, but different masses.

Joule A unit of energy in the mks system of units; the amount of work done by a force of 1 newton acting through a distance of 1 meter.

Kelvin Scale The temperature scale using absolute zero as zero and the melting point of ice as 273°.

Kilowatt-Hour A unit for measuring electrical energy, equal to 3.6×10^6 joules.

Kinetic Energy Energy due to motion, equal to $\frac{1}{2}mv^2$.

Latent Heat of Fusion The amount of heat necessary to melt a unit mass of a substance.

Latent Heat of Vaporization The amount of heat necessary to vaporize a unit mass of a substance.

Latitude The number of degrees an object is north or south of the equator.

Longitude The number of degrees an object is east or west of the prime or Greenwich meridian.

Magnetic Field The region in which a magnet affects another magnet.

Magnitude of a Star A number indicating the brightness of a star. A difference of 1 magnitude indicates a brightness ratio of about $2\frac{1}{2}$ times.

Mass The quantity of matter as evidenced by inertia.

Mechanical Equivalent of Heat The relationship between mechanical energy and heat energy; 1 calorie = 4.186 joules, or 1 Btu = 778 ft-lb.

Meteor An object from space called a meteoroid that enters the Earth's atmosphere.

Meteorite A meteor that has penetrated the atmosphere to the Earth's surface. Those striking the Moon's surface are also called meteorites.

Milky Way The spiral galaxy in which our solar system is located.

Moderator The material used in nuclear reactors to slow the neutrons to thermal speed.

Molality The number of moles of a solute dissolved in 1,000 grams of a solvent.

Molarity The number of moles of a solute in 1 liter of solution.

Mole Avogadro's number (6.02×10^{23}) of particles of whatever chemical species we are dealing with.

Molecule The smallest particle of any substance capable of independent existence.

Molecular Orbital A region of space or an energy level which may be occupied by a pair of electrons associated with two or more nuclei in a molecule.

Momentum The product of the mass of an object and its velocity.

Nebula A dust or gas cloud in space.

Neutralization The reaction between hydronium and hydroxide ions to produce water.

Neutrino A neutral subatomic particle with a negligible mass.

Neutron A nuclear particle with no charge and a mass of 1.675×10^{-24} gram.

Newton That force necessary to give a 1-kilogram mass an acceleration of 1 m/sec^2.

Nodes The places where the orbit of the Moon intersects the plane of the ecliptic.

Nonpolar Molecule A molecule with a symmetric electrical charge distribution.

Nucleons The particles inside the nucleus of an atom.

Orbit The path one body takes around another body.

Orbital The region of space that may be occupied by a pair of electrons in a given energy sublevel of an atom or molecule.

Osmotic Pressure The pressure developed across a semipermeable membrane separating solutions of different concentration.

Oxidation A chemical process in which electrons are given up.

Perihelion The point in the orbit of a planet or a comet which is nearest the Sun.

Perigee The point in the orbit of a satellite which is nearest the Earth.

pH The negative logarithm of the hydronium ion concentration.

Photosynthesis The process by which green plants convert carbon dioxide to water and carbohydrates.

Polar Molecule A molecule with an asymmetric distribution of electrical charge.

Polymer A complex molecule formed by the combination of many simple molecules.

Power The rate of doing work.

Precession The conical motion of the axis of a spinning object.

Proton A nuclear particle carrying 1.6×10^{-19} coulomb of positive charge and having a mass of 1.673×10^{-24} gram.

Ptolemaic System A planetary system with a stationary Earth at the center.

Quantum A unit of radiant energy.

Radiation Transfer of heat energy by electromagnetic waves.

Radioactivity The spontaneous emission of particles and rays from a substance.

Radioisotopes Isotopes that are radioactive.

Reduction A chemical process in which electrons are gained.

Revolution The motion of one body around another.

Rotation The turning of a body about an interior axis.

Salt An ionic compound containing a positive ion other than the hydronium ion and a negative ion other than the hydroxide ion.

Satellite An object orbiting another of larger size.

Scientific Notation A method of writing numbers in exponential form.

Scintillation The tiny flashes of light produced when an ionizing particle strikes a fluorescent material.

Scintillation Counter A device used to detect and count ionizing particles or rays by the scintillations produced in a fluorescent crystal.

Sidereal Day The interval of time between two successive passages of a star or the vernal equinox across a meridian.

Solar Day The time from true noon to true noon.

Solar Eclipse The obscuration of light when the shadow of the Moon falls upon the Earth and within that shadow the Moon blots out the Sun.

Specific Heat The amount of heat needed to raise the temperature of a unit mass of a substance 1 degree.

Spring Tide The high tide produced when the Sun and the Moon act together.

Stellar Parallax The apparent displacement of a star when viewed from two different positions.

Sunspots Dark spots observed on the surface of the Sun.

Surface Tension The force required to break a unit length of liquid surface film.

Synodical Month The interval of time between consecutive full moons.

Temperature A measure of the average linear kinetic energy of the molecules in a substance.

Thermal Capacity The amount of heat required to raise the temperature of an entire object 1 degree

Tide The alternate rising and falling of the surfaces of large bodies of water.

Transmutation The changing of one element into another by bombarding the nucleus.

Transuranic Elements Elements above atomic number 92.

Unsaturated Molecule A molecule containing one or more multiple bonds where atoms may be added to the molecule.

Valence The combining capacity of an element.

Valence Electrons The outer-energy-level electrons of an atom.

Van de Graaff Machine An electrostatic generator capable of producing a steady output of several million volts to accelerate charged particles.

Vapor Pressure The equilibrium pressure exerted by the vapor of a liquid at a given temperature.

Volt The energy change of 1 coulomb of charge in moving between two points in a circuit, expressed in joules per coulomb.

Weight The gravitational pull of the Earth on an object.

Wilson Cloud Chamber A cloud chamber used to observe the tracks of ionizing particles by means of condensation of supersaturated vapor on the ions produced along the track of the particle.

Work Action performed on an object, and defined as a force times its displacement.

Zenith The point on the celestial sphere directly above an observer.

Index